To Ann

enter he

the strange tales

of the Shabby Tattler—

[signature]

16. May 11.

http://alangilliland.blogspot.com

The FLIGHT of BIRDS

Published in Great Britain by
Raven's Quill (publishing) Ltd.,
63, High Street, Billingshurst, West Sussex, RH14 9QP
01403-782489
www.ravensquill.com

British Library Cataloguing in Publication Data
A CIP record for this book can be obtained from the British
Library.

ISBN – 9780955548628

Printed and bound in Great Britain
....

The
FLIGHT
of
BIRDS

Alan
HOWARD

Raven's Quill Ltd.

A Strange Bird

"Where d'you think you be headed to, me little lady?"

Kate Pegler jumped. That scabrous voice from the briar hedge tore a bloody rent in the smooth skin of her solitude, and beads of sweat, like blood, welled up in the wound.

"Who... who's there?" she started, "what do you want?"

"Just me. What I want to know is what you be doin' in these here woods," the voice grated.

Kate peered anxiously sideways, yet could see no human shape in the matted undergrowth. She was about to run when the voice, as if sensing her growing panic, chuckled harshly, but with an unthreatening and almost comical whine, "You ain't goin' to run out on me, are yer? I ain't goin to hurt yer, now. Only goin' to tell yer, warn yer, like. These here woods ain't always right friendly to them what don't know their ways about."

A figure unravelled its tasselled form from the shadowed leafiness of the unkempt hedgerow. It emerged, crowned with a shredded top-hat from which lank dark locks hung dense, framing a pinky-grey, uncouth visage, swarthy yet not bearded, cocked to one side above sloping, powerful shoulders as the figure stooped to part the dense tangle of thorns in which he seemed to have been taking his ease.

As he straightened up, she noticed that a black patch covered the man's left eye. But as the light struck his face, the iris of his right eye dazzled her with its cerulean blue, enchanted her and overrode her instinct to flight, so bright and cheerful it was. The creases about it were playful, laughing even, in the friendliest way, while his swarthy brow arched quizzically.

"That's better. I can see yer ain't affrighted by the outer form like a fool be. Yer can see right through to the inner virtue, I reckon." The stranger at his full height towered like a sooty chimney over Katie. She stood her ground, matching him eye-to-eye, for there was a strange becomingness about this grubby figure that excited curiosity more than fear.

"But I shouldn't talk to strangers alone, like this," she replied with a calmness which surprised her.

"Ha! You're the stranger hereabouts, me little spatchcock." The stranger laughed, exposing a full set of perfectly white teeth totally at variance with his ragged outer demeanour. "Y' ain't been here barely five minutes, and yer callin' me a stranger already?"

"I didn't mean that," she admitted, laughing. "What I meant was, outside one's family…"

"I knows yer meanin', but it makes little difference, because your family's the outsiders hereabouts. You're the strangers here, definite. The villagers, now: them's family. Them's family like what yer never reckoned on. Them's tighter than a banker's braces. Yer won't get nothin' outer them insider ten years, if yer foller my meanin'. Yer the foreigners here! My advice ter you's this – yer'd do well to listen to good heed when it's offered. An mine's good heed."

"I'm sorry," Kate offered him a small hand of conciliation, " I didn't mean to be rude or unfriendly, it's just that my dad…"

"Parents is parents, and I don't blame yer. I cut a rude jib, I reckon, an who'm I to warn yer agin them what's sails are set fairer than mine, apparently? They says the eye's fer seein', but I says the eye's fer deceivin'. Yer best watch out

8

for them in particular what looks good ter the eye, if yer take my meanin'. Yer heed me on this and I'm satisfied. There's been strange goings on in these here woods of late. Signs, they says... Omens."

"Omens of what? What's been happening?"

"There's tell of unrested souls in these there woods, awaitin' of the lord's doom in the second comin'."

"Oh, rubbish! Omens, indeed. You're just pulling my leg. That's obviously a tale to frighten away strangers like me; to keep us out."

"I don't say I believe it, and I don't say I don't," the man grinned wickedly at her and winked. "There yer go then. I done my duty. I warned yer. Don't say I didn't. I only done it because there's somethin' special about yer; about yer comin here at this time, after all the other appenin's of late."

"What things?" Kate was perplexed by the contradictions embodied in this old man: her trust of him and his friendliness set against the mysterious nature of his warnings and predictions.

"Well, there's the birds. Them birds been actin' mighty peculiar of late. Missin' where they ought ter be and then suddenly appearin' where they didn't ought ter. Like the seasons are out of kilter."

"What do you mean?"

"Well, the other day them birds suddenly appears all along the roof ridge of the east wing of the house."

"Surely birds quite often gather and perch together."

"Not like that! Not all different types together, singing."

"Singing?"

"Yes, and then they all goes silent, like, as if in mourning, then as sudden all departin' with a mighty flappin' of wings over into these here woods. I never seen its like afore. An then..." The old man paused, as if for dramatic effect.

Kate obliged and asked, "Then what?" She found herself being drawn into his world against her better judgement.

9

"That roof were the wing of the house what burnt down, and with them all in it, that's all." He looked at her intently.

"Who?" She was beginning get the hang of his style, now.

"The lord and lady. An, they say, his mistress."

"His lover?"

"Yes. T'is said she haunts the house on account of what he done to her." The man looked at Kate keenly, sizing up her reactions. "T'is said she was his prisoner. Prisoner and mistress."

Kate suddenly felt uncomfortable with the way the conversation seemed to be going. "I've just remembered. I'm late. I've got to…"

"But of course you have, me dear," he said, fetching her a gentle clap across the shoulder from which she strangely did not wince, and added: "I can see yer uneasy, gel. I'll be goin' off, then. Now, if you ever needs me urgent, like – for anything. Any emergency; whistle thrice, like this."

The man put two fingers in his mouth and, pursing his lips, let forth a shrieking blast. "Go on then. Try it."

To humour him, Kate tried. After a couple of feeble attempts she got the hang of it and laughed as he clapped her on the back, crying: "Well done, gel. I reckon you got the hang of that, now. I'd better be off. Don't forget."

"But how will you hear me? I mean, you're not always going to be within earshot."

"Don't worry about that. I'll hear you, one way or t'other."

As he turned his back to go, Kate, unable to comprehend this last suggestion at all, hastily asked: "What's your name?"

"Don't go under a partickler name, I don't," he replied, "there's them as calls after me, 'Shabby Tattler', on account of me appearance, like. That's as good as any, I reckon."

Before Kate could collect her wits to question him further, he was gone. She was left with a strange impression of the man. He was as a shaft of warm sunlight cutting through the gloom of this dismal uncivilized place to which her father had so recently dragged her from the buzzing familiarity of the city.

But why did he say that about her whistling if she needed him urgently? Why would she want to? Why should she need to? And how would he hear her if she did? Was he following her? He didn't act like one of these weird stalkers she had been warned about. There was nothing tense or neurotic about him. But what was he warning her about, she wondered.

A shadow spread across her path and she shivered involuntarily as she made her way back towards the cottage her father had rented on the outskirts of the village.

2

A New Life

"How long have you been here, then?" Kate asked Robert Ruddock, as they ambled slowly along the lane that led from the bus stop towards her father's cottage on the Eastern outskirts of Yarnfold.

Robert was a sturdy handsome youth, with blondish hair and very pale blue eyes. His clothes were very ordinary, countrified in her eyes, and his general bearing was slightly uncouth, yet attractive in its masculinity.

Kate had met him one morning at the bus stop and found that he took the bus to the same school and they had agreed to meet on the bus home.

"I only arrived at the start of the year," answered Robert. "My Dad took a job as a woodsman and gamekeeper at Fugglesham Court – that's the big estate – and we've got a cottage at the edge of the woods. So you're in old Tom's cottage, are you?"

"I don't know. It's the last one as you leave the village along this lane."

"Yeah, that's the one," said Robert, "the old man died a couple of years back. The cottage has been rented out since. He was a right character, so they told me. He used to ride an old nag into the village on a Thursday evening after he'd been paid, go to the pub and get completely hammered, spending at least half his wages. Then they used to throw him across

12

his horse and the old thing would plod home with him, unconscious, hanging over it. And his wife would lift him off and put him to bed and take the rest of his wages. She was a big woman, so they said, and Thursday was his only chance to have a drink before she got hold of his money. So he used to make the most of it."

Kate laughed. "What happened to his wife, then, once he died?"

"They chucked her out. It was a tied cottage, belonging to the estate and the management reckoned he could make a lot more renting it out to the likes of you. No offence. If you're from London, how come you've moved here, then?" Robert grinned at her in a challenging way and Kate smiled back.

"None taken. We're not exactly rich, you know. My Dad came down here to live, to be somewhere near my Mum's grave."

"I'm sorry. I didn't know," said Robert.

"He couldn't bear to stay in the house where she died, and felt that living in the country would do me good. I'm not so sure. I had to leave all my friends behind."

"Well, you've got one here, now," replied Robert, looking sideways at her. "If you want one, that is."

"Thanks, you're very kind. It's a bit difficult, arriving halfway through the Spring Term in the second year of A-levels. Everyone knows each other and I feel a bit out of place."

They arrived at a junction where another lane crossed theirs. "My house is down that way," said Robert, "beyond Fugglesham Court. I'll show you around at the weekend. My Dad being gamekeeper means I get free access almost everywhere around here. So I know my way around pretty well by now. And I'll introduce you to some of my friends at school, too."

"Thanks. Don't you want to go home, now?" asked Kate, already hoping he wouldn't.

"No. I'll see you home first." Robert skipped a pace or two in front of her. "Anyway, there's a shortcut through the woods from your place to mine I can take."

The pair of them walked unhurriedly towards the now-visible whitewashed timber framed cottage where Kate now lived.

"It's really rather nice. Our cottage, I mean. It's all higgledy-piggledy. You have to walk uphill to bed in my bedroom. And when you get up in the dark, it's a bit like being drunk, difficult to stop yourself falling over. I'll get used to eventually, I suppose." Kate was warming to this affable lad, with his pleasant blue eyes, blondish hair and rather rangy frame bounding around her like an eager puppy.

They had reached the cottage now. "Come inside and meet my Dad. Would you like a cup of tea or coffee?" asked Kate as she opened the gate.

"Are you sure? Won't he mind?"

"Of course not. He's probably out in the orchard at the back. That's where he works when it's sunny like this. We'll take him a cup."

"Ok. Fine. Great."

Kate took him through the long living room to the kitchen in an annexe at the back. They made some tea and she gave him a tray to carry out into the garden.

Her father was sitting in a canvas director's chair, crouched over his papers on a folding table. He was wearing a woman's wide-brimmed basket-weave sunhat and a pair of wrap-around sunglasses. He had no shirt or shoes, only a pair of shorts.

Kate laughed at the incongruous sight he must present to someone who didn't know him, and turned to Robert: "That's my Mum's sunhat. He insists on wearing it. He says it's so much cooler than a normal hat. That's my Dad for you. He doesn't care what people think."

"Good for him," laughed Robert, and, to Kate's father,

"I'm Robert Ruddock, Sir. Pleased to meet you."

Kate's father rose and shook his hand. "John Pegler. So you know my daughter? Are you at the same school?"

"Yes, and I live only just over the way," replied Robert, pointing across towards the woods to the South. "So we get the same bus."

"Good. I'll be pleased to know she'll have someone to accompany her home in the evenings, especially once winter sets in."

"Dad! I'm not a baby, you know. I can manage quite well on my own," replied Kate.

"I know that dear. But these long dark lanes: it's not like the bright streets of London. So, yes, Robert, I will welcome your keeping my daughter company home from school."

"Rob, sir. Call me Rob. That's what my friends call me."

Fetching two more chairs they settled to a relaxing tea in the orchard. It was more than an hour later that Robert announced he must leave. Kate's father had engaged him in such an animated interrogation about the village and surroundings that Kate was able to sit passively and glance at them amusedly in turn, only occasionally throwing in a remark or two.

The two shook hands once again as Robert left, sealing what had been a very fast-growing friendship.

Kate was surprised. It had been the first time her father had shown any sign of high-spirits since Amelia had died two months earlier. Maybe this is a good sign, she thought. Maybe this marks a new beginning for him.

This contrast in him cast her mind back to that awful day in January.

Kate had been awakened suddenly one morning by a cry for help from her father.

Her mother, Amelia had, with her husband's help, got out of bed that morning, taken two paces into the room and frozen, wracked with pain. Kate rushed in to find her father struggling to hold her steady.

Amelia, though as thin as a bird now, had suddenly seemed to take on a deadweight that even his strength found difficult to bear. Every slight movement was accompanied by an uncontrollable scream from her mother.

Kate took Amelia's other shoulder, and the pair of them manoeuvred her back to the bed and laid her as gently as possible on it.

Kate couldn't help herself bursting into tears in sheer frustration at her helplessness as she whispered endearments into her mother's ear, stroking her hair. She looked across to her father and saw tears running down his cheeks as he fiddled with her morphine drip.

"Could you help me with this, Kate," he said, "I can't see properly."

Kate rushed round the bed, wiping away her own tears and hastily increased the rate of the pump's infusion.

Only a few days before they had cut these back because Amelia appeared to be undergoing a phase of remission from her cancer, experiencing much less pain and being able to go downstairs and walk around their house for the first time in months.

Soon the muscle-spasm that arched Amelia's back relaxed, and she subsided into a morphine-induced sleep.

"I'm afraid this looks like the end, Katie darling." Her father whispered. "The oncologist said it would reach her spine soon and that that would signal the final phase. We just have to accept it and make her as comfortable as possible."

"It can't be, can it?" cried Kate. "She was so well yesterday, walking about. She looked so happy as she looked at everything in the living room. She was on the mend."

"It often happens. Apparent remission. They said you can seem to get better for a while, then it hits you again, harder than ever," replied her father.

The Macmillan nurses called an hour later, changed her and made her more comfortable.

Amelia slipped slowly away. In the first hours she would open her eyes and look longingly at Katie or John, whoever was keeping watch, swabbing her brow and cleaning her mouth of the saliva gathering there and spilling over as she turned her head in a hopeless attempt to communicate. The only words they understood through the wheezing rattle of her attempts at speech were: "Thank you, thank you."

Later, she just laid passively, eyes closed, whimpering when any attempt was made to move her.

When Kate removed her oversized nappy to change her, she peed like a baby in the sudden rush of cold air.

She ceased eating. Kate and her father made numerous attempts to force teaspoons of water between her lips.

Towards the end her frail chest heaved in spasms as she took tiny gasps of air, three or four at a time, and then relaxed and didn't breathe for what seemed an eternity to Kate. Then she would repeat the process.

Her eyes were sunken in their sockets and her cheekbones and nose seemed to grow as the soft tissue dissolved beneath her almost translucent skin.

Seeing her mother visibly waste before her was too much for Kate, and it was almost with relief that she obeyed her father's instruction to "nip down to the shops to get us some dinner, or we'll starve."

When she returned, she saw her father standing quietly at the top of the stairs, looking vacant and lost.

"What is it?" She cried, running straight up the stairs to him, "What's happened?"

"She's dead. She died a few minutes ago. She just opened her eyes wide, took a deep breath and then collapsed back, giving a long sigh."

Kate ran in to her mother and was about to fly to the bed

17

to hug her, when she saw the strange expression of surprise in her mother's wide eyes and open mouth. She seemed beyond reach, now, untouchable. An involuntary shudder shook her to the core.

As Kate approached and looked down at the corpse of her mother, this cage in which her spirit had dwelt, it looked so empty. She gently pushed Amelia's lower jaw shut and closed her eyelids. Her mother's expression looked more peaceful now. More like her living self as she was in sleep.

But Kate would never forget that awful vision of life departed from this hollow shell, that had, in a different guise, borne Amelia through life and brought her, Katie, into being, now lying prostrate before her.

She leaned forward and kissed her mother on the brow, cupping her face in her hands, as Amelia had so often done when she thought Katie was asleep when she was a little girl.

Kate's recollections were interrupted by her father. "Nice lad, that Rob. Down to earth. Straightforward. I like that. Give us a hand with these tea things will you, Kate."

As he approached, she turned her head away from him.

"Are you alright?" John Pegler touched her on the shoulder. "It's mother, isn't it?"

Kate turned and they embraced. Kate's father hugged her tightly, as if by doing so he could somehow bring them all together again, bring his own dear Amelia back to life.

One day Kate was idly rummaging around in the attic. There were several trunks, of varying ages and styles, stacked against the eaves. Opening the first, she shone her torch inside. It was full of papers, letters and old photos. She decided to investigate this later.

In the next she found a treasure trove of old dresses, cloaks, boots and the like. She guessed they must have belonged to Amelia. She dragged out a bundle of likely looking dresses and hauled them down the loft-ladder to her bedroom.

Finding a beautiful dress in a crepe fabric cut on the bias in deep purple, with a triangular base hem, she ripped off her tee shirt and jeans, and put it on. It clung to her body like a skin. She went to her mother's full-length mirror, now in her room, and studied herself. It was fabulous. It made her look like a film star. She turned around. The dress swirled about her legs and settled gently to reveal her hips and thighs to be more shapely than she had ever imagined. She put on a pair of the soft leather, above the knee, boots.

She turned, and turned again, watching the skirt swirling gracefully, as if in slow motion. How lovely her mother must have appeared, wearing such an outfit.

She ran downstairs to show her father. At first he looked shocked, recognising his wife's outfits, then laughed: "I see you've been in the attic. That trunk's full of her oldest dresses," he explained, "ancient Biba dresses from the seventies she wore when we first met. She used to go to Oxfam shops in Kensington when she was a student."

"When did you meet, then?"

"Oh, back in eighty-six. That was two years before you were born. That dress suits you just as much as it did her. You know she could still fit into them until recently."

Going back upstairs she tried on several other dresses and tops of this type, soft cotton tee-shirts with balloon sleeves, unable to make up her mind which was the most sexy.

She resolved to wear them for school, regardless of their possible incongruity. She was sure their sheer elegance would be a hit with the boys, a total contrast to her modern or "Goth" companions. Worth a try, anyway, she thought.

Kate's friendship with Robert Ruddock grew as the term progressed. He showed her the short cut between their houses and she often took it to return from his cottage.

They had arranged that on the first Saturday of the Summer

half-term he would introduce her to the estate workers at Fugglesham Court and give her a guided tour of the stable courtyard and the outer buildings of the grand Elizabethan mansion.

As they walked around the grounds, Robert pointed out the various facets of the house: "Fugglesham Court is the seat of the Tercel family. They've been here since the 13th century, apparently.

It was originally a Great Hall house, but one Sir Gabriel de Tiercel, in the reign of Elizabeth, greatly expanded it into three wings. He built a West wing, matching the original, now the East wing and, joining the two wings, this great South façade with that gabled entrance in the middle.

He was a ruthless man, Gabriel. He removed the nearby hamlet on the South side of the house that housed his estate workers to make way for a grand vista and deer park. He was a fanatical hunter.

It's said he massacred the villagers when they objected, and there's other nasty tales about him as well, apparently, though I don't know myself. After a disastrous fire, in which he died, Gabriel's descendents further expanded the house on the north side into a series of courts, hence the present name."

"So who lives there now?" asked Kate, as they completed their tour around the outside of the buildings.

"Just the old General Tercel himself, and a few servants. We don't often see him. He's been a virtual recluse since his wife died, apparently."

"So he's all alone in that huge house? How sad." Kate felt a pang of compassion for a man with all that wealth but deprived of love and family.

"Oh, no. He's got a son, Gabriel. But he's always away. I've never seen him since I've been here."

They rounded the last court and returned through the great arch into the stable courtyard. "Want a cuppa before you go? I've got to help my Dad this afternoon in the woods, putting out the feed for the pheasants."

"Ok. Yes, thank you." Kate followed him into a sort of parlour.

"This is where Dad and the others eat when they're not out on the estate. It's empty at the moment, it not being lunchtime yet. I'm meeting him here soon."

He made her a cup of tea and passed her a huge biscuit-barrel. The windows in this room were so dusty that the courtyard outside was only hazily visible. As they drank their tea, Kate could see blurred figures passing to and fro outside.

"I'd better go," she said, "I know you're busy."

"Never too busy for you," answered Robert with a broad grin. "Next time you come round I'll take you out on the quad bike. It's brilliant. We use it to transport the feed for the pheasants around the woods where the paths are too small for a tractor. I'll have to get my Dad to agree, first. You'll have to cling on tight, you know, if you're not going to fall off, and I've got a spare helmet."

"Thanks. I'll really look forward to that," Kate said, as she walked towards the door. "Bye."

As she opened it she met the first of the estate workers trickling in for their lunch break. She walked to Robert's cottage and then down the lane towards the village and her home.

3

The hamlet

The next day Kate took the shortcut to Robert's house through the orchards and woods. It was the first time she had taken this path in this direction on her own. A few hundred yards into the woods she came to a junction from which four paths split from her own.

She was confused. She didn't remember this junction. When she had come this way with Rob, like a passenger in a car, she must have had left it to the driver to navigate. She chose what seemed the most likely route to Rob's house and proceeded into the wood.

Soon she realized the path was unfamiliar. Why hadn't she paid attention, she thought? Still, she felt this path was leading in the right direction at least. It must eventually bring her out somewhere near her destination, if not directly to it.

The path meandered through the deepening gloom as if it was undecided as to which way to go or, Kate thought, to deliberately confuse.

A cobweb caught her across the face and glued there. She had wiped her face with a shudder. She looked up. The sun shafted through the leaves, spotlighting the birds flitting from branch to branch. Though all seemed perfectly normal, she couldn't shake off the feeling that something was watching her.

Suddenly the warning of that weird man, Shabby Tattler,

came into her head. This feeling of being watched, she felt, must somehow involve the birds that he had said had been acting 'peculiar of late'. She dismissed the idea as ridiculous, a fantasy engendered by the old man's warning.

She strode ahead. But the feeling persisted, that somehow the birds were following her. A wren danced in a bush alongside her, whirring angrily. She felt as if she were trespassing on the birds' domain, a domain in which she, as a human, had no right.

Round a bend, the path led into a clearing. As she entered the glade, she saw that it was occupied by a hamlet of small cottages, more like hovels than homes. Standing and sitting in the shady doorways were some old villagers, eyeing her cagily.

The villagers appeared to be throwbacks to an earlier era, like the figures from a Constable painting. Dirty and dishevelled, they wore old-fashioned country smocks not seen for a hundred years at least, she reckoned. Perhaps they were a tribe of those old charcoal-burners she had heard inhabited the woods, eking out a primitive living, coppicing and making charcoal deep in the forest, self-sufficient in most things and almost completely isolated from modern society.

Their huts were rudimentary. Many had heavy hangings over their entrances instead of doors and wooden shutters over the window spaces, which had no glass. Pigs and cur-dogs rooted around, picking at and fighting over scraps in the muddy lanes between the huts. Chickens and ducks scratted in the dirt at the edges of the village and around the ponds.

She walked up to the nearest of the old villagers, introduced herself and asked with as much boldness as she could muster, "Is this the Fugglesham Estate? Do you people work for General Tercel?"

"Not on your nelly, Miss. We don't 'ave no truck with them evil de Teerzels nor with that Fugglesham Hall neither." The old man spat a huge gob onto the earth in front of Kate and

23

stamped on it with some venom, squashing it into the mud. "An we don't want no nosey-parkers nebbin' around on behalf of his Lordship nor nothin' like that."

The man jabbed his thumb disgustedly over his right shoulder as he said this, and Kate's eyes were drawn to the horizon behind him. Through a gap in the trees she could just make out a silhouette in the distance of a great house. It could only be Fugglesham Court.

"Why there it is!" she exclaimed.

"And there it'll stay, till the end," remarked the man ominously. "Who're you, then, if not spyin' out on us here?"

"I'm not a spy. Honestly. I'm nothing to do with Fugglesham or General Tercel. I moved here with my father recently after my mother died. We live in what used to be Old Tom's cottage, apparently." Kate did her best to nice to the old man, smiling and chattering in a friendly but not too inquisitive fashion.

After a time he mellowed, "My name's Jack Herne. I'm the head of this here village. That there's my brother, Frank. We're the fishermen what looks after the fish-stocks in the long pond and the rest. Them used to be the mill-ponds for the iron-works, but them's long gone."

Jack Herne pulled aside the curtain to his cottage, "Come inside and meet the missus. Bessie! Bessie Buntie! Where be you?" He peered into the darkness.

"I'm here stupid," she cried, clanging a wooden ladle on the side of a huge cast-iron cooking pot Kate could now just make out hanging over the embers of an open hearth in the middle of the hut.

Smoke curled up lazily towards a tattered hole in the apex of the roof. The whole room was smoky, and the roof-beams soot-blackened, as Kate discovered when she walked straight into one. She rubbed her head and her hands came away covered in black dust.

"If you can't see me, you must be getting blind's a bat,

24

Frankie boy," she laughed, "there's plenty here for even a blind man to be getting' a hold on."

Bessie Buntie was a large buxom cheerful-looking woman in a grubby yellow dress that hung like a tent to the floor. "All we got is a little bit o' bread and no cheese, but you're right welcome, sweetie, so long as you're not fussy."

She held out a rough chunk of hand-made bread that Kate did not dare refuse, for fear of offending her. "If you come again, I'm sure my Jack will go catch a nice trout for the young lady, won't you Jack. He's a good fisher, our Jack is."

"That I will, if you come back on our side," said Jack Herne. Kate wondered what he meant by "on our side" and guessed it had something to do with the villagers' animosity towards the Tercel family.

"I'd love to come again," said Kate eagerly. "I'm free at the weekends, though I have to go to school during the week,"

"Don't go much on weekends, we don't. Not since that day. What day is it then, today?" asked Jack.

"Er, Friday?" replied Kate, wondering how they could possibly not know.

"What's this school, then, where you work?" asked Bessie Buntie. "Do they pay well?"

"No." replied Kate, "They don't pay. I just go to learn."

"Like an apprentice, you mean," Bessie asked.

"Well no. Yes, I mean, sort of," Kate was confused. Were they teasing her? She didn't think so. They seemed to be just simple or rather, not simple, but ignorant.

Just then two large men dressed in green with red felt caps, looking rather like characters out of Robin Hood, walked up to the door. "You in there Jack Herne? We got a load of kindlin' for you and the folks."

Jack went to the door and greeted them. After a few minutes of chatter that Kate couldn't quite catch, Jack leaned back in and shouted: "Come on out Kate. This here's Jack Yaffler and that's Jack Eccles. They're woodsmen. They cut

25

our hurdles and kindling and such."

"How do you do?" asked Kate, "If you don't mind me saying, you seem to have a lot of Jacks around."

"Jack's a poplar name hereabouts. We got a Jack Straw, our pastor, and a Jack Nicker too," chuckled Bessie Buntie, " in fact you could say we got a Jack o' All Trades! No doubt you'll meet them bye-an-bye."

" Where's your cousin, then – Emmet Peel?" asked Jack Herne of Jack Yaffles.

"He's a law unto himself, he is. He comes and goes. You never know when he's going to turn up next, you don't. Last I heard he went south, but he'll be back in time for the meetin'," replied Jack Yaffles.

"What meeting is that?" inquired Kate.

"Beggin' your pardon, miss," replied Jack Herne, " but that's our business an none o' yours." ·

"Oh, I'm sorry, I didn't mean to be nosey," Kate blushed with embarrassment.

"Don't worry, miss, no offence given nor taken, I reckon," added his brother Frank, patting her on the shoulder. "But some matters is best left private, so to speak."

"Of course," said Kate, feeling a little less excluded by this touch of affection. She chewed on the chunk of bread, thinking that it did taste really good, if heavy and a little bit gritty.

While they were talking, Kate cast her eyes towards the silhouette of the distant house. A strange feeling came over her that it looked somehow different from here to the way she remembered it from her visits with Robert.

She decided that she would try to get a little closer to the house from this viewpoint on another occasion to fix in her mind the detail of its roofline and windows so that she could compare them with her close-up impressions.

She didn't dare head directly for the house to get a better view for fear of offending the villagers. Clearly there had been a major falling out in the past leading to this desire on their part to remain separate and hidden. She decided to keep the secret of their existence to herself until she had resolved the issue of the peculiar alienation permeating this hamlet and its aspect to the great house.

So she asked Jack Herne if he would guide her towards the village cottages and that he willingly did. They parted at the edge of the woods on a path that she found familiar. "That's as far as I'll go, me dear. Don't like to interfere with them outsider folks. Rather, let them be, like."

Kate spent the rest of the day looking up old farm workers costumes on the internet.

The nearest thing she could find to what she had seen was in some illustrations from an Elizabethan manuscript. But she thought this must just be a fluke, and decided to go to the main library in the nearby market town to research it more thoroughly, together with the history of the district.

The following morning she went straight to the house with the excuse of asking after Robert, who had been busy lately helping his father in his game-keeping role.

On being told he was not in the courtyard area, she said she would go in search of him.

She walked slowly round the whole house at a slight distance, comparing each façade with that in her memory. She decided it must have been the Eastern façade she had been looking at from the hidden hamlet. According to Robert, this was once the main façade when the house had been a great hall house. It had been superseded during the Elizabethan rebuilding of the house by the Southern façade and had then become the East wing.

Somehow, though, as she stared at it now, it seemed less imposing than it had been yesterday.

She looked back, away from the house, looking for the hamlet where she had been standing yesterday. There was no village to be seen, just the family's chapel and graveyard on the edge of woodland. It occurred to her that the village might only be visible from an upstairs window in the house and decided that somehow she must inveigle her way into the house and go upstairs to check it out.

In the meantime, she counted the windows on both floors and noted the gables on the roofline and the shape of the chimney stacks. There were six gables above the attic windows on this side. Except the Southernmost window, all the windows on the first floor were bricked up, and on the ground floor the wall was largely bare except at the north end, where two windows were set almost at ground level.

She returned home and helped her father in the orchard for the rest of the day.

The next morning she rose early, sneaked out of the house and ran along the path towards the junction where she had left Jack Herne two days earlier. She followed the path leading towards their village until she saw it through the trees.

Here she left the path and forced her way through the underbrush to a place she guessed would put her between the village and the house. Sure enough, she found a continuation of the clearing in which the hamlet stood and looking in the opposite direction, could see the house.

She was much closer to it now, and could make out its roofline and windows quite clearly. There were still six gables, but each stood at the apex of an arched window rising through a full story-height. Below these windows there was what looked like a nook for a door, and a series of undercroft windows, of which only the two at the north end were there yesterday when she had looked close-up.

Kate rubbed her eyes. What was going on? How could this same façade have changed so? It was impossible and yet here she was, looking at a different house. It was as if she were seeing this wing as it might have been when it was a great hall.

She crept forward stealthily, as if by making a noise she might suddenly send the whole illusion crashing down, for she felt it must be some trick of the light or perspective that made the house seem so different today.

Eventually she gained the edge of the wood and walked slowly forward until she reached a shady spot at the edge of the Eastern lawn. Here she sat down to think.

Something that was impossible was happening to her, here in this god-forsaken corner of the countryside. Peasants dressed in 16th century costumes, apparently, keeping themselves hidden away in a secret hamlet that couldn't be seen from the house, and yet from which the house could clearly be seen. A house that changed according to the way she approached it, as if she were seeing it in different times. And a strange yet not forbidding man who had appeared out of the blue and given her dire warnings of disasters to come.

She looked hard at the house. It remained just as it was when she had seen it from the woods.

She studied the windows. There were definitely no attic windows now; just these tall arched Gothic style windows with elegant stone tracery.

Her eye caught a movement at ground level. She saw a shadowy figure emerge from within a shadowed recess in the wall towards the southern end. It paused, its hunched form facing the wall for a moment. It turned briefly towards her, as if noticing her presence, then flew swiftly away to the North, hugging close to the wall before disappearing around the far corner

Thinking it must be Shabby Tattler, Kate wondered why he should be lurking there so furtively and race away when he saw her watching him. What could he have been doing in that recess? She hurried across the lawn towards the house.

Reaching the recess, Kate discovered that it was a small

arched porch with a heavy oak door. Strange that she hadn't noticed it the day before. She felt around until she found a handle and tried it. It was locked. "So, Shabby Tattler must have been locking it when I saw him. But why? And why did he flee so hurriedly when he saw me? What, behind that door," she wondered "could make him act like he did?"

Frustrated, Kate was about to go when she spotted an object lying in the grass by the entrance. It was a large black iron key. "He must have dropped it in his haste," she thought, "I'll try it in the lock."

"Kate!" It was Rob's voice calling her from across the lawn. Damn, she thought, I'll have to try again later. I hope he didn't see me pick it up.

"I'm coming!" She waved cheerily to him and trotted over to him. "I was just on my way round to see you," she lied.

"What were you doing up against that wall?" Rob asked.

"Oh, nothing. I just thought I saw something in the grass there, but it was just an old stick."

Robert looked at her a little curiously, but then said: "I was just going to go fishing. I've got the afternoon off. Do you want to come? It's a beautiful day and it's nice and peaceful down by the lake. I know a real suntrap down there. We could take a picnic."

"Oh, ok," she replied a little flatly, annoyed that she couldn't now resume her exploration, but relieved that he hadn't noticed the key. "I've nothing special to do today."

4

Fishing

The two of them returned to Robert's cottage where he gathered up his fishing gear and grabbed some food that he slung in a small rucksack.

They wandered idly down towards his quiet spot, Robert decapitating bracken tops with his folded rod and Kate admiring the butterflies flitting about the hedgerow.

Robert set up his fishing line, resting the rod on a stand and weighting the base. He didn't tell Kate that he had no intention of catching anything – he was using the wrong bait and had placed his rod in an unlikely spot – he wanted the excuse to keep her here as long as possible.

She watched the float settle as ripples spread out and slowly subsided. He laid out a towel and placed the food and a bottle of beer from one of his deep jacket pockets onto it.

"Right, sit you down and let's eat." He sat cross-legged, pulled out a penknife, jerked off the bottle top then started to cut the loaf into thick slices.

Kate sat beside him, watching with amusement his movements as he cut the cheese into rough chunks and folded them into the bread to form extremely crude sandwiches. He handed her one. As she started to chew she mused on the feeling of warm security that seemed to emanate from him and enfold her like a duvet. It was sense of complete familiarity, as if she had known him forever. Given the strangeness of this place, she wondered how it was that she had struck up an immediate intimacy of trust with two such different people as Rob and Shabby Tattler.

"Try this, it's nice with cheese," Robert insisted, as he gently force-fed her some beer from the bottle while her mouth was still full. Kate felt the melting of the bread, the pleasant mingling of the warm beer and ripe cheddar: a nutty acidity and creaminess she had never experienced, a novelty that seemed so appropriate to this place and her mood.

She lay back, glowing – watching his form against the clouds, listening to the breeze among the leaves and the small buzzing of insects, murmuring contentment. These gentle noises, the breeze tickling across the hairs on her skin, tempering the sun's warmth, were so soporific that she drifted into a dreamy sleep...

She is with Rob. They are walking hand-in-hand through the forest. It seems unusually tranquil.

Suddenly it dawns on her that she can hear no birdsong. The realization brings on a deep disquiet, a sense of profound foreboding.

She looks at Rob. He is smiling, and yet his smile seems unfamiliar. His eyes hollow, lifeless. It is as if time has slowed, as if they are wading in a dreamlike somnolence towards something awful. It feels as if the ground is slipping away from her: as fast as she tries to go forward she is held in a weightless void, treading water. A trembling shock of inevitability skitters up her spine.

Sunlight. A clearing ahead. A huddle of figures with their backs to her. Cloaked figures. A low incantation reaches her ears, indistinct, as if the sound were travelling through water, reverberating through her body.

Something furtive, uncanny, about their demeanour. A head, turning momentarily towards her and as quickly turning back. The gesture: confused? Caught out?

A murmuring. More faces, turning towards her, hidden under their hoods. What are they doing here? Why hiding like this? Who are they?

One advances towards her, arms outstretched. The hood slips back: a face, smiling, welcoming. An ashen, blood-drained face, gashed from temple to jaw, flesh hanging raggedly in strips from its bony cheek-bones...

The figure beckons her, keeps on coming towards her. Others turn and they too, approach. All are scarred, disfigured, maimed, some limbless, some split open from shoulder to waist, all chanting...

Kate grips Rob's arm tightly, utters a whimpering scream, turns and runs. Runs blindly into the forest, stumbling through a wasteland of dead thickets. But her running is slow motion and the thickets are like underwater weeds, enveloping her limbs and dragging her down...

A loud splash and flash roused her instantly. Kate turned away from the glare of the sun, which momentarily blinded her as she opened her eyes, and sat up.

Rob had vanished, leaving a mess of picnic leftovers and clothes scattered on the grass. Standing up, Kate looked out over the lake. Ripples were spreading from close to the small wooden jetty jutting out into the lake. She ran over to it. There was no sign of him. She walked along the jetty, peering into the water, heart beating fast.

There was a sudden splash beside her and a clammy hand gripped her ankle. She silently screamed and looked down.

"You idiot!" she laughed as Rob's head emerged, dripping water. He shook it, spraying her legs and skirt.

"Come on in, it's great," he laughed, "or the demon of the lake will drag you... to the muddy bottom!" He slapped a great clod of grey-brown goo onto her shoe.

"Stop it!"

"Come on in, then" he threatened.

33

"But I've got no swimming costume."

"Nor have I." He laughed, turned and dived under, flashing his bare buttocks before disappearing.

In a sudden impulse, as if to divest herself of those horrors of her imagining, she flung off her dress and shoes, hesitated, then cast off her bra and panties and quickly dived in before Rob surfaced again.

As she sputtered to the surface, she found herself face to face with him.

"It's easy, isn't it?" He beamed broadly at her with a hint of wickedness in his eyes. "Race you to the middle - where that post sticks out, see?"

"But what about reeds and things, can't they catch you and drag you under?" she asked, a little nervously.

"None here. Not towards the middle. Only near the edge of the lake. Come on." He turned and started swimming.

She raced after him, catching up with him and then overtaking him. Suddenly she found her ankle grasped again, herself pulled up short and somehow treading water in his loose embrace.

She put her hands on his shoulders to catch her breath. She could feels his muscles rippling under her fingers as he moved his arms to keep them both afloat. She slipped one arm round his neck and slid her other hand slowly down his chest, feeling muscle, tiny hard nipples, and the hairiness between.

He was grinning inanely in her face as her hand continued its exploratory meandering, fingering his belly-button, slipping lower...

Suddenly he wrenched free and started swimming towards the jetty, yelling over his shoulder, "Come on. Catch me if you can."

She chased after him and arrived at the jetty just as he heaved himself up and onto the pier in one movement, as effortless as an otter rising from the water into the sunshine, defying gravity.

Only inches from her eyes, the arch of his back in a cascade of sparkling water was followed by the flash of white angular buttocks and thighs. A sudden twist of his torso and he was sitting on the pier, grinning down at her, extending a helping hand, "Come on."

"But I'm naked. Turn away."

He turned his head to one side, but found her hand as she reached up, briefly squeezed it, grasped her wrist and lifted her bodily into the air.

"Oh!" Raised to his level, she was flicked about to sit beside him in the sunshine, naked. Glancing at his body beside her, she jumped up, hastily gathered up her clothes, ran to the towel on the grass, picked it up and wrapped herself up in it.

He approached her, stark naked, watching her expression as she took him in. He reached her and, looking directly into her eyes, snatched away the towel, whispering: "Don't. Let the sun do it. I want to see the droplets evaporate on your pearly skin."

He laid the towel down and bowed towards her, indicating her place. She burst out laughing at this ludicrous scene – his gallant gesture under these circumstances.

Giggling, she lay down obediently on her tummy and crossed her arms under her chin, looking sideways up at his brazen nudity.

He lay down beside her and turned her gently so that she lay on her back. He leaned over her and kissed her deeply, slowly. Moved by this, she touched his flanks with feathered fingers She returned his kiss with lips grown soft, drawing him into herself.

He began to press upon her. She pushed him back, away from her, muttering, "No. Not now, not here, not yet..."

She felt him tense, relax, slump back; felt his acute disappointment in the tightening of his mouth, the movement of his Adam's apple as he closed his eyes and sighed.

Suddenly she felt out of place, naked, here beside him. She reached out for her dress and hastily put it on.

"What are you doing?" Rob asked as he, too, hastily got dressed.

"I'm going home, " she retorted.

"You're not angry, are you?"

He looked so worried that it made her smile and stroked his cheek with the back of her hand. "No, I'm not. But I've got to go."

She ran off, leaving him standing there; foolish, bemused... pleased.

5

Shabby Tattler

"What were you doing by that hidden door in the East wing?" asked Kate.

Shabby Tattler looked at her, a little surprised. "Door? There ain't no door there, me dear," he replied.

"Yes there is, I'll show you." Kate led him round the yard to the east wing of the house and on to the shadowed recess.

On the way it occurred to her that it was very odd that she should have bumped into him like this, just when she had resolved to confront him with the key and ask why he had skulked off like that. Perhaps he was returning to retrieve the lost key when they met.

"Here it is." she announced triumphantly, looking back at him.

"What is?"

"The door – in this recess – look!" Suddenly she felt queer, a little giddy, as if the world was turning under her, confusing dream and reality.

"Ain't no door there, look. Just like I said."

Where the door had been just yesterday, a plain stone wall faced her. "How did that happen? There was a door. And there you were, locking it. And when you saw me, you ran off in a hurry. Why?"

"Not me. I ain't been here for awhile."

"But it was you. It must have been. You had a long

37

black cloak, just like now." She looked at him, searching desperately for an answer. He grinned back.

"You're having me on. It was you, and I can prove the door was there. You dropped the key! I've got it."

At this, his smile evaporated, "A key? Where've you got it?"

"There, see," she laughed. "It was you - you know about the key. I've got it, safe and sound, and I won't give it back until you tell me what this is all about - creeping around like a thief."

"That key. It ain't mine. If you got it, then it's yours to figure. It's a mystery right enough. But it's your mystery." He scratched his head and put his hat back on. "It's a puzzling' conundrum, all the same."

"But won't you help me?" she pleaded, suddenly uncertain, grabbing his arm, "if it wasn't you, then who was it? And how did the door disappear?"

"Well, this wall, she's as hard as rock. How you saw a door here's not easy to explain. Now how did you come upon it, like?"

"I came through the woods. Just before midday, I think. Because Rob came along just after and we went for a picnic by the lake."

"Rob? Weren't he curious? About the door, I mean?"

"No. He didn't see it, or the man. And I didn't show him the key."

"I see. Figured you'd keep it all to yourself, did ye?"

" Well, I... I didn't think, actually. And then he distracted me."

The old man thought awhile and then a sparkle lit his eye. "Just an idea, mind. But if you were to bring along that there key, just around the same time of day, like, along the very same route you followed yesterday. Then maybe that there door would appear like, all ready for unlockin'."

"That's crazy."

"No crazier than you grabbin' the key to a door as don't exist! And holdin' onto it, what's more."

"Ok. I'll try it. But what do you think will be inside?"

"I don't know for sure. But maybe this got to do with Black Martin."

"Black Martin? Who's he?"

"He's the feller you saw. What you mistook for me."

"Who is he?"

"Trouble! If you see him, steer well clear. Understand me? Steer well clear. 'Tis my idea you'll find summat mighty strange through that there door. So, you be careful, now. Tread right wary."

She grabbed his lapels, "Can't you come with me, please?"

"Can't do that. 'Tis your mystery to unravel, an none but you can do it, if my reckonin' be right."

Old man Tattler turned towards the woods and ambled off in his unhurried way, leaving ugly thoughts flapping about her head like crows about a carcass.

She resolved to return at noon the next day with the key, hoping against all commonsense that the door would reappear.

6

The room

As she entered the room, Kate noticed it was veiled in an
unnatural silence. Sunlight shafted obliquely down from
arched windows set high in its walls; too high to see out
of. The lower part had been bricked up, giving the whole a
church-aisle like appearance. Dust specks swirled upwards in
the shafts of light like smoke, as if her entry had disturbed a
profound stillness.

As her eyes became accustomed to the gloom, she started
to notice her surroundings. The room was cavernous, a vast
hall, the heavy forms of a crude hammer-beam roof just
discernible, rising into the darkness above the windows. The
walls were wood-panelled to half their height, overhung in
part by dull tapestries. In the centre of the west wall was set
a large fireplace, unlit, but with an impressive carved stone
mantel.

Picked out by a shaft of sunlight on the far side of the
room, she saw a half-lit hooded figure, seated before a frame
of peculiar construction. Beyond, a wood-panelled screen
crossed the width of the hall, into both ends of which were set
arched doors, presumably leading to further chambers. One
of these was open, but there was darkness beyond. The scene
had the thick dusty atmosphere of a Rembrandt painting.

With key in hand she had returned at the appointed hour.

The door was there, just as Shabby Tattler had predicted. She had unlocked it, entered, shut it carefully and climbed a narrow, steep, dark, spiral staircase. At the head of the stair he had found a second door with a key in the lock. Unlocking it, she had entered a dark hall set on first-floor level. She imagined a crypt-like vaulted under croft lying beneath this room into which little daylight flowed, and wondered how one could reach that and what it might contain.

She paused for a moment by the door, walked slowly forward. As she approached the seated figure, she could make out that it was a woman, dressed in a medieval sort of costume, sitting at what looked like a half-finished tapestry. This alone was fully lit by the shafting sun and was resplendent with colour.

The woman's head turned, and Kate saw indistinctly in the reflected light of the tapestry a seemingly beautiful face, framed in a hood of soft maroon velvet. The woman looked startled and her hands jumped briefly to her cheeks, and she uttered a strange little gurgling sound.

Kate paused, not wishing to alarm the lady.

The woman stood. She came slowly over to Kate and touched her face with the tips of her fingers, as if she was part blind. Then she grasped Kate by the shoulders and gently steered her into the full glare of the shaft of light. She stood before her, regarding her, caressing her face and neck and hair. Slowly the strange look of recognition that Kate thought she had seen in the woman's eyes faded, replaced by a look of loving sadness.

Kate was bewildered by this demonstration of clear affection on the woman's part. She stood still and let the woman continue exploring, somehow sensing the woman was dumb, speaking through her hands and the touch of fingertips. The woman embraced her now so tenderly that Kate dared not push her away. She felt hot tears trickle down

41

her cheeks. Why was the woman crying?

The woman pulled away, returned to her seat, took a sheet of odd-looking yellow paper out of a small drawer in a bureau beside her and began to write. She wrote fast and fluently, as if writing was her occupation.

Kate watched as the lady, finishing, sprinkled some powder over the page, shook it and blew lightly over it, sending small white clouds swirling in the shafts of lights.

The woman turned to Kate and offered it to her. The paper was almost translucent and heavy, the writing peculiar: a spidery italic, neatly formed. It took Kate a while to decipher it, to become accustomed to the strange script.

"Sweet Katie," it read, "you are returned at last to me. You are older now, but unmistakably mine. My happiness at seeing you is mingled with sorrow that it has been so long... that you have not sought me before now."

Kate's hands were quivering, making reading difficult. She was becoming confused and scared. Who was this woman, who knew her name and talked of her return, of an intimacy that could not be?

"You see my plight. I am struck dumb, a prisoner in this room. Only you can rescue me. Set me free, Katie, my darling daughter..."

At this point Kate dropped the letter, her hands shaking. She looked up at the woman: "I don't know who you are, how you know my name, or what game you are playing, but you are frightening me. Stop it! I am not your daughter. You are not my mother. My mother died four months ago."

As Kate bent to pick up the letter again, the woman approached, arms outstretched to embrace her.

"Stop it! Stop it. Go away. You are not my mother." Kate pushed her away and the woman's hood slipped as she stepped back into a shaft of sunlight. Kate fleetingly saw the auburn glow of her long hair, the delicate alabaster skin, the blue, blue eyes, the anguished sorrowful expression, so familiar… her own mother's face!

"It can't be! She's dead. Who are you?" Kate screamed.

The lady advanced towards her again. Kate turned and fled. Slamming the hall door and locking it, she ran down the winding stairs, in her haste careless of her arms scraping the rough stone walls.

Reaching the outer door, she opened it, pushed through, slammed it to behind her and, fumbling for the key, locked it again and collapsed in the arch, panting for breath.

As she regained her composure she noticed that, still gripped tight in her left hand, she had the crumpled paper of that letter. She stuffed it into her pocket and made her way back to her cottage and went straight up to her room.

She sat on her bed, took out the letter and unfurled it to look at it again. Its ink had smudged and run, but she could just read most of it. She slowly reread this mysterious letter, growing more and more agitated as she did so.

"…set me free, Katie, my darling daughter.

"They told me you were dead; they told me you had been killed in that dreadful massacre, along with all our family.

"But in my deepest heart I could not believe you dead. It has been my hope, sustaining me through all these cursed years of slavery, that you had escaped and would return one day… find a way… to free me… to avenge the ignominy of our fate.

"I see you are impatient and my silence frustrates you. So I will write no more, my darling Katie, except to repeat my utter joy in beholding you once again."

Who could this woman be, Kate wondered, who called herself her mother? How could she possibly know her name? Not only her name but the pet name only her mother had ever called her by: Katie? She recalled that shock of recognition she had felt as the facial features and even expression of her own mother had appeared so clearly in that of this strange woman. But what of her imprisonment? For

43

imprisoned she surely was. But by whom and why? Surely the old general couldn't have locked up his wife and pretended she had died? Maybe she had gone mad and had to be locked away to live in her delusions? But then his wife would have to have a twin sister, her own mother who was an only child. Impossible. If not that, what? And why mute, if, as she claimed, she was her own mother? A ghost imprisoned in a silence of the dead? Too absurd. The questions rampaging through her head were too disturbing to contemplate.

Who, Kate wondered, could she possibly turn to? Certainly not to anyone in the great house. She would have to reveal that she had stolen a key and sneaked into a part of the house that, to all appearances, didn't exist. They would rightly assume her to be mad. Who, then, would believe her preposterous tale? Rob? He was too straightforward to accept such craziness. She daren't risk losing his trust and intimacy.

There was the letter! This, at least, existed. And strange it was, too. Not written on any paper she had ever seen. It looked hand-made. And the script: so old-fashioned and scrawly, with funny flourishes. It could almost be medieval, Tudor or something.

Shabby Tattler! Suddenly that strange old man with the twinkling eye seemed to be her only hope. He it was who had said that the question of what lay beyond that door was her own mystery to unfold. Did he know more than he was letting on? She decided that the ragged tramp was the only one in whom she could confide her weird experiences in that room.

He had an openness to, if not knowledge of, the mysteries of this place. He almost seemed an integral thread in the fabric of strangeness that hung over the house and the woods surrounding.

She fell asleep fully dressed on her bed, her hand still clutching the letter. Her father, looking in on her later, decided

44

not to disturb her rest, and returned downstairs quietly to put her dinner in the oven, in case she should wake hungry.

7

The ring

Kate awoke with the room buzzing with flies. A shaft of sunlight forced open her eyelids and blinded her. She turned away from the brightness and noise. She covered her ears.

Still the flies persisted with their loud buzzing. They were in her head. She jumped out of bed and headed for the shower to wash away those dreadful flies. She had slept badly. She had a hangover. She could not decide whether the bizarre encounter yesterday had been a dream or had actually occurred.

She had the letter it was true. But how had she come by it? She felt as if she had been drugged, as if someone, someone who knew of her distress at her mother's death, had forged a letter from this woman purporting to be a reincarnation of Amelia, her mother, and implanted by suggestion the bizarre tale surrounding its appearance.

Kate didn't know what to do, whether to confront Shabby Tattler – for if there was a hoaxer, it must be him – or take the letter for analysis at some museum. But would they take her seriously? She was beginning to feel that her perception was becoming so kaleidoscopic she might lose her grounding altogether, and end up in a clinic, diagnosed schizophrenic or something weird.

She decided she needed something, an escape to the ordinary - Rob. He had a cheerful capacity she found quite charming. He was so matter-of-fact she found herself at ease in his company. His company would be just the tonic for her today.

"Come on, then, lazy bugger, Rob!" she shouted, lobbing a pebble up at Robert's bedroom window.

Rob's face appeared at the window of his cottage. "What time is it?"

"Nearly seven o'clock! Come on. We're going for a walk. You promised. Have you forgotten?"

"No, of course not. I'll be down in a minute."

She laughed. He was too polite to contradict her. He hadn't promised at all. She had just made it up. But he would come anyway.

The door opened. "Come in. Have you had any breakfast?"

"No. I'm starving. Look! I've picked some mushrooms." She hugged him and followed him into the kitchen. She made some tea and then sat in a corner of the kitchen, watching him as he fried some bacon and eggs to go with her fresh mushrooms.

He was strong, firm and simple. Not thick - but uncomplicated. There was no cunning, no deception in him. She liked him for this.

In his presence she felt inured to the traumas of the last few days.

As they ate, he asked: "Where shall we go, then?"

"I don't know. Away from here. I want to get away from everyone for a day."

"I know. We'll go for a long walk on the downs. There's a secret path that'll take us straight up. It's a bit steep, but no one will see us going," he replies, "and we'll take a proper picnic with us, with wine, to celebrate."

"Celebrate what?" asked Kate.

"Life," laughed Robert, "what else?"

Leaving Rob's cottage by the back door, they followed a track going west into the woods. To their right the woods were mainly overgrown stands of hazel and chestnut coppice. Older mixed oak woodland on their left rolled away towards the downs, giving way to beech and yew as it climbed into the still-deep shade of its northern slopes.

Down here, though, the climbing sun was beaming through the leaves, drawing a mist from the damp ground and creating a fine display of silvery shafts of light through which the couple walked, their figures alternately silhouetted and highlighted with gold.

Suddenly Rob started to his left and cried: "Here we are! My secret path."

He pointed towards a thick clump of seemingly impenetrable holly. "My dog found it. I call it 'Smugglers' Way', because it would have been perfect. Look!"

He laughed as he parted the bushes and Kate found herself being propelled gently through into a tunnel-like track way heading due south. It was set in a groove in the landscape, bordered by holly and ancient yew, so that it was dark and not a little spooky.

"Are you sure this is ok?" she touched his arm.

"Yeah, its great, isn't it?" He took her hand and led her on enthusiastically, "you can just imagine the smugglers using it, can't you? They could bring large teams of packhorses hidden down here to supply the big house, no problem. There are tales that the early lords got a lot of their money through smuggling. And I bet this was their road - its too deliberately made not to be. And the entrance at the top is just as well hidden, you'll see." ·

Climbing a steep gully bounded by the same holly and yew, though more stunted, they could still see nothing of the surrounding landscape. Eventually they came to a large spreading yew in the hollow centre of the path. "This is it, path's end!"

Rob scrambled up the chalky slope facing them, seemingly into the branches of the yew. He parted them and Kate screwed her eyes against the sudden brightness.

"Come on up" He hauled her into the sunlight and she found herself standing on the edge of the tree line on the upper slopes of the downs. The branches of this yew were actually lying on the ground, completely concealing the hollow rut beyond. "Good, eh?" he added.

"Yes, it would make a perfect smugglers' trail," she agreed.

The sun here was burning through the morning mists on the top of the downs, revealing glimpses of a shimmering sea away to the south. They set off along the ridge with the ground falling away to their right, revealing the forest far below stretching away to the north, wreathed in mist.

"No wonder they are called 'Hangers', these slopes," Rob said. "It feels as if you could jump straight out into the woods down there. We're going to the 'Ring'; its my favourite place at this time of day."

They soon came to a clump of beech trees, which they enter. The 'Ring' was a circle of beech planted in the confines of an ancient circular hill-fort, whose smooth trunks glowed marvellously in the morning light.

"Its magical," Kate exclaimed, looking around in awe.

"I know, and this is only the outer ring of old beech trees that remains now. So just imagine how amazing it must have been when this whole great circle was full of beech trees like this.

"What happened to all the others?" asked Kate.

"They were all blown down in the great storm of eighty-seven. Only the outer ones remained standing because they had much stronger roots, having taken for years the full force of the winds and protecting the trees in the centre. But that storm was a mighty one. Blew down half the trees in the county."

Kate wandered slowly between the trunks along the edge

of the wood. Distorted by the winds sweeping up from the sea, their writhing forms, caught fleetingly in shafts of light burning through swirling mists, made it seem as if the trees themselves were dancing.

She put her hand out to touch the nearest tree. She felt its smooth grey bark and looked at the sinuous curves of its branches stretching up towards the pale green canopy of leaves.

She whispered to Rob: "You know, these trees, up here on this bare hill looking out over the sea, are just so beautiful. It makes me feel somehow as if I belong here."

"So do I," Robert interrupted, "feel like that... being here with you, that is..."

He paused, awkwardly fumbling with his shirt.

As she turned to look at him, he suddenly embraced her. Kate smiled at him, relaxed in his arms and they kissed.

Kate nestled her head in the hollow of his shoulder. He lowered her gently onto the soft grassy bank that encircled the trees...

"Well, well, what have we here! A rural idyll, no less. The young shepherd and his ewe, nursing his flock!" A hard laugh accompanied this rude interruption.

Hastily Kate and Rob disentangled and started to pull on their clothes. Mortified, furious at being caught so flagrantly in their intimacy, Rob retorted: "What the hell are you doing here? Creeping up on us like that?"

"I could well ask you the same," replied the voice, chuckling.

Kate looked up to see the stranger staring blatantly at her breasts. Quickly covering herself, she cried: "Do you mind?"

"Not at all," replied the young man, smiling and gazing directly into her eyes, "your beauty complements that of the trees so perfectly."

Rob, doing up his belt, started as if to jump up and strike

the man, but Kate stayed his arm and said: "Look, please leave us. You've caused enough embarrassment already. Or do you intend to gloat over it?"

"Not at all - it was by pure chance I came upon you, and I apologize for my initial outburst. Unforgivable. I'm afraid it just popped out." With that the stranger, keeping his gaze fixed firmly upon her eyes, performed an ironic bow and retired.

"God. The bastard cheek! I'll..."

Kate put her hand over his mouth and gently laughing, said: "It was our fault, really - we were far too careless. Someone was bound to come along."

"I suppose," Rob grumbled.

"It's this place," she smiled at him, stroking his cheek, "it cast its glamour upon us and we entered its dream, careless of the mundane world."

"Yeah, right." Rob grudgingly agreed. "I think we'd better go back. I'd like to know who that cheeky bugger was, all the same. 'Shepherd and his ewe...' I'll give him shepherd next time I see him, jumped up little squirt."

"Calm down. It really doesn't matter," she replied. "Except that he has seen me naked," she thinks to herself, "and the way he looked at me like that - so directly. Its as if he dismissed Rob as being of no account. I wonder who he could be?"

They said little as they made their way down the hanger on one of the main paths, each preoccupied with their own coming to terms with this gross intrusion on their intimacy. Each with diametrically opposed conclusions except in their curiosity concerning the identity of the intruder.

They parted at the gate to her father's cottage in the village. "Thank you for a wonderful day, Rob. Don't let that silly man spoil its magic. Promise?"

"Ok. I'll see you tomorrow, then."

She reached up and kissed him briefly: "Bye."

8

Shabby Tattler

It had been over a week since Kate had seen him last. He had suddenly appeared before her as she was leaving her cottage one afternoon, thinking she would kill some time with Robert

She knew there was no point in asking him where he'd been or where he lived. He only appeared when it suited him, and the only means he had given her for summoning him was so absurd she hadn't dared try it.

"Hmm. So it seems to be true, then." Shabby Tattler stroked his chin contemplatively, eyeing her keenly, as if sizing her up, as they strolled along the sunlit path towards the woods.

"What does? Who is she?" Kate had told of her adventure in the hidden room and her meeting with the secretive woodland villagers. He had asked to see the letter and had read it silently when she fetched it out from the cottage for him.

"Dumb, you say?"

"Yes - at least she was silent and only wrote me this note," added Kate, handing him the letter, "Who is she, do you know?"

"Well then. That there lady, she's familiar to me, from a long time ago, long time ago."

"How?" Kate looked at him expectantly.

"First off. We're goin' to need a place to sit. Because its a tale what'll be a long time in the telling', if it's goin' to be told right. If you wants to hear it said right."

"I do, I do. Who is she? How do you know her? Is she alive, then?"

"Now this here bank looks suitable enough. Let's settle us down here a bit, and I'll gather me memories right up. Just gimme one minute."

He settled in the long grass and laid back, head against the root of an old beech tree. He picked himself a juicy stalk of grass and chewed it, gazing up through the leaves at the blue sky.

Kate had to follow suit, knowing there was no hurrying him when he was in a story-telling mood, however eager she was.

"I been around a bit, Kate, me girl. I seen things and heard things the like o' which takes some believin'. Well, 'twas like this. Long ago, there was a legend of an imprisoned woman in this here house. A gruesome tale it is, too. But I'll tell it you if you're minded to listen. But listen you must. No interruptin', no questions till I've done with me tale complete, like. Understand?"

"I promise. I won't say a word."

"Alright! Here we go. Now the lady, she don't come into it straightaway. But you just bide you time. She'll enter it, bye and bye. Just you be patient."

And so he began:

"It were several hundred year bygone. The lord o' the manor was a certain Gabriel de Tiercel…"

"But isn't their name 'Tercel'?"

"Are you telling' this tale, or am I?"

"Oh, sorry. You are. I'll shut up."

"Good. This Gabriel, he were right ambitious, frighteningly so. Weren't nothin' he wouldn't do, 'tis said, to farther the same. And he did so. Fugglesham Hall it was, when he growed up; Fugglesham Court it was by the time he were done.

"'Tis said much of his money were made illegal, like. He were tight with a gang o' smugglers what did him proper service, during them wars waged across the channel. He made a right fistful out of them wars, providin' for her majesty's troops and, 'tis said, them's of her enemies too.

"Trouble was, the smugglers' Captain, one Falco Basard, and 'is sidekick, Gormer Scart, they was smart. They figured that they could lay a finger on a goodly part o' the gains of that trade, or they could lay a finger on him, Gabriel, now Sir Gabriel, if he didn't play ball.

"They got right high-minded and forward with the master, with threats and such. But they weren't smarter than that man, for they hadn't bargained with his new man. This man was twice as evil as the pair of them put together..."

9

A new man comes

It was a fine morning in September when the stranger
turned up at the gate. He was a tall, powerfully built man
with a striking mane of silver hair, contrasting starkly with his
heavy black eyebrows and large moustache. He wore a grey
cloak with a black velvet jacket that had a single broad silver
stripe down each sleeve to the cuff. He wore a blackened
armoured breastplate over his doublet, which was of a silvery
grey. Unlike the English at this time, he wore black Venetian
breeches with no codpiece and had long thick black leather
riding boots, with baggy uppers to the mid-thigh.

He rode a black mare with a silver fox fur trimmed saddle
and a pair of wheel-lock pistol holsters on either side. He
carried two more tucked into the tops of his boots, and a
longer rifled breech-loading wheel-lock petronel in a holster
on his left side. He carried a long sword, an estoc, at his
side, together with a mace and a dagger. His eyes were so
dark they appeared coal black and glittered with malice as
they peered out from under his black helmet. He had a pack
behind his saddle in which was carried the rest of his armour.
He was a mobile arsenal.

He leaped from his horse, throwing the reins into the face
of the guard challenging him and demanded he take his horse
to the stables to be watered and fed.

When the guard protested and tried to bar his way, the

stranger grabbed the spear out of his hands, snapped it in two over his back, and lifted him bodily into the air and threw him into a water trough.

The stranger strode through the gate towards Fugglesham Hall followed by a small troop of skittering guards urging each other on to challenge him but falling over themselves to get away whenever he turned to face them.

The man hammered on the outer door of the hall until a face appeared in its grill. "Tell Sir Gabriel de Tiercel that White Whiskey John is here and would see him," growled the stranger.

"Are you expected?" asked the face in the opening, only to have its nose pinched violently and nearly dragged through the small aperture.

"Do as you're told man, or I'll run you through, door or no door," replied the stranger, holding the man trapped by his nose and unsheathing his huge sword. With a twist of his hand the stranger shoved the face back through the aperture with a loud crack of cartilage and bone, and the little man scurried off to report to his master, blood pouring from his broken nose.

"So he's here, then," laughed Sir Gabriel when the man reported the assault by a stranger at the door. "Get out of here and get cleaned up, you baggage. You're making the devil of a mess of my floor."

The doorman scuttled out, wailing quietly to himself, to the kitchens where he could be attended to by the scullery-maid, Bessie Buntie.

"Oh what 'ave you done to yourself, now, Phyp Spadger, you careless man," cried Bessie, snatching up a cloth and dipping it in cold water before slapping it on his face.

"It weren't me wot done it. It were the stranger. He 'tagged me through the door, he did. The bastard broke by dose."

"Don't worry, Phyp, I'll soon 'ave you sorted out." She

squeezed the bridge of his nose hard and cracked the cartilage back into place. He howled with pain but she held him firm until the pressure stopped the bleeding.

"Now let's get you cleaned up, me lad, afore the master comes calling for you again." She wiped his clothes and soaked up the spilt blood before sitting him down by the huge cooking fire and pouring him a hot cup of soup.

"I'll get that bugger, I will. Just you wait," Phyp Spadger sat fuming, threatening and moaning by turns, watched with amusement by the cooks and maids.

"Don't reckon you'll be doin' much along them lines, do you, Binkie?" laughed little Polly Washdish, wiping the dough from her hands.

"Not likely! I seed the man. Built like a Shire horse, he is," replied Binkie Scop. "I'd like to get a bit that meat between my thighs, I would," she cackled through her nearly toothless mouth.

"What you see in a little runt like him, then, Bessie Buntie?" said Polly, pointing derisively at the small hunched frame of the whimpering doorman. "If you sat on him he'd disappear up your jacksie."

"I don't know what your Jack would have to say if he were to find out about you and Phyp," laughed Binkie Scop.

"Put him on a hook's end and go fishin' for his self, I reckon," added Polly.

"He'd catch his self nowt but another old trout, with a bait like that," shouted Binkie, slapping her thighs with glee.

They all hooted and cackled with laughter. Phyp Spadger turned puce and announced with as much dignity as he could muster: "I got to get back to the great hall, I has. I've had enough of your chatter for one day."

He strutted out, adding, "Some of us got appointments upstairs, and some of us don't. An there's an end of it."

The cackling group of cooks, wash-dishes and under-maids looked at one another in amazement and then, as he slammed the door, burst into renewed guffaws of laughter. Bessie Buntie grunted and sat on her pride.

White Whiskey John stood with his helmet under his left arm before Sir Gabriel de Tiercel. The two men eyed one another in appraisal. The pursuing guards and minions of his Lordship looked on apprehensively.

"Well, John, I'm glad you've come," said Sir Gabriel, "we've a lot of work to do."

"Glad to be of service, your Lordship," replied White Whiskey John, bowing ironically in the most obsequious manner, "Your will is my desire."

"Sit! Sit, man. I'm not a Lord, yet. We've much to talk about. Boys!" called Sir Gabriel, "Fetch wine for my friend, here, and food, and then leave us."

"I see you had a little trouble at the gate," added Sir Gabriel.

"Not I, Sir," replied Whiskey John. " Not I. Just a little understanding that needed to be reached, that's all."

"I see, I see," chuckled Sir Gabriel. "I can see we will get along fine, you and I."

"That we will, Sir, that we will."

The servants retired as Sir Gabriel and his guest settled into conversation in the glow of the great hearth.

Word reached Falco Basard in the forest that there was a new man in the household of Sir Gabriel de Tiercel.

"What? What the hell is going on here? Who the hell does he think he is? I run this damned show. Gabriel – he doesn't have a fucking clue what's goin' on. Who the hell does he think he is? I'll 'ave the bastard on a bloody gallows if he tries to cross me, I will." Falco Basard stormed up and down the tiny hall of his storehouse for contraband, hidden deep in the woods. "Gormer? Gormer Scart! Where are you, you lazy bastard?"

Gormer Scart, a tall, dark, narrow-shouldered individual wearing an almost black greenly iridescent garment, stood by his master's shoulder.

"Ere I am, Capt'n. I done what you said." Gormer Scart stooped over the seated figure of his boss, peering down at the back of his head over his long hooked nose, thinking to himself, "one day I'm going break that skull of yours, Falco Basard."

"What was that?" Falco turned and looked up at him, "I 'aven't bloody well said anything yet..."

Gormer Scart stood up straight and answered: "I took all them cannon over the Downs to the port, like what you ordered me to."

"Oh, yes. That," Falco acknowledged, "But we've got more important matters need attendin' to. There's a new man up at the house. By name of..."

"White Whiskey John. I know," butted in his henchman, "I found out from the sailors down there. He's a right piece of shit. A German mercenary Reiter, a pistoleer who's been fighting these wars for over ten years for whoever bids the highest. But they say he's a rat who's got religion, now, and wants to spread it like the plague."

"We've all got religion, ain't we boys?" chuckled Falco Basard, "blessed be those what helps their selves, cos they shall inherit the bleedin' lot, eh?"

The gang members brayed with laughter. Gormer Scart stood his ground without a hint of a smile on his face. "No. You got me wrong. This boy's different. It ain't money with him no more, and that makes him dangerous. We can't turn him. He's unbendable, they say, like the path of the executioner's axe. Woe betide any bugger crosses him, they say. He skewers you through with that big sword of his or his bloody firearms. They say he's got five of them pistols and a long gun. And if that ain't enough, he whacks you with that iron mace of his."

"We'll see about that, won't we boys?" laughed Falco. The gang members chuckled nervously. White Whiskey John's reputation had preceded him, as he always intended it should, terror doing half of his work for him before even he started.

"Who told you all this, anyway?" asked Falco in irritation at his henchman's undermining of his own position as the man to be feared.

"It's all around the dockyards," replied Gormer Scart, "and he's brought himself a lunatic Lutheran preacher man by name of Parson Mew, along with his sons, Crocker Mew and Sprat Mew, and an idiot called Saith Fool. He's a massive bugger, he is. Thick as a post but hard as oak. He does what he's told and it's White Whiskey John what does the telling."

"Come on, now," started Falco Basard.

"No, I seed it meself," continued Gormer Scart. "Parson Mew was a preachin' with his two sons either side of him and Saith Fool sat behind; and up comes four good Catholic boys, rapiers a gleamin' and tells him to clear off with his sacrilegious claptrap. Well, the Parson, he carries on a preachin' like it were only the Word of the Lord what could move him.

Well, these boys warned him again and again he carried on spoutin' them bible mysteries in English, if you please. That riled up these good boys sommat rotten and they set to removing this rabble-rousing Protestant filth from the streets.

Parson Mew, he just raised his hand like in a blessing over these boys and yon Saith Fool steps up to his full height, seven foot if he's an inch, and holds out his arms and spins like a capstan out of control, clubbing these boys to kingdom come.

One gets it behind the ear and it comes right off, blood spurtin' everywhere…"

"Get away with you," started one of the crew.

"No. I mean it. He's got great iron-studded gloves like a bloody mace on the end of his arms. The second one's skull was stove in like an eggshell. The third lost half his jaw and the fourth scarpered like a deer. That man grunted, "Sorry, but you mustn't abuse the Word of the Lord like that." Can you believe it? He was apologizing to them he's killed and half killed, like he'd just farted in good company, or something."

The crew burst out laughing at this. All except Falco Basard, who was scowling now, seeing in this new bunch a real and potent threat to his own hard-won franchise.

"I'd best go and report the loading of the cannon to Sir Gabriel, " he mused, "and take a long hard look at this White Whiskey John."

10

Falco Basard

"Ah, Captain, welcome," Sir Gabriel de Tiercel clapped Falco Basard on the shoulder as he ushered him into his study. "Meet my new assistant, White Whiskey John.

He's come over from Germany at my request. I've brought him in to sort out my affairs here at home, and those damned villagers and their damned refusal to give up their Catholic blasphemy. They're traitors to Elizabeth, every damned one of them. Whiskey John – meet Falco Basard, Captain of my trading fleet."

White Whiskey John stepped forward from the window in which his powerful frame had been silhouetted, allowing Falco Basard a first glimpse of the face of his rival. The pair shook hands with a firmness betokening their instant mutual hostility.

"Nice to see you," said Falco Basard, "your reputation precedes you."

"Does it indeed," replied Whiskey John, "my reputation?"

"As a disseminator of the true faith," interrupted Sir Gabriel, "isn't that so, Falco?"

"As you say, sir. But I could've dealt with them Catholics myself, if you'd asked me." With this first probing remark Falco Basard looked keenly between his master and White Whiskey John for clues as to the latter's standing in relation to himself.

"Oh, but I think you're busy enough, already, don't you? I wouldn't want you wasting your time chasing around the woods after recalcitrant peasants. Your job is far too important for that. Looking after my trading interests is your forte, after all. Generating wealth and avoiding taxes, eh?" Sir Gabriel laughed. White Whiskey John smirked unpleasantly at Falco Basard as if to say, "know your place, man, and it isn't here."

Falco Basard smiled falsely and replied, "Of course, of course. Put like that I see that I am too important to spare on wild-goose chases. And talking of money, I'd like to bring to your attention, Sir, that the boys are getting restless, like. They done their jobs but ain't been paid for three month since. There's a reckonin' due there, and that right soon, if you understand my meaning." He glanced slyly at White Whiskey John as he said these last words, wondering if the man got his drift.

"A reckoning? Of course. See to it will you, John? Pay the good Captain and his crew their dues," replied Sir Gabriel.

"Pardon me Sir…" started Falco Basard.

"Didn't I tell you? White Whiskey John is my purser from now on. You'll report to him the details of all our transactions and he'll sort out your dues. That sort of thing I find so tedious. It'll give me room to devote more time to planning our strategies for the future. There's a great future in the Mediterranean trade with the Spanish. I intend to hire a few persuasive merchantmen to seek out those richly laden vessels and relieve them of their cargoes. You've got contacts in that direction, I take it, Falco old boy. I must talk to you about it sometime. See him out, will you, John?"

With that gesture Sir Gabriel de Tiercel dismissed Falco Basard, relegating his role to that of an employee, outside his confidence. Falco shot a glance of pure hatred at White Whiskey John, who merely smiled sweetly back, saying: "Do come and see me soon – about your wages, I mean – my office is in the rear court. But I'm sure you know where."

"So," thought Falco, as he strode out of the door to the courtyard, "he's even been given the room I use when I'm here. The bastard. I'll get him. I'll get them both."

Falco heard the drumming of hooves as he was mounting his horse in the courtyard and he looked out towards the arched entrance to see Sir Gabriel's younger brother, Michael, clatter into the cobbled yard astride his heavy horse.

"Mornin' to you, Sir," Falco cried in greeting. "I see there's a new man takin' over Sir Gabriel's affairs, by name of White Whiskey John. Seems to be right close to Sir Gabriel already, by the looks of it. Even taken over the purse strings. Now that should make your life easier, I reckon."

"Purse strings? What do you mean?" replied Michael, as he lowered himself from the saddle. His vast bulk quivered as he walked towards Falco's horse. "What do you know of him?"

"Well, only good, accordin' ter his Lordship," said Falco cautiously, awaiting the reply he was hopefully engineering.

"And otherwise?" asked Michael, "What other reports have you heard?"

"Oh, nothing," replied Falco, grinning cheerily, "at least, not nothing I can report in this company," he added confidentially, nodding his head sideways up towards an open window in the courtyard offices.

Michael de Tiercel looked up to see a face recede into the shadows. He leaned towards Falco and said in an urgent but quiet voice, "You and I need to have a talk, man. I'll meet you at the great oak at midday."

"Certainly, sir," replied Falco Basard, "at midday, then."

As Falco Basard rode up Michael de Tiercel was waiting under the shade of the great oak at the far end of the estate. He was on a different horse and wore a hooded cloak of deep green, looking every inch the conspirator Falco hoped he was about to become.

"Halloa, there," called Falco, as he approached. "Did anyone see you come?"

"No," replied the de Tiercel uncertainly, "I don't think so."

"You can't be too careful, you know. Not with the likes of White Whiskey John." Falco Basard dismounted and looked around for a long time, making sure there was no movement in the nearby trees or bushes that might indicate someone watching.

"There's another stranger arrived," announced Michael. "Black Martin, they called him. He's White Whiskey John's aide, apparently. And he's brought a Lutheran preacher, Parson Mew with his two sons, Spratt and Crocker, and a giant of a man called Saith Fool. He's an idiot, apparently."

"But not one you want to tangle with, " said Falco Basard. "I heard about him already. A regular troop of fanatics, by the looks of it," said Falco. "They was called the Black Riders, or Devils Riders, back over in the Low Countries during them wars, you know, on account of their penchant for rape and plunder, so I'm told. I would try to get rid of them as soon as you can, if I were you, Master Michael. With Whiskey John holding the purse-strings you could find your allowance being cut and then how would you pay for your whores, eh?"

"Whores? I don't know what you mean." Michael de Tiercel reddened so that the fat wattles overhanging his collar took on the colour of a turkey's.

"Come along now, Sir, your secret's safe with me. I've got me own spies, you know. Self-protection. But you ain't going to enjoy them long nights in the upstairs room behind the inn with that little Catholic redhead much longer. Not unless you think of a plan to get rid of that man and his crew."

"What do you mean?" asked Michael de Tiercel, nervously playing with his reins.

"Catholic whore. That's what I mean…"

"She's not a whore. She's just… poor. That's why I give her

money." Blustered Michael. "She loves…"

"Your money! Long as you got it, that is. She's a Catholic, and you pay her for sex. White Whiskey John, now, he hates Catholics and he don't approve of no whoring, leastwise, not between a Protestant which you are said to be, beggin' your pardon, and a Catholic. Brats out of wedlock and out of religion. It just won't do, see."

"I suppose you're right," mumbled Michael de Tiercel, "but what can I do?"

"Send out spies. Get something on him. Ruin his reputation. He must have a pretty black past, having been a soldier of fortune for so long. This Protestant thing. It's got to be a cover. A means to get power. He's seed which way the winds blowing and he's set his sails fair, I reckon." Falco Basard looked intently into the shadowed face of Michael de Tiercel, trying to discern whether his shaft had hit home.

It had. He could see beads of sweat trickling down that blubbery skin, dripping off his jowls onto his saddle. The man was his. He smiled. Enough for one day, he thought to himself, I'll let the bugger stew for a bit like a dumpling in this soup he has found himself in, before I spoon him out with a ladle.

"Reckon we'd better go, afore someone misses you and comes asking questions," shouted Falco, spurring his horse and riding quickly towards the woods in which he had his headquarters.

11

White Whiskey John

"Down to work, then," Sir Gabriel de Tiercel thumped the table. "It's a delicate business I brought you here for."

"Tact is my middle name," replied Whiskey John, smiling and stroking between thumb and forefinger his chin, where so lately a comely pointed beard had sat. He had changed his style for reasons known only to him.

"Well, before I tell you of my affairs I must have your assurance as to your absolute discretion." Sir Gabriel looked into the black eyes of Whiskey John, eyes empty of feeling, revealing nothing. "I rely on you to execute my bidding, whatever it may be."

"They called me Wurchangel in the wars, 'Destroying Angel' in your tongue," replied White Whiskey John. "I am as described. I now employ those talents purely in the Lord's service."

"Excellent, excellent." Sir Gabriel smiled. "I know I can rely on you. But, so that we understand one another more fully, I must tell you that I have looked into your credentials before calling upon you."

"Naturally, sir. Impeccable, I trust?" John cocked his head slightly, wondering where Sir Gabriel was leading.

"Impeccable. But for one, how shall I put it, oversight."

"Oversight, sir? I'm afraid I don't quite follow you."
Whiskey John's palms began to sweat, and he placed them

upon his lap.

"Certain documents came into my possession in the course of my inquiry. I believe you may know of what kind, my Dear John." Sir Gabriel was enjoying Whiskey John's discomfiture, certain as he was that there were compromising documents other than those he held, and therefore knowing that White Whiskey John was, at this moment, frantically trying to figure out which of these had come into his possession. "Documents that, in the final analysis, guarantee your loyalty."

"Of course, sir. Loyalty you shall have." White Whiskey John spat the words out through gritted teeth, realizing that he had been out-manoeuvred by this English would-be aristocrat. "And what is the nature of these businesses I am to be relied upon to carry out?"

"Good. Now that we fully understand one another, I can reveal the true extent of my problems. Have another cup, won't you?" Sir Gabriel proffered the decanter. "I am beset by problems. First and foremost, Falco Basard, whom I have been using to carry out my discrete trading operations with continental Europe, has become most obtuse of late. Ideas beyond his station, to the point of blackmail, no less. He has threatened that, unless I give him personally a half-share in the contraband business, which as you now know, ranges from cannon, guns, and other weapons to wine, spirits, silk and spices, he will inform the authorities and, on the promise of a pardon, give them the details of all the transactions I have masterminded during these past seven years in the wars in the lowlands. I would lose my home; my fortune, my liberty and possibly my life were he to do so. He must be stopped. And soon."

"I see. He seems a dangerous man, to me. Not one to be underestimated." White Whiskey John continued stroking his ghost of a beard. "You have, if I may say so, estranged him still further by so blatantly replacing him with myself as your closest confidante. I think I must first do everything I can to bring him into my confidence, to make him feel that I need him and will continue to rely on him, so that his guard becomes relaxed. I will start by insisting that I pay his men a bonus and double his own dues to show my goodwill. I may even be able to draw him into a plot to remove you, Sir Gabriel, and have you replaced as head of this household by your brother, Michael…"

"What? Michael? Are you mad?" Sir Gabriel de Tiercel sputtered, spilling his wine.

"I said, draw him into a plot, Sir," repeated Whiskey John, slowly and calmly, "a plot to which you would be privy at all times. You see, my spies tell me that, even as he was leaving, he met your brother in the courtyard, and they appeared to be talking in undertones. So, I would insinuate myself into their confidence by proposing such a plot myself, and thus achieve the dual goals of easing his suspicions about me and of uncovering a real plot if there is one. Then Falco Basard will be considerably easier to dispose of."

"I don't believe for a minute that Michael would dream of plotting against me. He hasn't got the wit."

"But Falco Basard has. He will try to get some leverage over your brother and then use that to persuade him to usurp your station. Mark my words. I know men better than you. Brotherly love is a convenience quickly dropped where self-interest rears its ugly head."

White Whiskey John paused to let this sink in. He reached into to his jacket and from a pocket pulled out a pipe and some tobacco. He slowly filled the basin and lit it with a match, pulling in short sharp bursts on the mouthpiece until the little brazier was glowing.

"Have you tried this, Sir? It's the latest fashion in London." He handed Sir Gabriel the little instrument. "Now suck, inhale gently, the smoke, Sir, and then breathe out."

Sir Gabriel inhaled sharply, and then coughed hard, tears coming to his eyes.

"Try again, Sir, but less fiercely. That's better, Sir. It brings a peace and clear-headedness to one's deliberations, you will find. You may keep it, Sir. It is called a pipe. And the weed is tobacco. From the Indies. It will be a new thing in business. One that you should consider."

After allowing Sir Gabriel time to regain his equilibrium after the initial rush, Whiskey John spoke again. "As to your second great matter, Sir?"

"Oh, that. It's these damned villagers of mine. They refuse to worship in my chapel any more. Since I threw out their damned priest. That reminds me. Is Parson Mew installed, yet? I look forward to his first sermon on Sunday. The last parson was an incoherent babbler."

"Yes, he is, Sir. And a finer preacher of the Lord's Word you won't find this side of Germany, Sir."

"Good. Now, about these villagers of mine: they've taken to sneaking off every Sunday and Holy day into the woods to a secret rendezvous where the infernal priest spouts his Roman nonsense to their eternal satisfaction. I won't have it! Do you hear? It just won't do. They're mine, and they'll damned well worship as I tell them. Find the damned recusants out and persuade them back, force them back if necessary, or make an example of them, if they refuse."

"We'll bring them into line, one way or another, Sir."

"And what's more, their damned village is too close to the house. I can see it from my new great hall. It's an eyesore, sir. A filthy damned disgrace and smelly to boot. I want it removed to a farther location. From the front of the house I want a view all the way to the Downs. That stinking village is in the way. I want it moved."

"Was that your third matter?" inquired White Whiskey John.

"No. That's a matter of extreme delicacy. It is a matter of the utmost tact. It is the matter closest to my heart." Sir Gabriel de Tiercel paused. He pondered whether he dared, even with the securities he held against betrayal by Whiskey John, to reveal this affair to the man. It seemed to him a matter beyond solution.

Eventually he plucked up the courage to speak: "I am in love, Sir, with a beautiful woman…"

"I have seen her. Your wife, Phyllis, is unsurpassingly lovely to look at," interrupted Whiskey John.

"Not my wife, you fool – her sister – I'm in love with her sister. I'm in love with Amelia Linnece, younger sister of my wife and second daughter of Sir William Linnece. I have had her, sir. We met first when I married her elder sister, Phyllis.

I had her soon after and she bore me a child, a girl named Kate. For Phyllis's sake, Amelia kept silent. She refused to name the father, thank god. To cover up their shame, Amelia and Sir William's wife, Rosie, were closeted together during the pregnancy, so that none would know whose child it was, save their trusted midwife and nanny. So Sir William passed the child off as his late-begotten youngest daughter.
Sir William suspects me of being the father. But still Amelia keeps silent.

So to avoid disgrace, he is going to marry her off to a down-at-heel Catholic aristocrat, Lord Barnaby Stave-Carew, who is completely besotted with her, and her father's wealth, no doubt.

The man is a Catholic. He is grossly fat. He is an in-bred idiot. To allow him to plunder Sir William's fortune through Amelia cannot be tolerated – not after all my efforts to secure it. I won't let it happen. To let that weak, incompetent, cowering, crass, wheezing, dribbling mass wed my darling Amelia? I cannot let this happen. You understand? I can't bear the thought of that soft pink excuse for a man smothering her with slobbery kisses and laying his vast blubbery bulk over her delicate, exquisite body; covering her like some great toad.

It is unbearable enough seeing young Kate and having to

71

pretend to be her brother-in-law. I cannot touch her, hold her, and kiss her even, as I would my own daughter. But can you imagine, on top of that, having to entertain the presence of this filth, knowing that soon he will lie abed of my own sweet Amelia?

I must have Amelia. Somehow I must have her. And you must find a way." Sir Gabriel paused for breath. "Above all else, you must find a way."

White Whiskey John looked at his master. "They say trouble comes in threes," he thought, "but they don't come much bigger than these three."

To Sir Gabriel, he said, "I shall need a little time to reflect. I shall find a solution, rest assured." Bowing, he took his leave.

"Call Black Martin to me, will you?" White Whiskey John leaned out of the door to his office in the yard, waving to one of the grooms. "Tell him I want to speak with him. Tell him that it is urgent."

"Right away, Sir." The groom, Joe Ben, ran off in search of the new boss's right-hand man.

He was a sprightly boy, and Whiskey John had taken a shine to him. His lithe young body swelled through his doublet and hose in the most becoming way, and his innocent laughter tinkled like a sweet bell in his ears. Whiskey John had never understood the attraction of women, with their soft sagging bodies and high-pitched squawking voices.

His soldierly upbringing had brought him only into intimacy with the firm comradely musculature of his fellow warriors. Here only was true fellowship possible, a union of body, soul and mind, united in purpose unto death.

Women were, for him, suitable prey for rape and mutilation in the frenzy of victory, to be sloughed off in the aftermath of that ecstatic paroxysm of slaughter that followed battle.

As Joe Ben came bounding round the corner, his glossy black curls bouncing in the sunlight, Whiskey John allowed himself a smile in the direction of his discrete desire. The boy smiled back, his blue eyes flashing warmth. He will suffice, thought John, for the duration of this assignment. The boy danced away happily in the direction of his mounts, having pleased his new master.

John's gaze was drawn back to the entrance through which Black Martin now came, Tall, slightly hunched about the shoulders, but with a flowing gait which covered the ground with great rapidity, his deep blue cloak flowed behind him in two long tails, such was his speed. He almost seemed to float over the ground.

"You summoned me?" asked Black Martin, in his peculiar sing song voice. White Whiskey John had picked him up a few years earlier in the Netherlands, where he had been working as a spy for the Duke of Alva before turning wholeheartedly to the Protestant cause and becoming a double agent.

"Yes. I want you to find the secret location of the Catholic worship in the woods. I want to know who goes there and where they come from. I want to know who is hiding the priest, and where he is being hidden. You'll have to recruit a local who knows the lay of the land. That little rat, Phyp Spadger, the doorman, whose nose I broke the day I came, seems a good choice. He's a nasty greedy, power-hungry little squirt. Bribe him. Give him a promotion and promises of more. He'll soon forget his resentment for his nose."

"I've already sounded him out. He's spying for me in the kitchens already. Seems they insulted him something rotten and he's keen to show them whose boss." Black Martin turned on his heel to go.

"Oh, and look in at the Linnece household, will you?" Whiskey John added. "Install a pair of eyes and ears there too. They're Sir Gabriel's wife's family, but Sir William is a covert Catholic it appears. There might be some little secrets to be had there."

73

12

Black Martin

The following morning a message was conveyed to the neighbouring manor of Runswick Abbey, home of Sir William Linnece and his family, with an invitation from Sir Gabriel de Tiercel to hunt with him on that Friday and bring his family so that Phyllis might spend the day with her mother and sisters, ending with a dinner in the great hall after the hunt.

Black Martin, as White Whiskey John's aide was charged with attending the ladies while John rode behind his master and Sir William. He fetched them by carriage to Fugglesham Court and oversaw their pleasures until Sir Gabriel's return.

At the feast he discretely observed their behaviour and that of their master, Sir William. He noted that, while overtly the two gentlemen exchanged pleasantries as equals, Sir William had the air of an altogether more powerful lord, and that Sir Gabriel went out of his way not to incur his displeasure.

That evening he again escorted the party home. During the course of the day he had secured the attention of the young lady chaperoning young Kate Linnece and arranged a secret assignment for the following Monday.

At dawn on Sunday Black Martin rose from his cot, threw a grey hooded half-cape, such as the peasants wore, over a smock, rough leggings and coarse felt shoes which he wore to complete his disguise. He slipped a dagger into his belt and picked up a long staff with a good clubbing end.

In the half-light he slipped out from his lodgings in the courtyard and made his way without a torch along the path that skirted the hamlet of Fugglesham and led towards the forest.

The mist hung heavy over the landscape as Black Martin took up his post hidden in a clump of bushes at the forest's edge beside that path he deemed to be the one most likely to be used by those recusant villagers determined to worship in the old ways of Marian Catholicism.

He despised these backward people, whose embrace of and dogged adherence to Catholicism had been so easily manipulated by the cynical incorporation of their more primitive beliefs and rituals into its own all-encompassing dogma.

He chewed on a strip of meat and rubbed his arms and legs to keep warm as he waited, hoping that the rising sun, now piercing the upper branches of the trees, would not wholly burn off the fog, for he wished to join the procession unnoticed as it passed by and so to discover the location of these secret services.

Soon the first stirrings within the wattle huts of the village were followed by the appearance of figures emerging and gathering in dark huddles in the rude streets. At a word from one of these, a ragged procession of hooded bodies started towards the woods and Black Martin's hiding-place.

As the first of these groups reached him, he noted carefully the face of that one who had spoken and, as the last group passed by, he swung into his place at the tail of the queue and shuffled along in their style towards their rendezvous.

They reached a clearing in the woods as the sun, arcing up through the mists, pierced the ring of trees and shone clear and bright upon an altar adorned with elaborate silverware and behind it a seven-foot high wooden carved crucifix.

Standing at the side of the altar was the priest, Jack Straw, so recently outlawed by Sir Gabriel from his domains. Black Martin watched as the service began. The incessant chanting of the responses and the priest's incantations were just beginning to lull him into a stupor when a movement at the side caught his eye.

A small group of figures, attired in long cloaks with hoods had arrived and silently took up station to the left of the altar, but closer than that of the general congregation.

With their backs three-quarters to him, Martin could not make out whom they were until, as the priest was taking communion, the hood of one of them slipped off, revealing Sir William himself. Quickly replacing it, Sir William glowered as he scanned the congregation to see if anyone had noticed it was he and then resumed his stance.

With a start, Black Martin realized that the small group must consist of the whole Linnece household. They were covert Catholics. Recusants! Black Martin realized that it must be they who were secreting the outlawed priest in their household and organizing these subversive congregations.

The priest, Jack Straw, then turned to this group and summoned one of them to the altar. As the man turned to face the congregation and threw back his hood to reveal his face, Jack Straw introduced him: "Hear, good people gathered here today in the Lord's presence, the words of this man, John Ball*. He will preach our sermon today."

The man John Ball poised himself and then began, in a deep voice that resonated around the glade:

" Ah, ye good people, the matters goeth not well to pass in England, nor shall not do till everything be common, and that there be no villains nor gentlemen, but that we may be all united together, and that the lords be no greater masters than we be."

"United as one body, praise the Lord," answered the congregation.

What have we deserved, or why should we be kept thus in

servitude? We be all come from one father and one mother, Adam and Eve: whereby can they say or show that they be greater lords than we be, saving but they cause us to win and labour for that which they spend?"

"From one father and one mother came we. How then one greater than another be?"

"They are clothed in velvet and camlet furred with grise, and we be vestured with poor cloth"

"When Adam delved and Eve span, who was then the Gentleman?"

"They have their wines, spices and good bread, and we have the rye, the bran and the straw, and drink water."

"And the good Lord will turn our water into wine, ere long!"

"They dwell in fair houses, and we have the pain and travail, rain and wind in the fields; and by that that comes from our labours they keep and maintain their estates."

"He who endures labour's pain, henceforth will reap labour's gain!"

"We are called their bondmen, and unless we readily do them service, we are beaten; and we have no sovereign to whom we may complain, nor will hear us nor do us right."

"Our sovereign is ourselves, and ourselves our remedy. If our sovereign heed us not, then there shall no sovereign be, No bondage but our own, imposed, and by this our labour shall be free!"

The congregation's united voice rose to crescendo as the preaching came to an end.

Black Martin couldn't believe what he was hearing. Not only were Sir William Linnece and his family holding court to a Catholic gathering, their preacher was preaching sedition, equality of Lord and commoner; universal suffrage! It was incredible.

Here were so-called reactionaries, recusant 'Catholic' peasants, being preaching a revolution more radical by far than that achieved by Protestantism in a hundred years. Black

Martin couldn't believe what he was hearing.

This had implications far greater than the squabbling between the Protestant and Catholic nobilities that did not touch the question of their sovereign right to rule, whichever group achieved ascendancy.

Black Martin was confused. "How could Sir William," he thought, "with all his privileges, be a party to such seditious talk? Surely he could not intend to give up his own status to join a revolutionary band of peasants with no hope of success? Perhaps his intention was to nurture them, to foment full-scale revolution by the peasant class to overthrow the Monarchy.

That must be it! It could only be that he was intending to use such a revolt to reinstate a Catholic regime. Maybe there were others like himself, all over the country, using the disaffection of the largely traditional and Catholic peasantry to install a religious fundamentalist Church-run state untempered by the whims and vagaries of an inherited Monarchy."

Black Martin's imagination began to run riot. "Could it possibly be that they plan a state, or federation of states, run something along the lines of the Swiss Cantons with their democratically-elected leaders. But then the urban cantons of Switzerland had come to be ruled by city councils that were themselves controlled by a small oligarchy of wealthy merchants."

He had seen these states in action; fought their armies and been beaten by them. He could see the power in the idea: its attraction for a merchantman risen to the rank of knight, now faced with persecution and loss of wealth because of his religion. Black Martin admired his constructed idea of this man. "If true, then Sir William Linnece and his kind would be truly a danger to the whole Protestant revolution, which had gained sway by gaining the allegiance of those in power, the aristocracy. An overtly Catholic democracy run by an oligarchy of merchants. What a volte-face!"

Black Martin stepped quietly backwards until he could slip behind a tree, and there he hid until the service ended and the congregation returned to their homes.

Sure enough, as soon as all the peasants had left, the priest, Jack Straw, and their preacher, John Ball, turned to the family who threw back their hoods and began a friendly exchange that Black Martin could not pick up. Their servants gathered up the silverware and table and the group processed in the direction of Runswick Manor.

Black Martin hastened back to report this discovery to White Whiskey John without detailing the content of the sermon or its enthusiastic reception. He was torn between two loyalties: that to his own ideals and that to the self-interest that served his current master.

He was attracted by the revolutionary idea of overthrowing the Monarchy, an extreme idea from which his own Protestant revolution had baulked. Now his own Faith was associated with the very aristocracy he so hated, and through such a revolt, would necessarily be overthrown alongside it.

He determined to reach Sir William and sound him out on where he stood. "But how?" he thought, "We do not move in the same circles and I cannot approach him merely to converse. But then, if he is truly as he seems, an originator and organizer of such a revolutionary idea, then surely he will respond to a direct and forthright approach. But if not, then I will have betrayed myself in so acting."

Black Martin kept his tryst with the chaperone of young Kate Linnece in the shelter of a summerhouse some distance from Runswick Abbey. While he felt about her clothing and caressed her skin as lovers do, he slyly pressed her for more intimate knowledge of the Linnece family, for their persuasions and the opinions that swayed them regarding religion, home and family, their sense of justice and fair-play.

He gently prized from her the secret of where Jack Straw

was hid; that John Ball was an itinerant preacher who was going from parish to parish, passed from patron to sympathetic patron, with his message of a kingdom of heaven upon earth in which all earthly kings are overthrown and each man becomes ruler of himself.

He concluded that Sir William Linnece must be as deeply involved in revolutionary plotting as he had suspected; that there must be others – many others – whom he must discover. He was in turmoil regarding his own beliefs and urges and how best to fulfil them now. Should he turn, as he had turned once already, from spy for a Catholic King and Emperor to passionate warrior-advocate of Lutheran Protestantism, back now to this crazy idea of a Catholic revolutionary democracy, or a revolutionary democracy achieved through an appeal to Catholicism?

"What are you holding back?" White Whiskey John's question took Black Martin aback.

He prevaricated. "What do you mean, holding back?"

"You know full well what I mean, and I mean to know it." White Whiskey John's threats were always effective because never empty.

Martin knew better than not to reluctantly hand him a suitably juicy titbit. "Ok. Jack Straw wasn't the only preacher in that glade. There was another, John Ball. Sir William Linnece brought him. He was with their party. So presumably he is also hiding in Sir William's Abbey."

"Really? I wonder what the significance of that could be?" Whiskey John stroked his beardless chin.

This habit of his will one day betray him for the dandy he once was before 'getting religion', thought Black Martin, who knew more about him than Whiskey John suspected. It suited him to serve this master for the time being, while he sought out his own dark path in life.

13

Kate Linnece

"Come to me, my darling," Amelia Linnece gestured to her younger sister, Kate. "Tell me what is troubling you."

"I had a dream," whispered Kate, curling into her sister's lap. "In my dream you were my mummy. Mummy wasn't there. Just you."

"Don't be silly, my darling, I'm your sister. Of course mummy was there."

"But she wasn't. I was laying on your tummy, so warm, and I could hear your heartbeat, just like always." Kate looked into her sister's eyes. "Mummy's heartbeat isn't the same you know. It's slower, and different."

Amelia held her daughter close, afraid, so afraid she might let her secret out. "You're just imagining it, Katie my darling. You know our mummy is your mummy."

Katie snuggled into her sister's warm soft bosom and clung to her. "I know you're my mummy. You are. You just are." She looked up into her sister's face. "Sing me that song, the one you used to sing to me at night. It's so nice and tickly down my neck."

"Oh, alright. But promise me you won't tell anyone about your dream about me being your Mummy."

"No I won't; it's a secret between us." Katie giggled: "You know, from here your nostrils look huge, like two caves."

Amelia held her close. She stroked her hair and her temples, singing her favourite lullaby until slowly her dear Katie subsided into a deep sleep.

14

The lake

"Come on out Kate Linnece! I know you're in there."
Robin peered between the leaves of the sweet bay hedge
running along the outer wall of the kitchen gardens. "If you
don't come out now, this monster's coming to get you."

A squeak of fearful delight emanated from a point about
five yards further down, betraying her hiding place. Little
Kate shrunk back into a tiny ball in the dry hollow between a
bush and the brickwork, covering her eyes with her fingers as
if by doing so she made herself invisible.

She could hear the rustling of branches being parted and
the crunch of old dried leaves drawing nearer. She loved this
anticipation of being found, of the moment when Robin
would suddenly grab her, crying, "Boo!" She peeped through
her ever so slightly parted fingers and saw a black shadow,
bent double, prizing the branches to make a path towards
her. It looked like a hunched demon with no head and Kate
squeaked again involuntarily, nearly wetting herself.

"Boo!" Her hands were torn from her face to reveal Rob's
grinning face a few inches away. She jumped at him and clung
to him in sheer relief for a second, before turning to lead the
way on hands and knees out from under the hedge.

Robin was eight years old, two years older than her. He
had a curly mop of blondish hair and ruddy cheeks and eyes
so blue and a special smile that she knew was all hers and

she loved him. He was the huntsman's son, and should have been out helping his father, but because Kate had taken such a shine to him, Sir William had given special dispensation to allow him to play with her under the watchful eye of her nurse. So he was always in and out of the house, especially the servants quarters where Kate liked to spend a good part of the day with her nanny, watching the cooks' steaming cauldrons and the big roasts and the chopping and dicing on the great table and the scrubbing and lathering of the laundry on the big wash-boards and the whole steamy chaotic mess of it all from which magically every day emerged her impeccably presented meals on their beautiful china and her scented clothes all neatly pressed which her nanny fussed endlessly over as she dressed her each morning and which she always got dirty before lunchtime.

Sometimes she was allowed to eat in the great dining hall with Papa and Mama on the long table she could hardly see over, with Amelia on her right and Phyllis on her left when she was visiting with her scary husband, Sir Gabriel, who always looked at her too hard so that she tried to make herself invisible by looking up at the patterns on the plaster ceiling or by wriggling on the bench closer to her sister Amelia, who she knew was her real mummy and would protect her from him. Sir Gabriel always sat at the other end of the table from Papa, with his horrid boy, Raphael, who was a year older than her and a bully, on his right hand, and his fat younger brother, Michael, on his left. She called them the three demons. Phyllis sat between Kate and the little demon, Raphael, or Raphe, as he called himself. Raphe used to reach round his mother and pinch Kate to make her squeak at dinner-table, and he used to try and chase her afterwards, but Robin would always appear as if by magic just as he was about to catch her and stand between them with his legs apart and his arms folded as if to say, "go on, try it!" But Raphe never did. He would slink away scowling and using bad words.

Kate didn't like it when the de Tiercel's came, much as she liked her eldest sister, Phyllis, because there was always a lot of looking going on, as if nobody could think of anything nice to say, and she was too busy trying to hide her eyes from the three staring demons.

"What shall we play next?" shouted Robin, as he ran around her in circles on the grass. "Let's go on the lake!"

"Oh, can we, Nanna? Can we?" Kate turned to her nanny, sitting with legs crossed under her, leaning against an old lime tree, with needle in her hand, as ever. "Rob can row. You know he can."

"Well alright, but as only far as the willow island. And don't get caught up in the weeds." Nanny always fretted when they went out on the boat, but Rob was a good rower, because he had been rowing since he was six, and they never got into trouble.

"Take me to our Hidey," cried Kate imperiously as she clambered aboard while Robin held the little rowing boat steady. He hopped in lightly and gathered up the oars as if he were a real man, and rowed them across the shiny waters, through the reeds and big flat lilies, towards their own private hideaway.

Their hideaway was entirely hidden by the gently rustling branches of a great willow that hung right down to the water. From inside it looked like a green waterfall, and its rustling leaves were as soothing as the sound of a real waterfall.

It was a tiny island, more a promontory whose neck had drowned, separating it from the shore at the great willow's foot by a few yards. It stood about six inches above water level, and was surrounded by a ring of reeds except at one point; their landing-place.

Kate leaned back and shut her eyes to let the strands of tiny leaves wash over her neck as they passed under the curtain, tickling her skin like feathers. She loved this moment, being stroked as if by elves, whom she had decided certainly lived here among these magically green-leaved branches.

She leaped ashore and ran to her special place, a mossy mound around which Rob had planted bluebells and columbine, chequered fritillary and iris near its shore, purple foxglove and pink geranium to succeed, and finally ever-so-deep blue flowering plumbagos on either side to make a throne for a fairy-princess, which is what he said she was.

Robin tethered their little ship and came to her. They lay back, heads together on the soft cushion and gazed up at the sunlight flickering through their leafy curtain.

"One day we're going to runaway and I'm going to live here in Fairyland, with you as my handsome prince," said Kate with a dreamy seriousness in her face. "I don't like grown-ups, with their horrid stares and their great clumsy bodies. Except Amelia, of course, and Phyllis. But they don't count."

"Why?" asked Robin.

"Because they're my sisters, of course!" replied Kate. She sat up and looked down at Robin gravely. "Can you keep a secret?"

"Of course I can," he replied, "why?"

"Because I'm going to tell you one. But first, you must promise to be my prince and carry me off to Fairyland."

"Alright. I promise," Robin laughed, "now, tell."

"Amelia is my mummy." Kate stared at Robin, who stared at her wide-eyed, as if she were mad.

"Don't be silly. She's your sister. She can't be your mummy as well." Robin laughed.

"She is. I know. It's a secret, see. And I'm not supposed to know. But I do." Kate looked proud and defiant and hurt.

Robin fell silent, moved by her expression. They sat still for a long time, listening to the breeze.

"How do you know? I mean, if it is true, how did you find out?"

"Her heart told me," explained Kate. "You know how when you do this…" and she placed her head on his chest, with her ear to his heart, "you can hear the heart-beat thumping loudly. Bu-boom, bu-boom, bu-boom? Well, I did. And Amelia's heart is my mummy's heart, from before."

"From before what?" asked Robin, not wanting his little Kate to move her head from its resting-place.

"Your voice sounds all hollow in there," Kate remarked. "No. From before I was born. I remember."

"You can't possibly remember from before you were born. You weren't alive then. Properly alive, I mean"

"But I do remember. As soon as I heard it I recognized it. The noise it made was just the same, from when I was… inside my mummy's tummy." Kate looked up into Rob's forget-me-not eyes. "You believe me, don't you? You must."

"I believe you," said Robin, stroking her hair. He fingered the streak of silver that ran back from above her forehead on the left-hand side, wondering at its strangeness, "I believe you."

"Why?" asked Kate abruptly.

" Because you're you."

Kate relaxed and they lay awhile, thinking their own thoughts. A cloud came over the sun and Kate shivered. "I think we'd better get back," said Rob, "before Nanny starts worrying."

Robin rowed the boat back slowly, loathe to end their small intimacy, while Kate sat watching him, trailing her fingers in the water, shh-shh, as the oars pushed the boat forward in little spurts.

At the shore Kate rejoined her nanny, who had been sitting all the while under her tree. She was asleep now. Kate picked a dandelion and blew it gently near her face so that the little seeds floated all around her, landing in her hair and on her eyelids and open mouth. "Pthth! Prumth!" Nanny awoke with a start, spitting seeds out of her mouth. "Kate! You little demon!" she cried, when she realized what had happened, "I'll get you for that!"

Kate dashed away towards the house, "Catch me if you can." Her nanny got up stiffly, grabbed her sewing, and lumbered after her, holding her fist to her back, sore with prolonged sitting.

15

Gabriel de Tiercel

Sir Gabriel paced up and down the length of his study, his hands locked tight behind his back. "I don't believe it. How dare you say Sir William is behind it all? He's my father-in-law. He's my wife's father. I owe him my position. His influence elevated me to this rank. I won't have it!"

"It is true, sir. Black Martin was at the Catholics' secret service in the woods. Sir William and his entire household were there. The priest, Jack Straw, returned with them to their home. They are hiding him, sir. They are Catholics. Recusants, sir. Traitors to our Faith and our Queen." White Whiskey John watched coldly as Sir Gabriel absorbed the meaning of his words.

"But he couldn't be betraying me like this with my own servants, my own peasants. Behind my back." Gabriel sat down heavily behind his desk and held his head in his hands. "What am I going to do? This is impossible. What in heaven am I going to do, with Sir William leading these damn traitors?"

"If you will listen to me, sir. I think I have the solution. To this and all your other problems. If you will give me free rein, sir, I can get you Amelia; end this Catholic rebellion; ensure your peasants never disobey you again, and get their cluster of hovels removed to a better location."

Sir Gabriel looked up from between his hands, "What?

How? Out with it man."

"Kill them all, sir." Whiskey John paused, waiting for the explosion.

Sir Gabriel leaped from his chair, knocking it flying back. "What the hell do you think you are saying, man? Kill them all? Sir William? His family? My own daughter? All my villagers? You're insane."

"Insane? I think not. Listen to me now. I can get you everything you want if you follow my instructions closely. Do you want to hear me?" Whiskey John walked over to Sir Gabriel and grasped his shoulder firmly with his right hand and led him gently forward, talking now in low undertones: "This is what we must do. Next Sunday, when the recusants go to their holy mass in the woods, you and I and my men will make as if to go hunting. I will instruct Falco Basard and his crew, who have no love of Catholics, to raze the village once it is clear of all the recusant worshippers, but letting those that remain escape, then hurry to meet Black Martin, who will lead them to the villager's place of worship.

They'll fall upon the traitors as they worship their idols and massacre them, every one. Sir William and his family will be first. Black Martin, in disguise, will make sure that Amelia and your daughter, Kate, are not harmed until we, you and my men, ride to the rescue. First you will snatch up Kate and ride off with her. I will ride away with Amelia to that hut deep in the woods I showed you yesterday. It is secure. I had it made myself for just this purpose. It is fitted out sufficient to receive the lady Linnece."

"But my daughter?" Sir Gabriel turned sharply to Whiskey John, "what am I to do with her?"

"As you whisk her away, you will pretend to her that you have rescued her. You will say you were out hunting with us when you came upon the massacre too late to save her family. You will ride to her home first and report the massacre there. You will say that your men, led by me, are attacking the gang,

90

led by Falco Basard, who killed Sir William and family. You will lead Sir William's men to help avenge this foul treachery.

Meanwhile, my men, who didn't attack Falco's men as we would have Kate believe, because there are too many of them, will, having helped in the massacre, leave the unsuspecting Falco Basard to enjoy the spoils.

Having killed the priest, the Linnece family and all the recusants on the spot, Falco's men will indulge in the rape of the womenfolk and pillage of the corpses. While they are distracted, my men will ride them down. By then you, with Sir William's men, should have arrived, and jointly we will kill them to the last man. Then we'll ride back to Fugglesham Court and announce the massacre of the villagers and the Linnece family by Falco Basard and his crew to all there.

We will say that we were out hunting when we caught them red-handed and killed them all, but were too late to save Sir William or his family. Your wife, Phyllis, will be devastated at the loss of her parents and dear sisters, and you will have to comfort her, saying that at least you were able to avenge their deaths and save her youngest sister, Kate."

"My god, man, we can't do this," groaned Sir William. "It's just too much."

"We can do this, sir. We must do it, if you are to have Amelia and protect her and her children from that fat slob Lord Barnaby Stave-Carew. Don't you see? You will have Amelia all to yourself. No one will know she is alive. We will devise a prison for her, sir, in which you may visit her as often as you will, and make love to her as you will."

"That's enough! Don't go any further down that road." Sir Gabriel paused, his mind whirring in confusion.

"Let me continue. With the Linnece family gone, you are rid of the Catholic conspiracy, those villagers who dared defy you and Falco Basard and his henchmen, who will take upon themselves all the blame. Any survivors among them will be hunted down and killed as outlaws. No one will shelter them.

You can have the village rebuilt further away as you wanted. The peasants with whom you replace the dead ones will not dare persist in recusancy for fear of their own lives.

Your family will inherit, through your wife, Phyllis, all the Linnece family's wealth and property. Your son, Raphe, will be heir to that estate when he reaches maturity. Your daughter will be brought up within your household as your own, out of your love for her family, and provided for according to her rank.

Don't you see, sir, it's perfect in its way. Through one day's black deeds everything falls into place and all your problems are solved."

"But what of Amelia? I can't keep her locked in a hut deep in the woods forever. We must find another solution for her." Sir Gabriel was already convinced. He was planning ahead. He was in awe of the elegance of White Whiskey John's solution. It seemed to him already accomplished. He could see a lifetime of bliss ahead with his adored Amelia secured.

"I have thought of that. Once the fuss has died down and life returns to normal and you to your routines; routines which involve frequent visits to and many hours spent in your armoury in the old hall of the East Wing, the one which is always kept under lock and key..." White Whiskey John looked slyly across at his master and watched the grin spread across his face as it dawned on Sir Gabriel where he was leading, "Then we will smuggle her into that wing, where a silken prison will have been prepared for her, and your experiments with metallurgy, on which you are so keen, as I know, will preoccupy you more and more as you seek to advance the art of war and weaponry, if you get my meaning, sir."

"Of course, of course," Sir Gabriel almost cried with glee, "You're brilliant, Whiskey John, diabolically brilliant. We'll equip it with soft furnishings, a double bed with canopies in the solar; the great hall's fireplace will burn strong with the fire of my metallurgical experiments. Its high windows are ideal. No one can escape from there. And the walls are so thick no one will hear anyone crying out in there. Even my gunpowder experiments are barely audible in the rest of the house. And Phyllis knows better than to try and interrupt my work there. See to it, man."

16

Kate Linnece

"Why do I have to wear this, Amelia, dear? The hood's so heavy and it smells. It's rough on my face, too." Kate looked up at her elder sister plaintively. "And I don't like going to that dark wood to pray, with all those strange hooded people. Why can't we just pray in our chapel, like we used to? It was much nicer then."

Amelia looked at Katie and smiled weakly. "I know it was darling, but things have changed. We can no longer freely worship as we always did. The queen has changed, and no longer tolerates our way of doing things. There are spies who would hurt your father if they found out that we still go to mass."

"What do you mean? We were not hurting anyone before. Why should anyone hurt Papa?" Kate looked confused.

"I can't explain, Katie, dear. You will understand when you get older. But we must praise god as we always have, and that means, for the time being, we must go out into the woods to pray with our friends." Amelia pulled on Katie's tiny boots, "We must go down now, to join the family."

"Are those people our friends? I've never seen them before, at least, most of them. I recognize some of our people, but all those others?" Katie tripped alongside her sister, hopping to keep up as Amelia strode down the long hall.

"They are our friends in Faith," replied her sister, "and

those are the best kind of friends. They will never betray us, even though they would be richly rewarded for doing so."

"But then why do we have to hide? Wear these ugly cloaks as if we were peasants?" Katie persisted, as they walked down a side passage to the small herb garden where Sir William and his family were gathering.

"Because there are others who would betray us. You must never talk to anyone about this. About going into the woods to mass. Do you understand, Katie, dear? This is most important."

"No, I won't." Kate frowned. This new turn in her life frightened her. This talk of people peeking and peering and threatening to hurt her family. Who were they? Why would they want to? All this made the woods a darker place. Where tall trees brooded silently, leaning over her, watching her small frame as she passed under them as quietly as possible so as not to upset them. She could feel their branches swishing, swaying towards her, brushing her, reaching out to claw at her.

Kate clung tight to Amelia's hand and tried to press as close as possible to her protective form as they made their way through the little-trodden pathway that led to the clearing deep in the forest.

Suddenly she heard a louder swishing and felt a branch grasping at her other hand and tugging, trying to drag her away into the darkness. She uttered a little scream and wrenched her hand away and put it her mouth as she jumped towards her sister, nearly tripping her up.

Just as she did this, she glanced at the shadow that had tried to steal her away and there was Robin, peeping through the leaves, grinning widely. A wave of relief swept over her. It was Rob. He would protect her from those awful trees.

"What are you doing? You nearly made me trip. What's the matter? Why did you cry out like that?" Amelia's tone swung between irritation and concern as she stopped for a minute and looked straight into Katie's eyes.

"Oh, it was nothing. I thought I saw a bogie-man. You know, spying on us. But he wasn't," she chuckled nervously. "Its all those things you were saying. They frightened me a bit." Katie looked up at her sister. "But I'm alright now. Quick, or we'll get left behind."

"You're right, come on," Amelia turned and they both ran a few paces until they had rejoined the family group.

Kate kept looking back and to the side, catching occasional glimpses of her dear protective Rob, who was flitting, unseen by the party, through the trees to their left like a woodland elf. Kate thought that's what he must be, to be so stealthy, and felt at ease now, under his watchful eye.

As they approached the clearing, Kate could see that the priest, Jack Straw, was already there, with his gorgeous vestments, and the large wooden crucifix that used to be in their chapel standing behind him. The silver chalice, plate and candlesticks that always adorned that place were resting before him on a rough wooden trestle. A crowd of hooded people were gathered there, too, mostly with their backs to the approaching party. The low chant of their responses followed the priest's singsong utterances in a language she did not understand, did not want to understand. She hated Latin. Her tutor said she could be a scholar one day if she tried, but she didn't see why she needed to be.

Her family took up a position on the left of the main congregation as the service proceeded. Sir William, looking large and dark and very menacing under his huge cloak, winked at her and nodded reassurance. She looked around behind her and there was Rob, grinning at her from only a couple of feet away, but completely hidden from the rest. She smiled at him and turned back towards the altar. She started to sing...

Kate wondered if Rob could hear her own thin high voice above the chanting of the congregation and was listening for her own voice intently when she became aware of another sound. It was a distant low drumming noise together with the tuneless din of distant geese. Then she recognized it as the sound of the hunt approaching.

It was getting closer and louder, and Kate turned to see if she could catch sight of the deer running before it. She was not alone in turning. The whole congregation turned as one towards to approaching din. Surprise and confusion were in their eyes. Several started to shuffle as the realization dawned on them: their secret mass was discovered. They were themselves the quarry.

A horde of riders thundered into the clearing. Rob leapt on Kate and knocked her to the ground and dragged her back into the undergrowth. He pulled her into a hollow oak at the edge of the clearing. Petrified, Kate clung tight to Rob, watched the unfolding horror of the massacre, her mother and father shot down, Amelia snatched by White Whiskey John and carried away on his horse. Suddenly she heard Sir Gabriel's voice calling out for his "darling Kate" and would have run out had Rob not grabbed her and held her down. With his hand clamped firmly over her mouth she had to watch the crucifixion of their priest, the rape and massacre of all the villagers, including Rob's father.

17

Amelia Linnece

Flung over the saddle of White Whiskey John's horse as he rode away from the clearing, Amelia's last sight of her beloved Katie had been when young Robin the huntsman's son hurled himself from nowhere at her and knocked her to the ground out of the path of an oncoming horseman, and then dragged her by the shoulders into the bushes behind them.

She had been unable to run after Kate because her own legs had collapsed with the shock of seeing her parents slaughtered before her eyes, and she had resigned herself to dying in that clearing with them.

Whiskey John whipped his horse along the narrow path through the woods. The briars and bushes beat Amelia's legs and face and bare arms, lacerating her pale skin with welts of red, oozing blood. She could not cry out: bounced on the hard horn of the saddle, she fought for breath, the air crushed from her lungs with each stride.

Soon he slowed the horse to a trot and while still in motion, dragged her hands behind her back and tied them together with a thong. He then hoisted her once more into the air like a puppet and dropped her into the saddle in front of him with her legs on either side.

They reached a tiny clearing in which stood a rude but sturdy hut. Leaping down from the horse, he turned and lifted her down a little more gently and placed her on the ground. "Stay there," he ordered, as he went to the door of the hut and unlocked it. Her legs were too weak to move anyway and, overcome by vertigo, she lay on her back, crying.

Whiskey John reappeared and, lifting her up, carried her into the hut that was to be her prison and put her down on the cot in the semi-darkness.

"Here you are, milady. Make yourself comfortable. This is your new home."

She looked around. The bed had a mattress, covers and a pillow. There was a padded chair and a table. There was a fireplace with a fire already burning in it. There was a lamp on the table. She looked up. There were three small openings high up: too small to climb through. The roof was timber, with sturdy batons beneath the thatch: too thick for her strength.

"Begging your pardon, Miss Amelia, but I must do this, for your own safety." White Whiskey John placed a leather belt around her waist and pulled it tight. "Can you still breathe? Good." He took a chain attached to ringlet in the corner, halfway between her bed and the chair, and attached it to the lock on her belt.

"There, now. You can't go and hurt yourself in the fire now, can you?" He looked at her. "And this," he said, opening a small cupboard in the wall to reveal a toilet niche, "is for when you… So you won't suffer from the smell."

"Very clever. You've thought of everything. But why am I here?" Amelia stood with her head cocked back defiantly. "When Sir Gabriel de Tiercel finds out about the massacre and my abduction, you'll all be dead men."

White Whiskey John looked at her calmly and smiled. "Is that so? I'll worry about him when the time comes. No one will ever find you here; so don't bother crying out. Make yourself at home. There's some food in that cupboard, and milk and water. I've got to go."

He turned and left her, locking the door behind him, ignoring her screams and pleas for mercy. Eventually Amelia stopped yelling and crying as she realized she was completely alone. No one could hear her. No one would come to her rescue.

In her mind a succession of ghastly images swirled one after another; the flash of guns, her father's head disintegrating before her, the gaping hole opening up in her mother's breast and her look of surprise and bewilderment, and Katie's small body, bowled over and dragged to safety...

Dragged to safety. Katie was alive. She prayed that her darling daughter was still alive. "Thank God," she thought, "thank God we let Robin be her playmate. He must have followed us to be near her. He must be hiding her now. He has such a sensible head on his shoulders he'll know what to do."

She was tired. So tired. She went back in her mind, over and over, to those last few minutes, trying to make some sense out of them, trying to piece together some meaning...

She tried to imagine what Katie was doing now. She was a witness to the whole massacre. Surely if they caught her they would kill her? Where would Robin take her? He must be aware of the mortal danger they were in. She knew that his father was among those attending the service, and so was almost certainly dead. She knew he had relatives all through the district. Perhaps he would take her to one of them, sufficiently far away to be out of danger? She knew that she could trust him, young though he was, to bring her Katie through this alive.

18

White Whiskey John

White Whiskey John rode back to the scene of the ongoing massacre. He met Black Martin who was sitting on his horse hidden in the woods at the edge of the tumult.

"Did you kill the other woman as I instructed and mutilate her face?" he asked as he reined in his horse.

"I did all that. She's here, on this horse, ready to be put beside her father and mother's corpses." Black Martin pointed to a twisted corpse laid over the horse. The woman's height, build and hair colour were the same as Amelia's. "No one will know it is not her, except for her clothes, which I will change once we get them back to Runswick Abbey. I've bloodied these so that it's not too obvious."

"Well done. Put this over her clothing." Whiskey John threw down Amelia's cloak. "Now we just wait for Sir Gabriel."

"Right. But we've got a problem." Black Martin interrupted him, "young Kate's vanished. She may be dead – among the corpses – who can tell? Sir Gabriel couldn't find her to rescue her and he's mightily upset. I managed to get him off to the Linnece household to warn them. They should be back any minute now."

"Good. Where are my men?"

"Hidden just beyond the river," Black Martin replied.

"I'll go to meet them and await Sir Gabriel's arrival. While we're killing Falco and his crew you sneak in and place the "body", then you search for Kate among the bodies. Her grey streak will make her easy to find. If you can't find her, then find a girl of a similar age and height and hair colour to Kate, then blow the top of her head off and damage her face, so that her hair and face are impossible to recognize. Then carve her up a bit so her clothing won't give her away. Put her there beside the others. She'll have to do for Kate's body. We'll sort the body out properly once we get back to the Linnece house. It's imperative that Phyllis is convinced she's dead. We don't want official search parties being sent out to find her because if the girl's still alive she might tell what happened. She's a witness and we're all dead men if she talks. It's Gabriel's fault. If he had reached her first, as I told him to, then we wouldn't be in this mess. If you don't find her among the dead, we'll have to send our own search parties out in secret to find her. When we find her we're going to have to kill her. No harm done there, because Gabriel will already think she's dead. We can't take her back to Sir Gabriel. It's going to be hard enough to keep Amelia's presence a secret, let alone have a daughter to cope with."

White Whiskey John rode to the rendezvous beyond the river and waited. A few minutes later he heard the thunder of approaching horsemen and Sir Gabriel with the Linnece household rode into view.

"Young Kate's dead too," Whiskey John said quietly as the two men met.

Gabriel froze for a moment, staring hard at Whiskey John, before turning to his men, "I don't want one of Falco's bastards left alive."

The troop, led by Sir Gabriel and White Whiskey John, bore down on the unsuspecting revellers. The Linnece men and Whiskey John's fighters cut Falco Basard's men, caught with their breeches down and for the most part in various stages of fornication, to pieces.

Gormer Scart, Falco's aide, alone of the debauchees, had the presence of mind to leap to his horse and, seizing a spear embedded in the chest of one of the villagers, charged straight for Sir Gabriel as he rode into the clearing. He thrust his weapon clean through Sir Gabriel's left shoulder as he swerved to avoid the blow aimed at his heart. Sir Gabriel was lifted off his horse and fell to his right as the spear snapped. His head hit White Whiskey John's left boot as he went down between the hooves of the two horses.

As Gormer Scart raised his long slashing sword to strike at Whiskey John's side, Whiskey John stretched his left arm out so that the barrel of his pistol discharged not a foot from Gormer's face. The charge took him in the throat and his head rolled back as blood fountained into the air from his partially severed neck. The raised sword swept down towards John, but glanced harmlessly off the pistol's barrel.

Falco Basard, taking advantage of Gormer Scart's spirited attack, leaped on foot towards Sir Gabriel's prone body, taking his sword in both hands made to impale his master into the ground. Crocker Mew arrived at this moment behind White Whiskey John. He reared his horse. The horse kicked out, knocking Falco off balance. Whiskey John turned and shot with his other pistol, hitting Falco in the thigh.

Falco slashed wildly out, unhorsing another rider by taking off his leg at the knee, then drove his sword into the underbelly of Crocker Mew's horse. He seized the sword of the fallen horseman and lunged at Crocker Mew as his horse keeled over backwards. As he fell, Crocker Mew took the sword-thrust in his calf; he slashed towards Falco, catching him on the wrist. Falco's sword remained stuck through Crocker's leg with his hand firmly gripping it, while Falco grabbed the stump of his arm to stop the blood pulsing out.

He yelled a foul curse as he fell upon the unconscious Sir Gabriel and bit at his neck, attempting to tear his throat out with his teeth. Sir Gabriel's rough collar saved his life as White Whiskey John, dismounting, kicked Falco Basard hard in the ribs with his heavy boot. Falco rose to his feet, releasing his handless arm, and went for his dagger with his left hand. Whiskey John calmly raised both barrels of the pistols he had taken from his boot-tops, but before he could aim and discharge them, the giant, Saith Fool, strode forward and grabbing Falco by shoulder with one hand, wrapped his huge hand around his face and snapped his neck like a chicken.

Half-naked men were being beheaded, impaled or slashed to pieces all over the clearing. In a few minutes there was just the groaning of the not-yet dead breaking the sudden quiet that descended on the gathering. Whiskey John's men stealthily went round making sure there were no witnesses surviving among the women while "finishing off" their tormentors. Their swords penetrated both the rapers and the raped. The Linnece men had been engaged in attacking those able to fight and by the time they had accomplished their task, John's men had completed their grisly duty too. Not one man, woman or child from among the worshippers or Falco Basard's bandits, remained alive.

White Whiskey John casually pulled Falco's sword from Crocker Mew's leg and tossed it to him, the hand still clutching the hilt, saying; "Keep it Mew. Souvenir of a good day's work done. And bind your leg, man, before you bleed to death on me."

Crocker Mew grimaced as he tied a tourniquet around his thigh. "I've lost my horse to that bastard Falco Basard. I'll take his horse too."

Whiskey John knelt by Sir Gabriel and felt his shoulder. "No bones broken. He should survive, if it doesn't get infected." He lifted Sir Gabriel into a sitting position and, holding his neck crooked in his arm, grasped the spear shaft and drove it on through the shoulder. He grabbed the spear behind the shoulder and pulled it out. He then stuffed the now profusely bleeding holes on either side with large wax plugs he had in a pouch at his side and held them in tight as he called for assistance.

Sprat Mew, the preacher's other son, came forward and bound the wounds tight so that the plugs sealed the holes front and back.

"Get him on a litter and back to Fugglesham Court quickly, Crocker Mew. You and Sprat clean the wound up, fast as you can. Make sure there's no cloth left in the hole, or he'll get infected and die. Pour clean boiled water through it to flush it and tip a bit of this whiskey through for good measure, then replug it with these." He took out another small bag containing two more waxen plugs. "Then see to yourself, man, before you bleed to death."

As Mew's boys rode away with Sir Gabriel strapped to a litter between them and the giant Saith Fool trotting behind, White Whiskey John turned to Black Martin, who had just arrived: "Well, that's made the job of passing off bodies as Amelia and Kate easier. Neither Sir Gabriel nor his wife, Phyllis, will be able to tell it's not them by the time we've finished. Did you find a girl's body for Kate?"

"Yes. It's all done. No one will know in the heat of battle it's not her. She's next to the other body," replied Black Martin.

"Then you take all the family's bodies back to the Linnece household and steal one each of Kate's and Amelia's dresses. Keep the servants away. Tell them it's too gory a sight until you cleaned them up a bit. Don't forget to cut up the outfits and rub blood and mud into them. Then arrange for the dead family members to be laid out for viewing, and I will bring Sir Gabriel, if he's fit enough, and Phyllis."

They walked over to the Linnece family group. White Whiskey John bent over the entangled bodies of Sir William, his wife, Rose, and the corpses masquerading as Amelia and her daughter. "My God what a mess we made. Finish this business, then tell the boys to pack Lord Stave-Carew into a sack – what's left of him – and take that back to Runswick Abbey, along with the others. Send a messenger to his own house to tell them of his tragic demise at the hands of Falco Basard and his gang. Tell them he died heroically trying to defend his wife-to-be. I'm off to console Sir Gabriel's wife and make sure Sir Gabriel is properly taken care of. We don't need him dying on us now. Not after all we've gone through here."

White Whiskey John put one of his discharged pistols in Falco Basard's left hand and stuffed another into the top of his right boot, before mounting his horse and riding back to Fugglesham Court.

19

A contract

Whiskey John entered Sir Gabriel's study. "Have you cleaned the wound and checked there is no cloth inside? Did you pour whiskey through it?" Whiskey John interrogated Parson Mew's two sons. "Did you plug it tight and stop the bleeding?"

"Yes, we did all that," replied Crocker Mew, "and the bleeding has eased off. It looks quite a clean puncture. I reckon he'll live."

"Has he woken at all? Has he spoken?" Whiskey John leaned over Sir Gabriel and listened to his breathing: "Good. It isn't too fast." He felt his head. "Nor has he a fever, which is a good sign."

At that moment Phyllis stepped out of the shadows: "Now, tell me what happened? They say my parents are dead. Amelia and Kate, too. How? Why? And how did Sir Gabriel and yourselves happen to be there and not save them?"

White Whiskey John stroked his missing beard involuntarily. He knew he would have to be cool and clear. The woman was far too collected. She should be in hysterics. Did she suspect something? "Well, ma'am, I'm not sure how much you know."

"What do you mean, know?"

"Well, did you know that your father and your family were secret Catholics? That's how they came to be in the woods

107

there. They were holding a covert mass." Whiskey John looked keenly at Phyllis as she replied.

"Of course I knew they were. Father was sheltering Sir Gabriel's priest. But who attacked them? And why? I want to know who killed them. And no lies. I'll see through them. My mother, father and sisters were murdered there. I want the truth. It wasn't Sir Gabriel, was it? He has developed a rabid hatred for Catholics and all their works. He's a wild, unruly man. If it was Sir Gabriel, I want to know, now."

"Of course it wasn't Sir Gabriel. We were out hunting when we heard a commotion somewhere in the woods and turned aside to investigate. We came upon the scene of the massacre, but too late to save them. It was Falco Basard and his evil cutthroats murdering and raping. Your family was already dead. We didn't have enough men, so we sent for Sir William's household. When they arrived, we set upon them and killed them all, every last one."

"What happened to my husband?"

"He was attacked by Gormer Scart, who ran him through with a spear, and then Falco Basard himself as he fell. Crocker Mew, here, Saith Fool and I saved his life, killing them both. Then we brought him back here. Your family's remains we took to Runswick Abbey. Black Martin is overseeing their laying out and awaits your arrival."

"You're no lover of Catholics, yourself, are you Master John? Didn't I hear that you, with your Mew friends there, were just back from fighting them in the Spanish Netherlands? You killed a good many, I believe? Even of your own countrymen for not abjuring their Catholic Faith?" Phyllis de Tiercel stood still as a statue, only her eyes and mouth moving as she tried to penetrate the guard of this evil newcomer, as she regarded him. "How am I to trust the tale you tell?"

"Madam, I assure you, that in the service of Sir Gabriel I have put all that behind me. I came here to escape the persecutions of both sides. Both are as bad as the other in that war. We came here seeking peace, didn't we?" Whiskey John directed his question towards the Mew clan, gathered around Sir Gabriel.

"Oh, yes, indeed," replied Parson Mew. "We are heartily sick of all the slaughter, aren't we boys?"

The brothers Mew nodded assent, and Saith Fool grunted.

"And why should Sir Gabriel want his own wife's, your, family dead, even if he did know they were recusants... I mean... practicing Catholics? No! We came upon them exactly as I said. And Sir Gabriel was wounded trying to revenge their deaths. He was too reckless in riding at them ahead of us and got caught in the side." White Whiskey John worked hard to allay her suspicions, wondering how well she loved Sir Gabriel if she was already so suspicious. Had an accusation of Sir Gabriel as father of young Kate reached her ears?

Phyllis turned to her husband and sat on the edge of his bed, took a cloth and dipped it into a basin and wrung it out before wiping his face and hair. She laid a hand gently on his chest and regarded him for a while silently. "You may all go now. Thank you. You did a good job here. Call my maid, Master John, will you please?"

"Certainly, Ma'am. When would you like to visit Runswick Abbey, Ma'am, to see the bodies... of your own family, that is?" Whiskey John bowed out of the room.

"When I'm certain Gabriel is alright," she replied. "I'll inform you when I need my horse."

"Right you are, Ma'am." Whiskey John closed the door to Sir Gabriel's chamber and strode down the passage, pushing aside the waiting servants. "The Master will live. Now fetch Milady's maidservant immediately to attend on her."

"Phyp Spadger! You wait outside Sir Gabriel's door. Let me know of any developments. But first get young Joe Ben. Tell him to saddle up. I've got a message for him to carry to Runswick Abbey. I'll be with Sir Gabriel's brother. Now hurry."

White Whiskey John made his way to the West wing where Sir Gabriel's younger brother, Michael, and his family had their apartments. He knocked loudly on the door to Michael's study.

"Come in," shouted Michael from within, "oh it's you, Whiskey John. And how is my brother? Will he live?"

"He will live, master Michael," replied Whiskey John, as he approached the seated brother. "Unfortunately for you."

"What do you mean, unfortunately?" Michael reddened with anger. "How dare you imply that I don't care for my own brother?"

"We don't choose our brothers, master Michael, but we do choose our friends. Falco Basard and all his evil crew are dead. And good riddance. They were getting above themselves of late, and in murdering the Linneces they undid themselves." Whiskey John now stood over Michael threateningly.

"Get out my light, man," blustered Michael. "How dare you stand over me like that?"

"You were seen with Falco Basard only recently in the courtyard after he left a meeting with Sir Gabriel and me. You were seen riding out to a rendezvous under the great oak. Perhaps you and he were in it together, eh? Planning the demise of all the family, including Sir Gabriel. After all, it was Gormer Scart and Falco who nearly killed him when Sir Gabriel discovered the massacre."

"How dare you! Shut up, this minute, or I'll have you..."

"What?" Whiskey John looked scathingly down at this spoiled feeble fat sibling, "You'll have me 'what?' precisely? No. I think you will be quiet and listen to me. Or it will go badly for you. I have enough witnesses to implicate you."

"But I'm innocent. I had nothing to do with the massacre."

"Maybe, maybe not. But Sir Gabriel doesn't know that.

When I tell him of your confidential meetings with Falco Basard and Falco's subsequent murder of the Linnece family and attempt on your brother's life, I think I can paint a pretty picture of jealousy and betrayal. A portrait that will stick. Don't you?"

"But that's ridiculous. Why would I kill the Linneces?"

"Black Martin overheard Sir William talking. Apparently Sir William caught one of your servants, Jack Nicker, pestering one of his servant girls. He was going to give him a good hiding when Jack suddenly pleaded that he knew of something 'what would be worth forgoing ten hidings for the knowledge of'. Questioned further, this Jack Nicker swore that you and Falco were plotting to get rid of Sir Gabriel and Phyllis, his daughter, so that you could take over. Sir William promised to go straight to Fugglesham Court directly after the service to warn Sir Gabriel, and ordered Jack Nicker locked up. But he escaped, and obviously came back to warn you. Then you sent him to Falco with orders to kill Sir William before he could warn Sir Gabriel."

"This is a complete lie. Jack Nicker never came to me with any such story." William jumped up, only to be roughly pushed back into his chair.

"Disprove it. Call Jack Nicker," White Whiskey John laughed.

"Why should I? He's got nothing to say, and you know it. You made the whole thing up."

"Call him, nonetheless."

Michael got up and went to the door, leaned out and shouted for his man. A servant's head popped out from a room at the end of the passage, saying: "He ain't here, sir. No one's seen him since early this morning."

Michael re-entered the room. "That doesn't mean anything. He could be anywhere. Though why he's gone without my permission, I'd like to know. But when he's back, he'll tell you himself I had nothing to do with it."

111

"He's got nothing to say on that matter, or any other. He's dead. Alongside Falco Basard and his gang. Where you sent him with orders to kill the Linneces. Now wriggle out of that one, if you can."

"But how can he be? I didn't send him." Michael collapsed back into the chair. "What was he doing there? It's impossible!"

"The fact that he was there with Falco Basard is enough to incriminate you, given Black Martin's statement. I'm afraid you are in deep, Michael, my dear fellow; in deep. Right over your head."

"But why? How? I don't understand. I only met Falco once. He arranged it. It wasn't about that at all."

"It was about your whore, wasn't it? He was going to blackmail you by threatening to reveal your whore, wasn't he? He drew you into this by threatening you with exposure." White Whiskey John looked with disdain at the boneless jelly of a man quivering in the seat below him.

"No. Yes. It was about her. But not like that. He wanted rid of you. Don't you see? He was using her to get me on his side to get rid of you. He was furious that you had replaced him in Sir Gabriel's favour. He wanted me to find out something compromising about you so that he could disgrace you."

"I see. And you think it would have stopped with that, do you? You think once he had you in his pocket he would have set you free again? No my friend, he would have used you to his own ends, to install you as head of the household, under his thumb, making his position unassailable."

"But why are you telling me all this? What do you want of me?"

"I only want what you want, my friend; your continued freedom to visit your whore to make up for what you lack at home. I want to be your guarantor of that freedom, in return for which I merely require your signature..."

"My signature? On what?"

"On your confession of your 'role' in the murders."
Whiskey John cocked his head to the side, eyeing Michael
with a faintly bored but amused air.

"My confession?" Michael's eyes started out of his head.

"Your confession. To be held securely in my custody against
any disloyalty on your part."

"Disloyalty? To whom?"

"To me of course."

"No. Never! You must be mad. I, confess to a murder I had
nothing to do with?"

"That's not how others will see it. I have enough evidence
against you to send you to the gallows. I have three witnesses
to the actions and of yourself and your co-conspirators. None
of whom, unfortunately for you, are in a position to deny the
charges against them."

"You did it! By God, you did it! You engineered the whole
thing, you bastard! You had them all killed and implicated
me. Why? What do you gain by killing them?"

"It doesn't matter. You will never know. What is certain is
that I hold your life in my hands at this moment. It's up to
you. A signature is all it takes to ensure your survival and
continued indulgence; to ensure your loyalty to me and all the
advantages to be had from my good offices."

"Advantages?"

"I know for a fact that Falco Basard was aiming to replace
Sir Gabriel – such a difficult, impetuous, hot-headed man,
don't you think – with yourself. A so much more even-
tempered, malleable master, shall we say."

"What are you saying? You would replace Sir Gabriel with
me?" Michael was thinking hard. As head of the de Tiercel
family, he and his would inherit all the de Tiercel and Linnece
Estates, provided Sir Gabriel's son failed to reach majority.
"But what about Phyllis and Raphe? How would you dispose
of them?"

"It's a long game I'm playing, and its better you don't know any details in my plans, provided you're willing to go along with them."

Michael smiled for the first time in this interview, thinking aloud, "Then I would really be free to do as I pleased. I could even install my mistress to the degree of comfort I would have her enjoy…"

"Precisely. You would be free to indulge to your heart's content; and I, to mine."

"Running my estate?"

"Exactly. Do we have a contract?"

"I think we understand one another, now. I think we do."

"Then sign." White Whiskey John held out the document, "sign your confession. It will be our bond, until death us do part."

They both laughed as Michael took the document and walked to the writing desk by the window, dipped his quill and, with a flourish, signed his death warrant.

White Whiskey John looked at him as he took the document, sprinkled some powder over it, waved it in the air, then rolled it up and slipped it into his sleeve: "You are my man, sir, as I am yours. Adieu."

White Whiskey John left that man, his head spinning with dreams of power. He made his way to the courtyard, where Joe Ben was saddled up and waiting. He hastily scribbled a note to Black Martin, sealed it, and handed it to the boy: "Hand to Black Martin himself, you understand? No one else."

"Right you are, sir," the boy galloped out through the cobbled arch and off in the direction of Runswick Abbey.

Just then Phyp Spadger came trotting up: "the Master's calling for you, sir. He's awake now, and quite lively, shouting and everything."

20

Gabriel de Tiercel

"What the hell happened, man? Out with it. What am I doing here? Who did this to me?" Sir Gabriel grabbed his wife, sitting beside him on the bed, by the shoulder and forced himself into a sitting position. "Aargh! My shoulder."

"Calm down, sir, you do yourself further hurt, straining like that." White Whiskey John walked up to his master. "You charged too impetuously, sir, ahead of us, and got caught in the shoulder by Gormer Scart's spear. He knocked you clean off your horse and you hit your head on my knee as you fell, knocking yourself out."

"Did I? I don't remember."

"Then Falco Basard leaped at you and was about to run you through with his sword when I shot him. He took poor Harald Sawyer's leg off at the knee and ran Crocker Mew's horse through and was aiming to kill him when Crocker sliced his hand off, sword and all. He jumped on you and was about to bite your throat out when big Saith Fool picked him up and snapped his neck like a turkey. Then we brought you back here, sir, in a litter, and had you cleaned up." Whiskey John sat down next to him and squeezed his good arm firmly, "I ought to tell you sir, before you upset yourself, that all the Linneces were killed; Sir William, Rose, his wife, Amelia and Kate, along with Sir Barnaby Rudgewick, who was killed heroically trying to defend the ladies, sir."

"Even young Kate killed, you say?" Sir Gabriel had taken

the hint. He did not betray himself. "Even Amelia? Oh no, both your dear sisters, Phyllis. I'm so sorry. I did everything I could…"

"He did, ma'am, and bravely, but too late, I'm afraid." Whiskey John commiserated as tactfully as he could. "Don't you think you should rest now, sir? I will escort Ma'am to Runswick Abbey to see to her kin."

"Yes, go now, dear," Sir Gabriel turned to Phyllis, "I'll be fine until you get back." He slumped back into the bed with a groan.

"Phyp Spadger! Come here." Whiskey John turned to the servant. "Take the lady to the courtyard and see her saddled up, and make sure my horse is ready. I'll just check Sir Gabriel's wound before I go."

Phyp Spadger led Phyllis to the door. Whiskey John made as if to inspect the wound as they departed. "You came close, sir, to forgetting, in front of your wife," he said reprovingly, "you'll have to be more wary."

" I know, I know. It's the wound. It's difficult to think straight. What's happened to Kate? Did you find her? Is she alive?"

"I don't know sir. We didn't find her. So I had someone about her size and colour messed up and placed with the bodies. Black Martin is dressing her as Kate even now so nobody, not even, Phyllis will be able to tell it isn't her. I had to do that sir, or Phyllis would have search parties out, and when they found her, the truth would be out about your part in it sir. She saw it all."

"What can we do then? Surely she'll go to someone and tell and then we're undone?"

"She won't go to anyone, sir. She's intelligent. Her whole family's been massacred. She knows you did it. She knows nobody would believe her. She'll go into hiding, most likely, and we'll find her. I'll send out secret search parties to scour the countryside until we find her. Then we'll bring her back in secret and keep her with her mother."

"Good. Well done, Whiskey John. I don't know what I'd have done without you. You think of everything."

"Thank you sir. Talking of her mother, Amelia that is, I don't think we can hide her in the forest for long. Someone is bound to come upon her sooner or later. You see, it that singing voice of hers. It's so beautiful and haunting. The noise will carry out of the shack through the woods. And it's so well known, someone will recognise who's it is. We'll have to move her to the East Wing as soon as possible. I'll see to it, Sir. Probably tomorrow night; once things have quietened down a bit."

"Excellent. Excellent, man. You are a genius. See to it as soon as all this fuss dies down. And we'll house Kate there too, when we find her. I want them warm and comfortable, mind. Kept in the style I would have my queen."

"It will be done, sir. I'll see to it. Only Black Martin and I will be privy to your secret, sir. I must go, or her ladyship will become suspicious."

White Whiskey John departed. Sir Gabriel's head was racing. He would now have Amelia all to himself in seclusion, together with his daughter, Kate. Amelia would be easier to control with her dear Katie by her side. He could be sure that Amelia would do nothing that might harm her daughter... his daughter. But where was Kate? His pulse raced suddenly and he was overcome by a blinding headache and collapsed back again onto the bed.

What if someone did find her before his own men? What if she did tell all she saw? He would be doomed if she was believed. She must be found, and quickly. Sir Gabriel tried to lift himself up into a sitting position, but as soon as he swung his legs over the edge of the bed and tried to stand, nausea forced him down again.

He lay still for a minute to try to gather his thoughts. Gradually his head cleared. What a time to be helpless, without even White Whiskey John to do his bidding or support him. He imagined his dear Kate, running wildly through the woods and then collapsing, exhausted, hungry and terrified, knowing that he, Sir Gabriel, her own father, had led the killing of her family and the kidnapping of her mother, Amelia. What if she was found by ruffians and attacked, even murdered?

He imagined Amelia, locked in her woodland cell, equally terrified, both for herself and her daughter and family. And he, unable to go to her to let her know that, though his prisoner, she would be safe, would be treated well, and, if only they could find her, even have her daughter returned to her as her own daughter; that, under his guardianship, she could at last, if not breathe the air of freedom, breathe that of freedom from the lie she had had to live under for all these years with regard to Kate.

He could then give her his promise that Kate would never be harmed, and would become her constant companion.

21

Kate Linnece

As dark enveloped the clearing and turned the bloody
ground black, Robin shook Kate. She awoke with a start,
visions of the horror resurging before her eyes. "Where
are we? Where's Mama and Papa and Amelia? What's
happening?"

Kate burst into tears as she remembered the details of
what had taken place before her that day. Robin cuddled her
until she could pull herself together enough to ask, "but that
horrid man took Amelia on his horse. Why did he take her?"

"I don't know," Robin answered, "I don't know why this
happened. But I do know Sir Gabriel must be the one in
charge, because he was there, looking for you. Why would he
be shouting for you, Kate?"

"I don't know. All I know is he always stares at me all
funny whenever he comes to visit and makes me feel like I
want to hide." Kate looked at Rob. "He stares at Amelia like
that too. You don't think he's stolen her, do you? He's always
looking at us like that, and he keeps touching Amelia sneakily
when no one's looking; no one but me, that is."

"But why would he want to steal her?" mused Rob. "He's
already married to her sister, Phyllis. And why would he want
to kill your Mummy and Daddy? They're his own parents-in-
law."

"Maybe they're not my Mama and Papa, like I told you

119

before. I know Amelia is my Mama. I can feel it. I know it's true. And you promised me you would believe me."

"You don't think?" Rob paused, wondering whether he dared say it. "You don't think Sir Gabriel could be your Papa? You said he looks funny at you and Amelia. If Amelia is your real Mama, then someone's got to be your real Papa."

"He can't be. I don't like him." Kate looked angry. "I don't want him to be my Papa."

"But if he was, then that would explain why only Amelia was taken and everyone else killed. He could be going to hide her away somewhere. That's why he wanted you. That's why he was shouting for you. And you know, after he had gone and that horrible man, White Whiskey John, came back, I recognized his black armour. I heard them say that they were going to dress up a woman as your Amelia and another girl as you, so they could fool Sir Gabriel's wife into thinking you two are dead."

"But why would they want to do that, if they had taken her themselves?"

"Because Sir Gabriel must be wanting to hide her somewhere and keep her all to himself and make her sister, Phyllis, think she is dead." Robin looked gravely at Kate, "and I think he must have wanted to steal you too. So you must be his daughter, then."

"But why would he want put me and Amelia, Mama, in prison if he loves us? Why don't we just go to live with him?"

"Because he's not allowed to. He's married to Phyllis, Amelia's sister, and so it's against the law. He could even be executed for it if they found out."

"Then he must be mad, mustn't he?" asked Kate, "Wanting to put us in prison and hide us away?"

Robin's brain was working furiously, now, trying to piece together the jigsaw. "No, not mad, just horribly evil and clever. I think I know what he's doing. With the Linnece's dead, and them only having daughters, he'll get all their estates through his wife. Or their son, Raphe, will. That must be it. That's why he killed Sir Barnaby Rudgewick too, because he was going to marry Amelia. Then his family could have inherited too. But now it all goes to the de Tiercel family. He would have killed you and Amelia too, but for one reason: you really must be his daughter and Amelia is your mother! So it must be true."

"How horrid." Kate shuddered at the thought of Raphe being her half-brother.

"Sir Gabriel was calling out for you at the start, before he went away. But then when he brought those other men back to kill all of Falco Basard's men, he got knocked out, and I heard Whiskey John tell Black Martin that he had taken Amelia to the cottage, wherever that is, and…"

"Does that mean that they've hidden her in a cottage?" asked Kate eagerly, "can we go and find it?"

"No, because I heard Whiskey John tell Black Martin that they must pretend you are dead, and that they are going to come and find you and kill you too, because you are a witness. So we mustn't go anywhere near any cottage where they will be. I think they mean to fool Sir Gabriel. All we know is, if Sir Gabriel finds you, he will make you a prisoner, and if White Whiskey John finds you he will kill you."

"What can we do, then?"

"First thing is, we've got to get away from here." Robin thought carefully, planning what they could do. "At least we're alive still. And nobody knows we're alive. All they know is they can't find you. They've all gone. They've taken all the bodies of your family with them. We've got to get out of here and far away before they come back. They've left all the villagers' and the outlaws' bodies here, so they will be back."

Robin pulled aside the bracken from the entrance to the hollow tree, and climbed out backwards. He leaned in and took Kate's hand. "Come on, now."

Kate crawled out stiffly and stood upright with difficulty. She had been curled up so long she could barely move. Robin rubbed her back vigorously until she loosened up and then took her hand and led her across the glade.

They picked their way gingerly between the mangled carcasses on the ground. Rob looked keenly to left and right, inspecting each corpse in turn, as if looking for something. "Why can't we just go straight away? Why are going through them? I don't want to see them," pleaded Kate, tears welling up in her eyes.

He led her to the edge of the clearing. "I'm sorry. But I'm looking for my father. I saw him go down over there somewhere. You sit here while I find him."

"But I don't want to be alone," cried Kate, clinging to his arm.

"It's alright, I'll only be a minute. And you can see me. But I must find him."

Kate sat with her arms tight about her knees as she watched Robin pick his way here and there through the corpses until he suddenly stopped, then knelt down. She saw him kneel, silent, still, for a whole minute before he leaned forward and put him arm out to touch something. Then he got up and bent over and reached down again and pulled at something. Then he stood upright, turned towards her, paused, looked over his shoulder for a moment and then walked quickly towards her.

She jumped up as he approached. "What was it? Did you find him?"

"I found him. He's dead. I closed his eyes." Rob looked at her solemnly. "Come on, we have to go now. We've got a long way ahead of us tonight."

"But what did you pick up?" asked Kate, as she took his hand.

"This," Robin pulled a shining knife with a seven inch blade out of its sheath, "we're going to need it. It was my father's hunting knife. I saw him kill a wild boar with it once."

They walked in silence along a forest path in a direction opposite to the two great houses. Robin had told Kate they mustn't talk for a long time until they were far enough away from the scene of the massacre to be out of danger.

Robin took Kate south towards the Downs, after cutting west for a couple of miles. They climbed through the thinning trees and scrubland until they reached the higher slopes of grassland where sheep grazed. It was a clear moonlit night and quite chilly.

Kate was thankful now that she had on this heavy woollen long coat with its ugly hood. Looking at Rob in his similar garment, she thought that they must look like a pair of elves passing silently through the moonlit landscape, on their way from one fairy dwelling to another, invisible to the big brutish men she had seen quite enough of for one lifetime.

"I'm hungry and thirsty," she said to Robin, tugging his coat. "When can we stop?"

"We can't, just yet," said Robin, turning to her, "but we can get a drink soon. There is a dew-pond not far ahead used for watering the sheep."

Kate trotted along behind him, a little more cheerful now, anticipating the long cool drink. She was hot now, under her big coat, because of all the walking.

"Here we are!" Robin exclaimed. They rounded a clump of large gorse bushes and there before them, glinting in the moonlight, was a sunken round pond. The moon was reflected in it as a perfect orb, surrounded by a halo of silken clouds.

"It's beautiful!" cried Kate, running towards it and throwing herself onto her tummy. She cupped her hands and slipped them into the cool water, sending ripples across the glassy surface. She lifted a handful of water to her lips and sipped it. It was good. She leaned further forward and dipped her chin in to sip directly from the pond itself.

Robin followed suit, and they both lapped at the water like a pair of wild creatures, their elbows in the air as they rested on their hands. Thirst quenched, Kate jumped up and ran around the pond so that she was facing Robin. He stood up too.

"You look like an elf. You are an elf!" cried Kate, in delight, as she started a little dance.

He laughed to see her skipping about so merrily, as if nothing had happened and it was quite normal to be out here like this under the moon. "You're an elf, too, and you've got a moon for a hat!" he cried. He began to dance too, and soon they were

Dancing and jigging and jumping about, watching each other's antics across the water. "I don't know which I prefer," Robin shouted, "you or your reflection."

"I like you! You're my very own elf-prince and you rescued me just like I said you would," she laughed, "and now you've got to take me to fairyland, like you promised. And we'll live, happy ever after in a land of flowers far from beastly giants."

Robin ran round to meet her and she ran towards him. She flew into his arms and they danced and danced until they both fell down, exhausted.

"I'm hungry." Kate looked at Rob expectantly. He could do anything. So where was the food?

Robin looked thoughtful for a while, then announced: "I know where we're going now. We're going to my cousins down at Glatting Harbour. Their village is really quiet. It's among the reed-beds in the estuary. They're all thatchers down there. I'll go and see old Bumble Clabitter. He'll find us a roof over our heads."

"But what about our food?" asked Kate, dismayed. She had never gone without before, and her tummy felt hollow and hurt a bit.

"There's an orchard, not far from here. We'll pass it on our way to Glatting. I'll get some apples there, and maybe some carrots too." Robin got to his feet and pulled Kate after him, "Come on. We need to get there before dawn, or we might get caught."

"Get caught? Do you mean you're going to steal them?" Kate's eyes widened at the thought of being a thief, of being caught. "Do elves steal?"

"They don't steal, exactly. They just pinch things, that's all," replied Robin, "because they know that nobody really owns anything at all. So they can't steal, see? Because there is nobody to steal from."

"Oh! Does that mean that Papa and Mama don't own..." suddenly she burst into tears, remembering her parents sudden and horrible deaths that very morning.

Rob pulled her to him and held her tight, felt her deep sobs shaking the pair of them. He stroked her hair under her hood until her sobbing subsided and she just leaned against him helplessly, feeling the closeness between them.

"There now," he said at last, "It's best to cry, you know. Can you walk now?"

"Yes, I think so," she whimpered. Then, wiping her arm roughly across her eyes, she stood erect and announced: "I've done with crying, now."

"That's a good girl," said Robin.

"Elf," answered Kate.

"That's a good elf,"

Kate smiled. Rob always knew how to humour her. "What's it like? In this reed village, Glatting whatsit?"

"Glatting Harbour. Oh, its nice enough." Robin elaborated to pass the time as they marched along. "All thatched houses of course. Very cosy. A long green with houses either side. And a river at one end. They all have punts, you know, to go among the reed-beds, cutting reeds. And Jill Blitter, my great auntie on my mother's side... oh, you'll love her. She's like a water-fairy. She lives out on her own in a little hut hidden in the reeds. Nobody could find us there, because nobody can ever find her, unless she wants to be found and, besides, those villagers are very close. I'm going to ask if we can stay with her until all the fuss dies down and we're sure nobody is out looking for us. But Bumble Clabitter will know best what to do. He's my great Uncle, you know, my Dad's mother's brother. He's got a great booming voice, carries right across the marshes, it does. And then there's Collier Jack; he's funny. He's got this great long hooked nose and the skinniest legs you ever saw. And his brother, Red Took, he's got skinny legs too, but always wears a tight red hose as if he was proud of them."

Kate laughed, "I can see him, I can see him."

"And those punts are fun," continued Robin, "they're not like my boat at all. They're flat-bottomed and sort of square and you push then along with a pole."

"Can I go in one?"

"Of course you can. You'll have to, if we go to live with Jill." Robin prattled on to keep her busy, "and the sunrise and sunsets are amazing from inside the reed-beds."

"Why?"

"Because you see the whole sky reflected in the smooth water full of reeds, it shines through them so that it looks magical. And at night the moon…"

"Like in the dewpond?" interrupted Kate.

"Yes, every night," he replied, "when the moon is out, that is, because you're in the middle of the water."

"Oh," Kate squeezed his hand, "Like a duck! Wack, wack! I think I'm going to like it, living with you in the middle of the water."

They reached the orchard Robin had told her about and he shimmied up a tree and threw her down a couple of apples, put some more into his satchel, and jumped down.

Kate bit eagerly into her first apple. It was sharp, but better than anything she had ever tasted, "Mmm." After a few more mouthfuls during which neither spoke, Kate threw away her core and asked, "does that make them my grandma and grandpa? Rose and Sir William? Because, if Amelia is my Mama…"

"Yes, I suppose it does."

"And they must have known all along. Why didn't they tell me, or let Amelia tell me? Why did Amelia pretend she was my sister?"

"Because Amelia isn't married. So she's not allowed to have a baby. Or nobody would marry her, I think," answered Rob.

The pair of them walked on silently for a while, watching the threadlike clouds passing the moon, making a pale halo around it. The path they were treading looked almost silver with bright jewels set in it where the puddles reflected the moon's light.

Kate turned to Robin, grasped his forearm, and forced him to stop. "You know, Rob, I'm going to rescue Mama. I swear I am. I don't care how long it takes, I'm going to find her and rescue her. I'm going to find her and kiss her and hug her and tell that I love her. Promise me you will help me do that, Rob, however long it takes?"

Robin looked at her and said: "Yes, I'll help you. And I'm going to avenge the murder of my father and your family. So help me God."

Suddenly Kate asked: "Why didn't you cry?"

"What do you mean?"

"When you found your daddy. You didn't cry." Kate looked earnestly into Rob's eyes.

"I know. I couldn't." He looked at her. "I don't know why."

"I would have."

"I know."

"Did you love him?"

"Yes. I can't quite believe he's not going to come back." Robin looked away.

Kate peered round him to see his face, and saw his chin quivering, saw tears beginning to trickle down his cheeks. "Oh, Rob, I'm sorry. I didn't mean..."

Robin sat down suddenly, as if someone had taken his legs away, and put his head between his knees and wrapped his arms around himself. Kate could see his frame shuddering beneath his cloak. She knelt before him and took his hands in hers and lifted them to her own face. He looked up and hugged her to him and released all his desolation in a long moaning cry.

They sat, wrapped in each other's arms, for a long, long time. Like a small boulder in the moonlight, thrown onto the road by a careless giant.

22

Kate

"And that there's the end of the tale of the Massacre of Fugglesham. As for the finding and the vengeance, I don't know exactly how this'll be accomplished, but 'tis said it be come to pass one day, and that right soon, accordin' to legend. It's got summat to do with them birds. "

"But you never described the massacre," Kate objected. "You have told the whole tale in great detail, all except the massacre itself. I don't understand. How can you possibly know so much, yet not know what actually happened there, in that clearing?"

"Its not a matter of what I know or don't know, me dear. It's a matter of how much you can take. There's time enough for you to find out about that massacre. And maybe then you'll regret askin' for so much. All I can guarantee is that you'll find out sooner than you may want to."

Old Shabby Tattler closed his tale and his eyes and lay back in the soft grassy bank with his hands behind his head, taking in the warmth of the day.

Kate, copying his actions as if to enter the spirit of affinity that she felt for this queer old tramp, lay back beside him and watched the drifting clouds, wondering about his strange, unlikely and horrific tale.

Suddenly he opened his eye and peered at her sideways from behind his brawny arm.

"What be your surname, dearie?" he asked.

"Pegler," she answered, "why?"

"That's strange. I could've sworn you'd be called after the name 'Linnece'.
Could've sworn it. That's a mystery to me, that is. I'm befuddled by that." He laid still awhile, his thoughts flitting among the rustling leaves like bees buzzing, until finally one alighted on his head and a look of incredulity spread across his brow. "You certain that's your name gal?"

"Of course I am."

"What were your mother's name, then?"

"Her name? It was Greengrove, I think."

"Don't figure, at all. I'm goin' to 'ave to mull it over awhile." He rolled towards her, eyeing her as if not quite believing her, "Don't suit me ideas at all, that don't. Got time enough to figure it, though, that we have."

He picked idly at a stalk of grass, nipping its individual seed-heads off, one by one. A cloud passed over the sun, the breeze suddenly got up and a small chill ran through her.

"Why is it you think my name should be Linnece?" she asked, half knowing what his answer would be.

"Because that were hers," he answered flatly. "The woman he took for his self, Amelia, what he snatched from the massacre, what died with him in that there fire. Linnece, she was called."

"What fire?"

"The fire what destroyed the East wing. The fire what killed her and him, Sir Gabriel, and his wife, Phyllis, Amelia's sister, and Phyllis's son, Raphe, and another man. All of them."

"But if it killed all of them, how come the Tercels are here still?"

"That's because you're forgettin' the baby…"

"Baby? What baby?" Kate started.

"Sir Gabriel and Amelia's son," replied Shabby Tattler laconically.

"You never told me about a baby." Kate was getting a little peeved by this drip-dripping of revelations.

"He came later, the baby she bore Sir Gabriel, some time after the massacre and Amelia's imprisonment."

"What happened to him? How did he survive? Was he a de Tiercel too?"

"That he was, a de Tiercel with a Linnece mother, just like Kate." The man opened his one eye and stared hard at Kate.

"But why do you think I should have that name?" she asked, trembling.

"Because of the legend. They say that when that Kate turns again, the end of the de Tiercels is nigh. That's why."

"And you think somehow that she could be me? The woman returning, or her descendent? Is that it?"

"Percisely! Because everythin' else fits into place around you. Like, its all comin' out in to the open again."

"How?"

"Your a seein' of the village what's not there. And a meetin' with them villagers long gone. And then them windows - what you saw from the village – them windows are not there neither.
Stands to reason, don't it? You saw the great hall like it was then. The wing what's burned down is what you saw. And have not you been inside it, according to you accountin' of it? And a seein' of the plight of that lady in her misery? You've some how been taken back to that there time. And for what? That's what I'm asking? For what? If not because your the one what's returnin', and goin' to end it all?"

Kate paled at the realization of what was implied by his assumption: that somehow she would become responsible for the end of the de Tiercels, for their deaths. "But I'm not! I can't be! You said it yourself! My name's not Linnece?"

"'Tis Kate, but."

"So?"

"Kate was her daughter's name, as you well remember, I

131

reckon"

"But not Linnece!"

"Then there's that grey fleck of hair on your forehead."

"What of it?"

"Grey Kate was her name, on account of the grey patch on her head. An that's right peculiar, that is."

" You're joking," spluttered Kate, feeling the noose of inevitability tighten around her throat.

"Never been more serious, I ain't. Then there's the other thing..."

"What other thing?"

"Your young friend. That lad's name's Robert. Rob Ruddock."

"Yes, so?"

"Robin Ruddock was his name, if you'd have listened to my tale. The lad what escaped with her. Rob Ruddock was his name."

"Now you're being silly. It can't have been."

"I swear it was, on me mother's grave, or I would if I could member where 'tis."

"Well it still doesn't add up, because I'm not a 'Linnece'."

Shabby Tattler sat upright slowly, rubbing his tousled hair in his hands, pondering the case for a while. At last a smile creased his face.

"I just 'ad an idea. Now, what if your Rob Ruddock was dissented direct, like, from the original, father to son? Then you could be descended, counterwise, from mother to daughter, couldn't you?"

"You mean, matrilinearly?"

"Don't know bout no matterlinnely, but I'd bet a purse-a-gold you're directly descended by the mother."

"Well, I might be able to find out. Dad knows a genealogist who could search our family tree. Though they usually only follow the surname back - the father's line."

"That's as maybe, but you're the gal alright! Anyways, we'll soon find out."

And with that he sprang to his feet with an agility that surprised her and started to walk away.

"But what about the fire? What happened to Kate? And what about the boy? You haven't told me about him yet!"

"That'll do for today. I'll tell you about that one next time we meet." Shabby Tattler casually doffed his hat to her without looking back before he disappeared beyond a bend in the path leading to the house.

"How do you know all this? How can you possibly know what happened? You're making it all up to frighten me, aren't you?" she shouted after him, to no avail. He did not return.

The clouds appeared to close upon one another. The weight of responsibility for the fates of those around her shrouded her in doubt. It was as if his sudden abandonment of her after his strange revelations was deliberate and intended to unnerve her. She found herself doubly alone.

For a while she crouched, immobile, like a bird in a covert beset by hunters, not knowing whether to stay or fly. She felt an unnatural darkness closing in on her, a sense of helplessness in the lugubrious presence of forces she could not comprehend, crushing her with claustrophobic dread.

It was as if all paths led to this path and her only way out of this was to enter the malign presence of this house of ghosts and pass through it, unravelling its heart of evil. She forced herself up and made her way cautiously in the direction of the house in the footsteps of that prescient man.

She wondered what his role was in all of this, who seemed to know, anticipate even, so much of this otherwise insoluble mystery. Was he somehow involved, not as an observer, but as a manipulator, puppet-master of this macabre play, conjuring appearances and disappearances, scenes of tragedy and comedy, with strings invisible to her, his intended audience?

As she neared the denser underbrush that marked the edge of the trail from the hidden village to the house she saw the familiar, expected, yet impossible outline of the great house, as it was prior to the fire which she now knew destroyed the East wing, so clearly visible to her now. She knew her way to the door in that wall which would lead her up those narrow stairs to that secluded room in which her own mother's distant female ancestor would be sitting, a sad prisoner, whose ultimate fate Kate now knew, and from whom she must try and elicit help in resolving this mystery.

23

The bright heir

"Top 'o the mornin' to you, Countess!"

Kate, lost in reverie as she walked the path from the hamlet to the house, started and looked behind her. A sweeping bow met her eye as a young man on horseback greeted her with a bombastic flourish. "May I inquire, Milady, which road you be takin', this fine mornin'? And what would a fine gentleman like moiself think of himself if he were to pass you by in the lonely reaches of these woods without taking such a lovely Lady under his personal protection? T'wouldn't bear thinking about, no indeed."

She had not heard his approach and wondered if he had ridden up on the grass to make his approach stealthy. It was the same young man who had so rudely intruded the day before.

Ignoring his flippancy, she retorted: "This road, obviously. And you shouldn't sneak up like that! You frightened me."

Ignoring her, he continued: "And what might be your destination, this beautiful day?"

"Does nothing put him out?" she wondered, then said: "The house, Fugglesham Court. And it's not a beautiful day."

"It is now that I've met you again. I thought you must be a ghost; the image of your pale skin has been haunting me so vividly. But here you are, splendid as a dream. Might I ask your name, my dreamy girl?"

"Kate. Kate Pegler."

In spite of her shock and the experience of yesterday she could not help but be amused at the peculiar manners of this rather beautiful young man. A smile fleetingly settled around the corners of her lips before she continued, "And you shouldn't keep appearing suddenly like this. It's scary. Who are you?"

"Gabriel." He pre-empted her next question with a broad grin and direct look: "Gabriel Tercel, at your service."

She burst into a giggle; "You? You're ferocious old General Tercel's son? Sorry. I didn't mean to be rude about your father."

"But you're right. He is ferocious. And I am his son. So extremely unlikely, don't you think?"

"Yes. I mean, no. Yes..." Kate blushed in confusion.

"Just so. But you have never met my mother, from who I inherit..."

"Your good looks," Kate blushed again, adding, "I mean, you certainly have not inherited..."

"The old boar's bristly character, I believe you meant to say." Gabriel laughed. "No. I'm your gay cavalier, not some boring old Puritan foot soldier, even if he is a General. General Bore. I'm as feisty as he is fusty."

Even as she relaxed and laughed, he leaned over her and put his arm around her waist and swept her up into the saddle in front of him. Surprised, she clung to his neck as he urged the horse into a gallop and thundered off across the lawns towards Fugglesham Court.

"Who's that?"

Robert, helping in the kennels, looked up as a horse clopped through the court up to the front entrance and its rider lowered a woman to the ground before himself dismounting. A groom took the bridle as the rider linked arms with the woman and they climbed the steps to the front door.

"That?" the kennel master looked up. "A course, you ain't seen 'im before. That's young Master Gabriel, fresh down from London for the summer 'ols. An I do believe…" he added, squinting hard, "that's young Miss Kate Wassername, from down the village what's with 'im. Them's new fangled - only recently come to live 'ere. Piglit, or sum such, them's called. They say she's right pretty, they does."

"Kate? You're sure?" Rob's cheeks were beginning to colour. "Gabriel, you say?"

"Oh yes. Him what's set to inherit the whole kit'n kaboodle when his dad pops his clogs. Lucky bugger. Don't reckon he works, nor ever had to, likely. They says he's a wastrel, spendin' all is family's loot on parties and such. He's got himself a regular reputation, has young Master Gabriel. An not much good on it, from what I hear."

"But what's Kate doing with him?" Rob mused out loud.

"Same as most," the hound master was only too keen to share his perceptions, "oh, them young lasses get their heads proper turned by young Master Gabriel, they does. An not just young lasses, if you get my meaning'."

He winked crudely at Rob, who turned disgustedly and stamped off.

"Now what'n blazes bit 'im, oi wonder?" The kennelman scratched his head before continuing the sweeping out. "Young folk. Ain't no tellin' with them. Ain't no steadiness in them, no more."

"Come and meet my father," Gabriel said, as he opened the front door.

"I can't, I'm not dressed," Kate flustered as he pressed her towards a door on the left of the great hall.

"Don't be silly," Gabriel laughed, "of course you can. It doesn't matter what you wear. Beauty such as yours needs no adornment. Believe me, I know."

Kate blushed deeply as he winked wickedly at her: "So you may wear whatever you like with equanimity. My father has an eye for aesthetic perfection in a woman. He will take to you immediately."

"Hold on," Kate stalled desperately, "show me a bit of the house first. Please? I've never been inside before. It's all a bit..."

"Overpowering? I know. It's not the most homely of places. Too damn large and gloomy." He smiled at her with a sweet understanding that completely disarmed her.

"Tell you what. I'll nip upstairs to get out of these riding togs and get a quick wash." He saw her concern. "No, don't worry. Into something more casual, that's all. To give you time to wander about a bit and get your bearings. There's lots to see."

"But what if I bump into..." she started.

"No fear. He's always ensconced in his study at this time of day." Gabriel was already leaping up the stairs as he spoke. Suddenly he paused, leaning over the banisters at the half-landing, "unless you'd prefer to keep me company, that is!"

Laughing, he bounded up the second flight and vanished, leaving Kate alone in this vast chamber.

She looked around, a little nervously at first, but then decided, "Why not?" She has been invited, after all, to explore. She determined to familiarize herself with as much of the house as possible.

She might even find clues to the mysterious east wing and its sorry occupant. Another secret entrance, perhaps?

On the whole, she thought, this was turning into an altogether happy coincidence, which she should exploit to the full, even if it meant playing him along for a bit.

After all, was it her fault that the scion of the house has taken to her so? But how would she explain this to Rob, who knew nothing of the mysterious lady or her own dilemma? She decided she would cross that hurdle when she came to it.

It really wasn't any of his business, was it?

She felt a twinge of guilt at her sudden callousness and promised she would confide in Robert at the first opportunity to present itself.

Kate decided to explore. There were three identical doors leading onto this hall: one to her right, one ahead and one to the left. She looked down at the beautifully polished parquet flooring and on the spur of the moment decided to pirouette upon it and go through whichever door faced her when she came to a stop.

She carefully turned the large brass knob to the door in front of her and opened it slowly. Before her stood a passage which led straight ahead to the southern porch. On her right two arched entrances led to a large dining hall with a stone fireplace set in its northern wall. She walked through the first of these. On her left the south-facing windows ran from floor to ceiling through this two-storey-high room. A huge table ran along its length surrounded by about twenty or more high-backed oak chairs. Oak panelling ran around the lower part of the walls. Above them tapestries hung, covering most of the bare walls. In niches along the walls stood sculptures and the ceiling was decorated by plastered geometric patterns resembling those of a wooden structured roof.

Kate shivered involuntarily. It felt to her as if the gloomy mysterious room in the East wing had been transposed to this new, brighter, location. The windows, instead of being high up and lanceolate, were from floor to ceiling, but the fireplace in the centre, the wood panelling and the tapestries above might all have been carried from the other. She reminded herself that probably the style of this room had been copied from the other when this became the main dining hall and the other abandoned. Though why the hangings had not been removed from the East wing at the time she could not answer.

The room overall was impressive but rather cold and uninviting. Looking back, she noticed that there were two small windows at first floor level above the passage through which she had just come. At the west end there were two more looking down from the upper floor of the West wing.

Kate pressed on and went through a door at the far end of the room on the southern side. She found herself in a much more cosily furnished oak panelled room with windows on three sides. This was the southernmost room of the West wing. It had a fireplace on its northern wall with a door on either side. The one she had just come through, and the other on the same wall beyond the fireplace.

It was furnished with a feminine taste, she decided: hung with many paintings and had comfortable couches and an escritoire. It must have been the summer drawing room for the lady of the house. Kate wondered if it was still used, now that there was none. It was certainly kept spotless, as if in memory of a loved one.

She passed through the other door, and found herself going through a series of rooms, each more extravagantly decorated than the last, all feminine, each from a different age and in a different style and dominant colour, with changing levels of intimacy and formality.

The centre room was the most formal, with beautiful French windows leading out onto the west lawns overlooking the great lake and landscaped park with its deer idly roaming.

Kate made her way into the last room of the series, a smaller, more intimate study, filled with photographs and more personal mementoes of times from beginning of the twentieth century. The last lady of the house perhaps retreated here when she wanted peace and quiet, just as she formally entertained in the centre rooms and more informally in the southern?

There was a strange atmosphere of reverential preservation about this whole wing. Kate could imagine the fusty old General pacing through these rooms on occasion, reliving his youth and childhood among the females of his clan, before he passed that watershed of manhood that drove him into the domain of the masculine, as Kate imagined it, the Eastern half of the house.

For it seemed to her already that this was how the house had been structured since its inception, with a sharp division of the sexes in the family, each at home in its own domain. East is male and West is female, and never the twain shall meet, in this family, at least. A schism through time, maybe driven by that original sin of the master of the clan, Sir Gabriel de Tiercel, all those centuries ago.

"Oh here you are!"

It was Gabriel, dashing Gabriel. Kate smiled. "Yes, here I am. In the domain of the female, I believe."

"Too right. It was my mother's study, and granny's before her." Gabriel waved his hand towards the photographs of two beautiful ladies.

"I can see where the looks come from," murmured Kate, "they are both very handsome women."

"Both died young, sad to say," added Gabriel. "It seems to be the curse of our tribe.
My mother was killed in a car crash when I was only five. So I really only remember her from the pictures in this room. She was thirty."

"But your father…"

"Is too old? Of course he was. He was thirty-seven when they married. She was twenty-three. He was fresh back from the Falklands, all mature and tanned and uniformed to the hilt. She was impressionable and fell for his panache. Panache? I hear you ask. Yes. The old General had it in abundance when he was young. Come on, a general at thirty seven?"

"Really? But what happened?"

Gabriel laughed. "To his panache? Or to Mama? Well, they went together. Wined and dined and honoured. Everybody

141

shook his hand. Then he killed her. Accidentally, of course. Drove her over a cliff in Perpignan while they were on holiday. Drunk, early one morning. She was unconscious and drowned in two inches of water in a ditch, apparently, while he was dead drunk. He survived, poor sod, with a permanent limp and his panache dashed forever. He retired from the army, retreated here and became the recluse we all know and love, I don't think."

"How sad. He must have loved her very much to have taken it so hard."

"He adored her to distraction, so they tell me. He blamed himself entirely. That's why he is so crochety." Gabriel looked at Kate for a long moment and added, "but come on, that's why you're here! The minute he sees you, he'll become more like his old self again."

"Me? Why?" Kate's hand jumped nervously to her chest.

"Because of your beauty. It'll remind him of his youth, of happier times. You don't mind, do you? Really? Meeting you would do him so much good. Would you do me the honour of allowing me to introduce you to him? Please?"

"But I'm not dressed. Look at me! I've only got my old jeans and jacket on. I was going to go for a walk. He can't see me like this."

"Whatever you wear becomes you." Gabriel knelt before her in an exaggerated show of humility that brought a smile to her face, and Kate knew that she would.

"Pleased to meet you." The old general took her hand in his, raised it towards him and gently brushed it with his lips in a gesture so old-fashioned and gallant that Kate felt a small tingle of delight shoot up her spine. His moustache tickled the back of her hand as he did this, adding to her amusement.

"I'm honoured, General. I've heard so much about you recently," she replied.

"Nothing good, I hope." He chuckled. "At least, not from

142

this fop of a boy, I'll warrant."

"Nothing but good, from your very amusing son, sir," she retorted.

"Good, good. I'm going to like you, my dear. What did you say your name was? I can never remember the first time. Not worth it, you see. Cluttering one's brain with names of people one's never likely to, nor often wants to, meet again. Waste of time. So much easier to ask again when one knows it's worth remembering. And if they're worth it, they'll not mind anyway. Don't you think so?" The general looked over his glasses, scrutinizing her.

"Which would you like me to answer first, sir?" Kate looked coolly at the old man without blinking, not allowing him to overawe her. "My name is Kate Pegler."

"Capital, capital! What an excellent young lady you've brought me, Master Gabriel. A cut above your usual class."

"Really, father. Show a little decorum. The young lady is present."

"A beautiful young lady. I am only too well aware, my dear boy. A very decorous young lady. I am very pleased to welcome you to my home. And I hope you will honour me with your company on many occasions in the future, my dear. This old stuffed jacket needs a good dusting down. You remind me, I think... and I hope you won't mind me saying this... of my own dear departed beautiful wife. Your demeanour, you know. Your candour. So refreshingly reminiscent..."

"But I haven't said anything yet..." started Kate.

"Precisely my point! Your saying that makes true my intuition, you see?" The general laughed and nudged her with his elbow. "Never wrong, where women are concerned, eh?"

"Er, no, I suppose not." Kate looked at Gabriel.

"Father. You're embarrassing Kate," interrupted Gabriel.

"Oh, dear. Sorry. Too much time alone, you know. It plays havoc with the social graces. A thousand pardons."

"Not at all, sir. I'm flattered by the comparison. I've seen photos of your wife. She was truly a lovely creature."

"Ah, yes. She was a gem. But how remiss of me. May I offer you a drink? Pink gin? Whiskey? A little sherry, perhaps?"

"No, thank you. I won't take up any more of your time, just at the moment. But if I may ask a favour?"

"By all means…"

"I would hugely appreciate it if at some time you could give me a guided tour of the house. What I have seen I have found fascinating. I would love to see it from the inside, so to speak."

"Of course. Delighted. Nothing would please me more. Name your day, and I shall be at your disposal for as long as you please."

"Thank you, sir. Goodbye."

"Please, dispense with the formality. I would be grateful if you would call me Peregrine… Perry, from henceforth."

Kate and Gabriel left the old general in his study. "Wow! I've never seen him take a shine to someone so quickly! Positively human! Whatever it is, I want some of that stuff you're taking. It's magic." Gabriel laughed, rubbing his thumb over his fingers in a 'gimme-money' gesture.

They entered the library. The walls were lined to the ceiling with books, ancient and modern, manuscripts among them. "God, this must be worth a fortune!" exclaimed Kate, staring at the case that housed the manuscripts.

"Yeah, many date back to the dissolution of the monasteries. Illuminated manuscripts and everything. Nobody reads them, of course. Just the odd scholar. Still, they look impressive I guess."

"As far back as that?" Kate was thinking furiously. "Do they contain any family history, or stuff like that?"

"Yeah, I guess so. You'd have to ask the general – Perry, to you – about that. I've never taken much interest. I'd flog the lot, if it was up to me."

"Thank God it isn't, then. You would as likely throw away your inheritance."

"Bah. Inheritance. A lot of happiness that deadweight brings anyone."

"You'll come to appreciate it as you get older."

"Rather, 'hope I die before I get old'," Gabriel laughed as he stumbled around the room, imitating a short-sighted old scholar poring over the dusty volumes of his collection.

"You're hopeless," laughed Kate.

"I would be, if I had to live with this lot all day. But instead, I have you. Let me paw over you to my heart's content, rather than these dusty tomes. I would trade the entire corpus of this knowledge for the deciphering of your sweet vellum-ptuous body."

"You're impossible!" Kate shook her head. "Look, I must go. I've got to cook the dinner tonight for my Dad. It's my turn."

"You cook, as well? How sweet. I love you already." Gabriel led her to the door onto the courtyard. "I can't abide kitchens, myself. So smelly. When can I see you again?"

"I don't know. It's up to you. Goodbye."

As Kate left through the outer courts she thought she saw Rob peering through a dusty window, but when she waved, the face withdrew as if stung by a wasp. "Strange," she thought, "I wonder if it was him. He can't be jealous, surely?"

24

Robert

"What is it?" Robert didn't go to the window, even though he knew it was Kate throwing pebbles up, clattering on the glass.

"I thought you were going to take me out on the bike today, on the pheasant run?" Kate's voice sounded small, insignificant, even.

"I can't. I've got to work." Robert was still hung over from the night before. It was payday and he'd gone down to the village pub with a couple of the lads from Fugglesham Court to get totally smashed. They did it most weeks, but he had joined them last night to try to obliterate Kate and that man from his consciousness.

He was consumed with rage. That effete rich young man had so blithely taken up with his Kate. Even worse, Kate seemed to be going along with it and even enjoying it. "Bitch!" He swore to himself. "Selfish cow! Just because the poncy bastard's filthy rich she thinks he'll make a better catch."

"Come on, Rob," pleaded Kate from the footpath below, "open the window. What's the matter with you?"

"I don't care to," replied Robert, opening the curtain just a crack to see how she reacted. "I'm busy today. Helping my father. And I'm sure you've got better things to do than hang around here."

"And what's that supposed to mean?" Kate planted her feet and stared up him. "I can see you peeking, what's going on?"

The curtains shuffled as his eye disappeared from view. "I know what it is!" crowed Kate, triumphantly, "it was you yesterday disappearing from that window in the yard as I left, wasn't it?"

"What if it was? What's it to you? You've got yourself a fancy-boy now, Kate Pegler, and I ain't one to come beggin' round after you." Robert sat on his bed and pulled on his socks.

"I haven't got a fancy boy, as you call him," retorted Kate, "I was invited in to meet the general, and so I went. And very nice he was too, if you must know."

"How comes you were up on his horse; Gabriel, I mean. How come he had you up there with him, eh?" Robert finished dressing and grabbed his work satchel, but paused to hear her reply.

"You great oaf, Rob, he gave me a lift, that's all," replied Kate, knowing that this wouldn't do at all as an excuse, knowing what Robert would say next.

"So you'll get up, or in, with anyone who offers you a lift, eh? Doesn't matter you don't know them from Adam. I'd be worried about you, if I cared, that is." He turned and slammed his bedroom door loudly and thumped down the stairs.

Kate, standing outside, paused, thinking how she could get out of this bind. How she could explain that it was the sheer charm of the man that won her over.

Robert emerged from the front door, "don't think I'm afraid to face you. But I ain't got time for wasters who lead you on then dump you the minute they find something more flashy." He strode past Kate and marched resolutely down the track towards Fugglesham Court.

"Look, Rob," Kate ran after him, "it's not like that. I wanted to get into the house, to meet the general. So when he offered, I accepted, see? He told me he was the general's son and that he would introduce me. That's why I went."

"Why should I believe you? What business you got with the general, then?" Robert continued to walk fast, staring straight ahead.

Kate grabbed his arm to slow him down, but he marched on, half dragging her along without looking round.

"I had to see him to ask him some questions about the history of the house for a school project. It's quite important to me. So this was the ideal way of getting to meet him." Kate squeezed Robert's arm. "Come on, don't be mean. It's got nothing to do with you and me."

"You seemed to be very friendly to him, laughing and joking and 'I'll see you soon', sort of thing. More than seems right to me," Robert looked at her for the first time.

"He's just funny, that's all," said Kate, looking up at him, "it's difficult not to find someone like that amusing. But amusing is all he is to me, honestly."

"Ok. If you say so."

"I do."

"But I don't like it. I don't like him. With his poncy walk and fancy manners." Robert slowed down a bit. "And in the yard they say he's a seducer, a philanderer."

"I'm sure he is, but that doesn't mean I'm going to be seduced by him."

"Maybe not. But they say he turns young girls' heads, with his talk and his money."

"Well, I'm not a sucker, Rob; you should know that. Unless of course you too…"

"Don't you start on me like that," Robert chuckled.

"Forgiven?"

"Yeh, forgiven. Just remember what I told you about his ways with women. Can't trust people like him. Users, that's what they are. Spit you out like a dry stone once they've had their fill of your flesh."

They walked on a little before Kate asked him, "well, what about my quad bike trip? When are we going to do that then?"

"I thought that was what you had come for?" laughed Rob, his good humour almost fully restored, "haven't you got the time now? Of course, if you're too busy to fit it in, I could…"

"Oh, shut up! Let's go now."

"Here we are, then!" Rob swung open a double door in the outer courtyard and walked ahead of her into the darkness. "Come on?"

"Oh, right." Kate looked at the fat wheeled bike and its small saddle. "Are you sure it's safe for me to get on as well? Where will I sit?"

"In front of me, across the saddle," Rob chuckled maliciously, "you know, just like you did on Gabriel's horse the other day. You didn't mind that, now, did you?"

"Ok. Ha, ha. Let's get on with it, shall we? And no more digs at me, ok? Or I'll just get off." Kate jumped onto the bike, and Rob slid on behind her and, reaching round her, took the handlebars and started the motor.

He revved up and accelerated off, skidding the bike in a sharp turn on the packed earth of the barn before roaring out of the doors and through the yard into the open.

He turned left as they reached the outer drive and they sped over the rough gravel towards the woods along the edge of the Downs. The bike bounced wildly as he drove it deliberately fast to scare Kate. She held onto the centre of the handlebars and pressed back with her body so that she nestled between his arms.

Robert delighted in feeling her fear and complete reliance on his ability to keep them upright on the increasingly bumpy track as it zigzagged up the steep northern escarpment of the Downs. He straddled the deep tractor tracks and bounced over the periodic grooves cut across the track in the chalk as rain run-offs.

149

At last he stopped in a darker section of the woods. Clumps of yew made this part seem almost tunnel-like in its gloom. Robert dismounted and went to a feeding station and refilled it. Then he mounted and continued to the next one. They hopped from one to the next until at last he said, "That's it. All done for today. How would you like to have a go?"

"Oh, I don't think I could. It seems far too dangerous."

"Don't worry, I'll take us back down and you can practice in an open field where it's nice and flat."

"Well, ok." Kate looked at him nervously.

"It's a doddle. You'll soon get the hang of it. Get on, and we'll head back."

Rob took her back down more slowly, demonstrating the clutch and gears and brakes as he did so. He rubbed his cheek against her face as he growled instructions into her ears. He could feel her responding to his touch and the tone of his voice. Her head leaned into his neck and she moved it in a slow stroking motion against his skin.

He was going very slowly now, to avoid any sudden bump cracking the heads together. He wondered how it was that every activity they engaged in turned into such sensuality. He had never managed this rapport with any other girl. It must be her, he decided, who somehow released him from his inhibitions and induced this skin-tingling state of euphoria.

He stopped the bike by a woodland hut with the excuse of collecting some stuff. He led her in, saying, "We may as well brew up, while we're here. It's used by the gamekeepers in the shooting season, but they always leave some long-life milk and teabags and biscuits."

He sat Kate down by the table while he put the kettle on. She looked around and saw a cast-iron freestanding log-burning stove in the middle of the hut, a rude bed frame, or cot, to one side, and the remains of an old hearth at the end. There was a doorway on the other side.

She got up and opened it. There was a little alcove with

a seat in it with a board laid on it. She lifted the board. The seat had a round hole in the middle. "How odd," she remarked, "it almost looks like a dunny."

"It is. Or was, rather. In the old days before toilets. This hut has been here for ages. If you look at the timbers, they're really solid, well built. This hut was obviously meant to be lived in at one time." Rob looked at her and smiled, "but now it only used in season as a shelter. We could use it as our secret hideaway, you know. No one comes here except in the shooting season." He winked at her. "There's a bed. In the cupboard, there's an inflatable mattress and sleeping bags in a steel trunk."

"I don't know," Kate looked around. "There's something funny about this place. It sort of gives me the creeps."

"Oh, rubbish. It's just a bit neglected, that's all. I could soon fix it up into a hovel fit for a princess!" Robert laughed as he handed her an enamel mug full of steaming tea. "Sugar?"

"No thanks," Kate seemed more subdued now.

Robert thought he detected in her voice a note of reluctance. He wondered whether his proposal had been going a bit too far, and hoped he hadn't put her off completely.

They sat in silence for a while. Rob looked at Kate. She sat, slightly hunched, her mug cupped in both hands. The vapour from the tea swirled in the shafting sunlight entering from the high windows.

Suddenly Kate, who had been looking around the room, inspecting each aspect of it with an intensity that made Rob keep a respectful silence, turned to him and asked: "Why are the windows so small and high up? Either a giant lived here, or whoever it was wasn't supposed to look out. It doesn't make sense. It makes the place feel…"

"…like a prison. I see what you mean. It is a bit spooky, now that I think about it. Why would anyone living in it not want to be able to look out?" Rob looked at Kate. She seemed to be turning pale and her expression was like someone who has realized something awful. "What's the matter? Are you all right?"

"I... I... don't know. I feel weird. As if someone has just sat on me. I feel like the breath is being crushed out me. Can we leave now, please? I've got to go." Kate jumped up and staggered, leaning on the table edge as she made her way towards the door.

"What is it? You look like you've seen a ghost." Rob rushed to her side and took her elbow, steering her towards the door. She looked as if she might faint. He led her to the quad bike in the sunshine of the path and sat her on it. She sat quite still, leaning forward on her hands, until she had regained her composure.

Rob re-entered the hut, rapidly cleared up and came outside again, sliding the heavy iron bolt of the studded door. "There now, I'll take you home."

Kate sat silent and rigid in his arms all the way back to her father's cottage. Rob helped her dismount and led her to the front door. He opened it and stood aside to let her pass.

She walked past him into the room without a word. "Kate. Is there anything I can do? You seem so strange, distraught. Not like you."

At this Kate turned and smiled weakly, "No, not at the moment. Thank you, Rob. You're so kind. I'm sorry. I'll be all right soon. I need to think. Go back now. I'll see you tomorrow, ok?"

"Ok. As long as you're sure you're alright."

"Yes. Don't worry."

Robert remounted his bike and roared off towards the great house, completely bemused by the sudden turn events had taken in that hut. It seemed to stem from the strangely high windows. Perhaps she was claustrophobic. He was determined to find out the next day.

25

The General

"You know, my dear girl, that I am well-disposed towards you. But you are asking for information about a deeply distressing episode in the history of our family. One best left dead and buried." The general turned and looked into Kate's eyes with a gaze that demanded honesty. "I cannot think why you should be interested in resurrecting things better left well alone. Unless you can convince me there is a reason of overriding importance for your quest, I am afraid I must decline to assist you. A school history project is not such a reason."

Kate's face, so full of enthusiasm till now, so hopeful of eliciting his help in unravelling the mysteries of this house, visibly collapsed into pained disappointment. She looked away, unable to find a way of telling the kind old gentleman her real reasons for asking.

She walked to the window of the library and looked out over the lawns. The sun shone hazily and the South Downs in the distance looked blue. The little church across the lawns was silhouetted against the silvery light.

"Something's troubling you, young lady. Why can you not speak?" The general walked to her side and leaned on the sill, looking out of the window. "I can feel this question is something that is important to you, personally. Am I right? Something beyond the reason you gave me."

153

He turned his head to look at her face. She was frowning and staring rigidly out of the window, as if frightened to look at him. "But I cannot see how the history of our house can have any significance to you. I really can't. You must help me to understand how if I am to be of help to you." He touched her shoulder.

Kate winced momentarily, and then relaxed. She looked at him with an anguished, almost pleading expression. "I don't know how," she started, "you see, it doesn't make sense to me, and you will think I am mad or something if I tell you."

"Try me. I must confess I am a little rusty where listening is concerned. But I assure you I will give you my best attention if you speak to me forthrightly, however absurd you think what you are saying may seem." General Tercel took her by the arm and led her to one of the deep leather armchairs and gently pushed her into it. "Now, relax, gather your thoughts, and then tell me about whatever it is that is troubling you."

"Thank you, I..." Kate stopped.

"Here, let me pour you a drink. A light sherry. To calm you. Just take your time." He wandered to one of the bookcases and pressed a book. The whole section of books started revolving and from the cavity emerged a drinks cabinet. "The house is full of surprises," he chuckled as he observed her eyes widen. "This is just a minor one."

He poured a sherry and passed it to her. She sipped quietly for a minute as he made himself a gin and tonic and returned to sit on a pouffe at her feet. She made to rise. "No, don't get up. I'm not so decrepit yet I cannot sit on an ottoman."

Kate laughed. He really was quite different from the image he projected to the outside world. As if reading her thoughts, he said: "Carrying the image of a crusty old dog really does have its advantages, you know, in my position. It relieves me of the burden of unwanted and troublesome guests and advantage-seekers, you know. And I really am quite happy in my own company."

"When we came here, earlier this summer," Kate began, "it was because my mother had just died, of cancer, after a long illness. My father couldn't bear to continue living in our London apartment, nice though it was. He needed to retreat to the countryside, and we buried my mother in the churchyard on the edge of the Wildbrooks not far from here. She was brought up in this area, you know."

"I'm sorry. You don't need to continue, if you don't want to, you know."

"No. I want to. I'm glad to have found someone I can talk to about it." Kate looked at him and he smiled kindly.

"I'm honoured that you think so."

"Well, not long after arriving, strange things started happening to me." She looked at him with concern. "Things to do with this house."

"What sort of things?"

"Well, first, I met this strange man, with a patch over one eye and a long cloak and a broad-rimmed slouch hat. He just popped out of a hedge one day. He gave me a warning that strange things were afoot."

"I'll have the men find him and run him out of the area, if he's threatening you," said the General. "Don't you worry about him."

"No. You mustn't. I mean. He wasn't threatening me. He was warning me, as a friend would. I trust him. I don't know why. There's just something about him I cannot help but like and trust, odd though he looks."

"Well, I don't know. There are some pretty queer folk around, nowadays. You need to be careful."

"Then... I don't know how to say this. Then I saw a ghost."

"A ghost?"

"Yes. I can only describe her as a ghost. She was dressed in a hooded cloak too, and was weaving a tapestry. But when she turned to me. It was my mother." Kate shuddered.

"Go on. I'm listening."

"It couldn't have been, but it was. It was my mother, except that she couldn't speak. She wrote me a note. And this was the most frightening bit. In the note she called me 'her darling Katie'. She couldn't have known. But she did. 'Katie' is the name my mother called me. Only my mother ever called me 'Katie', you see. I was terrified."

"You say she wrote you a note. Does it exist? Have you still got it?"

"Yes, at home. How could a ghost write on a piece of paper?"

"If it was a ghost. Maybe it was someone playing tricks on you, knowing how upset you are about your mother's death." The general leaned forward and patted her knee. Kate found this gesture oddly comforting, not threatening. "Where did this happen? At your cottage? In the woods? Where?"

"Here."

"Here? In my house?" the general started back, spilling his drink. "In this house? But how? You've never been here. Except the day before yesterday, with my son."

"I have. I'm sorry. I don't know how to tell you. It's all so confusing. I didn't burgle your house. Honestly." Kate's eyes started bubbling. She wiped away the trickle. "You see I picked up a key, which a man in a cloak dropped on the grass outside the door..."

"You picked up a key? Why didn't you return it to him?"

"He just ran off."

"A cloaked man. Not the one who warned you?"

"No. Not him. I thought it was, so I asked him next time I saw him. And he denied it, but said he knew the man. And that the key was mine to use. That I must go through that door. I know it sounds mad. But I did. I felt compelled to."

"I don't understand. Through which door did you feel compelled to go?"

"The door in the East wing. The one in the recess halfway

156

along."

"But there isn't a door there, my dear. How could you?" The general looked at her quizzically, doubtfully.

"You see! I told you I couldn't tell you. Nobody will believe me. They'll think I'm mad, just like I said." Kate jumped up and made for the door.

"Hold on, stop!" General Tercel's voice assumed a tone of command. "Just come back here, young lady. And calm yourself down. I didn't say I didn't believe you when you say you saw a door. I just said there isn't one. Now come and sit down. You must tell me the rest."

"I unlocked that door and went in, and up a stone spiral staircase. I found myself in a great hall, with windows high up. And there she was. I ran away after I read her note."

"So you saw the ghost of your mother, apparently, in the East wing of this house and you still have the note she gave you? Is that right?"

"Yes."

"May I see it? The note?"

"Yes, of course. Look, I'm terribly sorry. I didn't mean to break in. I just couldn't help myself. I had to know what the old man's portents and omens were all about."

"Portents and omens?"

"Yes. To do with birds doing strange things in the woods and perching on the East wing. And a massacre or something."

"A massacre? Where did you hear of a massacre? When was it?"

" I'm not sure. When the house was built, apparently. He said it was at the time of a Gabriel de Tiercel..."

"de Tiercel? You know, do you, that de Tiercel is the old way of spelling our name? Strange. I wonder how he knew. I wonder who he is."

"I don't know. He said I had something to do with it – that I was wrapped up in it somehow – or I wouldn't have seen

157

these things. Then I met her. My mother. Not my mother. But she knew me. She had tears in her eyes and called me…"

"…'my darling Katie'. Yes. Well, we've got plenty of food for thought, here, already." The general patted her again. "Now look here. I'll tell what we'll do. You bring me the letter, and I'll take look at it. We'll find out if it is a forgery or a hoax, and then we'll take it from there, eh?"

"Ok," Kate answered meekly. She felt exposed and vulnerable.

"Don't worry, my dear. I'm not questioning your honesty or your sanity. It is a strange matter, to be sure. But we will find a way through it. I will help you. For you see, I know something of the events you have just described. They have an element of truth to them."

He got up and took her hand and pulled her up from her seat and led her to the door. "Come tomorrow with the letter. I will, in the meantime, do a little research through the family records, and see what I can come up with."

"Oh, thank you. You don't think I'm losing my marbles, then?"

"Quite probably, but then how many people have marbles to lose?" General Tercel winked at her, "off you go, now. Come back after lunch tomorrow, to give me time to rummage around in the family's midden-heap."

"Bye," Kate stood on tiptoe and kissed his cheek. "Thank you for believing in me."

At this show of tenderness the general blushed with a pleasure he had not felt for many years. He watched her leave the room, and then turned to that section of books devoted to the family's affairs.

26

Kate

The next morning Kate dressed carefully and put on her make up. The General had only seen her in rough clothing and she wanted to impress him. She needed his help.

As she reached the outer gate of Fugglesham Court and walked in through the pedestrian side gate, the great wrought-iron main gates started to creak open to allow the general's magnificent old Rolls, with uniformed chauffeur, to make its stately passage out.

Kate peered into its windows to see if it was carrying Peregrine Tercel himself, and she half-waved the document she held in her hand, as if by doing so she could bring the vehicle to a halt. But the black limousine rolled on.

She watched its wheels crunching on the gravel drive, stirring a cloud of dust as the square-backed car purred into the distance. The general's sharp-beaked profile appeared in the long rear window as if he had turned to look at her. She felt a vague prickling sensation in the back of her neck. This scene seemed for all the world to have sprung from another era, like a ghostly Brideshead Revisited. She could almost hear the silken-voiced narration of Jeremy Irons inside her head and wondered whether she was not being drawn into a similarly unreal world of class and privilege in her incipient relationship with this strange house and its intriguing occupants.

"Damn!" she thought. "What am I going to do now? I've brought the letter he wants to see and he's gone out. I'll just have to go back home with it."

She stood for a full minute in the middle of the drive, foolishly watching the vanishing point of the long drive's rows of lime trees. She could picture the camera close behind her head as the car drove sedately away, just catching the silhouette of the general's head before rising up and back, to reveal an elegant figure from a bygone age, knee-length blue-black skirt wafting in the breeze, diminishing to a pathetic insignificance standing between the great gate-posts, slowly swinging shut as the car disappeared into a dusty haze.

Pure symmetry. The next shot takes the same camera height and distance, but in front of her, standing before the now closed gates, with the great house in the far distance, now zooming down and in to just in front of her, forlornly holding her letter before tracking back as she walks forward on her way back to her house, with the gates diminishing as she passes the pairs of lime trees until they can no longer be discerned.

Kate's reverie was interrupted by a noise: the soft purring of a contented cat, growing louder. She looked round. The gate was in the distance now. She must have walked all this way in her trance-like state. She looked ahead. The noise turned into a small cloud of dust from which a black silhouette emerged. It was General Tercel's car! Her heart jumped. He had seen her and he had turned around and was coming for her. Or was he? Surely not?

The car drew up alongside her, and the chauffeur stepped out and walked round to the rear passenger door, opened it and gestured her to alight. "Come along, dear girl," the general's voice beckoned, "I'll give you a lift to the house."

Kate climbed aboard and sat down next to the general in the huge, leather-scented seat as the chauffeur closed the door silently, resumed his place and started the car.

"You were coming to see me, I take it? Not Gabriel?"

"No, not Gabriel."

"Please forgive me, for not stopping immediately. I didn't recognise you back there." The General coughed. "I thought when I saw you I was dreaming. Someone from my past. It took me a while to realise. Where did you get that dress?"

"Oh, it's an old one of my mum's. Biba. Dad says it was a favourite of hers – when they first went out together. Do you like it?"

"Lovely. It fits you perfectly," the general looked at her face and then down at her hands. "That must be the letter?"

"Yes, sir, it is. Do you want to see it?"

"Of course, but not yet. It's too dark in here for my old eyes. Show me when we reach the house. Have you had any further thoughts about what you told me?" The general looked out of the window across the deer park towards the lake. "I love that view. It is so tranquil. You wouldn't think anything bad could happen in a world that contains such a perfect view, would you? But then I'm a spoiled old man. You probably see things differently."

"No. Yes. I mean the view. It is perfect and peaceful, as you say. But as for the rest, I'm confused. So many things seem to be happening to me, strange, unreal things, that I don't know what to think or believe at the moment."

"Well, let's just see what we can discover from an examination of your letter, and then proceed from there. It's always a bad idea to jump ahead of oneself in an unusual situation. We'll take it one step at a time shall we, and see where it leads us."

With that, the general signalled to Kate to let things be for the moment, so she sat back and took in the scene as viewed from the luxurious coachwork of this antique Rolls Royce. Her Brideshead feeling came flooding back with a neck-tingling satisfaction as she allowed herself to be administered to by the general's chauffeur and butler as they passed into the house and his private study. It was all so bizarre, the opening of doors, the taking of her coat, the brushing of dust from her shoes before entering the inner precincts of Fugglesham Court as an official guest of its proprietor.

"Alright, Martin, you may leave us, now. And make sure we are not disturbed. Not by anyone, including Master Gabriel."

"Yes, sir." The butler withdrew.

"Now then. A whiskey is called for. Helps me concentrate, you know." The general smiled as he pushed his magic button. He obviously drew a childlike pleasure from playing with the house's gadgets. "What will you have?"

"An orange juice will be fine thank you."

"Damn! I'll have to call the butler then. Orange juice is not something I stock."

"Oh, it doesn't matter. A gin and tonic will do. Have you got lime?"

"Of course. Gin and tonic it is. Ice?"

"Only a little, please."

The general poured and served the drinks, and then beckoned Kate over to the desk by the window. "Now show me this letter. I can see better in this light."

Kate unfolded the letter. It was a peculiar texture. General Tercel picked it up, fingered it thoughtfully for a while, and then sat down to study the handwriting style and the content of the letter.

Kate sipped her drink slowly as the general pored over the manuscript, drew out a large magnifying glass from a drawer in the desk and scrutinized the writing. He seemed to take forever, and Kate began to twitch uncomfortably. Was he thinking she had forged it? She broke the silence: "What do you think?"

"Kate, my dear, you have me confused. To all appearances it seems genuine. The script, the vellum, the quill type and the ink all seem to be concomitant with having been written

162

around the time of 16th century. Impossible, I know. But it does look like the genuine article. It is deeply disturbing." General Tercel looked up at Kate and raised his eyebrows. "I am foxed by this conundrum. How did you say you came by it?"

Kate repeated the story of her encounter in the hidden room in the East wing with the mysterious lady, 'her mother'.

"I wonder." The general paused, "I know. I have similar manuscripts from our household written around the same time. I'll fetch them and we can compare the paper and inks used."

He rose and went to a bookshelf, pressed on one side of it and the whole swung round to reveal the library beyond. "Another of my tricks," he chuckled, "I won't be a moment."

He disappeared and after a brief interval, reappeared with a sheaf of similar papers. "Now then. Somewhere amongst these is the one I am looking for. Ah, here it is. Now look."

He laid the new manuscript next to the letter Kate had brought. They seemed very similar. Kate looked more closely. Even the handwriting looked the same! "It can't be!" she cried, "Both look the same."

"Yes. It appears they are by the same hand. Look at the signature." The general handed Kate the magnifying glass. She stared hard, first at one, then at the other. They were identical! The very same signature: "Amelia Linnece", the same flowery script, the same flourishes and arabesques around the main letters.

"But it can't be! I saw this one written in front of my eyes. She dusted it and blew on it before handing it to me. It can't be!" Kate looked in terror at the old man.

"I'm afraid it is. Even the vellum is the same. It is the type made for this house at the time. All the correspondence was written on it. Though this one," the general pointed to his own letter, "was written before the massacre. Amelia wrote it to her own parents while staying here with her sister, Phyllis.

See?"

Kate read the letter through. Yes, there was no hint of the trouble that was to follow, though Kate thought she detected a hint of dissimulation in these words to her parents. Was Amelia covering up something, even at this point? Had she had the baby, Kate, fathered by Gabriel out of wedlock, at this time? She couldn't figure it out from the relatively short epistle.

"This leaves us with an impossibility, I think," said the general thoughtfully, "you were given a letter, addressed to you personally, but written in the sixteenth century, judging by its ageing. There's only one thing to do."

"What's that?"

"I'm going to take it to the British Museum, to have both letters analysed and dated. Then we shall know for sure." General Tercel laid his hand gently on Kate's shoulder, "that is, if you don't mind parting with your letter?"

"Of course not. I want to find out. But what if they are identical, in age and everything? What then?" Kate's eyes pleaded with the old man for an answer, an answer that somehow could make sense of it all.

"Now look, my dear, I think you should sit down." General Tercel beckoned her to a chair. "You and I must have a talk. I have been looking through the histories of the time. You see, records were indeed kept concerning the massacre, both the official family version, and versions of the 'legend' as it was put about by villagers orally until recorded in writing about ten years later when the dreadful fire took place and an official inquiry was launched into all the events leading up to it. But how much do you know already?"

"Well, there is what the old man, Shabby Tattler, told me, after I told him about my finding the key and then meeting the lady in the East wing."

Kate told the general the bare bones of the story up to the point where Shabby Tattler had left off; when the children had escaped to the village in the marshes and Amelia was about to be taken to the East wing as a prisoner of Sir Gabriel de Tiercel. She didn't tell him about the curse or of its supposed coming to pass, as Tattler predicted it would, through her, Kate Pegler. How could she? It was predicting that she would somehow be instrumental in bringing about the end, the deaths, of the old general and his beautiful young son. She could not face this possibility herself.

"Extraordinary!" the general leaned back in his chair. "The detail, the parallels with the official history are quite extraordinary. This tale, if true, fills in many gaps in that version of events; gives them a totally new meaning. I find it difficult to believe. Where did this man get his information? It seems impossible that he could know so much. I mean, how could he know about the escaped children? How could he possibly know, eh? They disappeared from history, to all intents and purposes. In the official history they were listed as dead, and indeed Kate Linnece was buried alongside her parents in the church of Runswick Abbey. But local legend says that they survived and that they would return one day to avenge the deaths of the Linneces and the villagers. But whom could they, Kate and Robin, if they had survived, have told? Who wrote it down with all that detail, and where, so that this man Tattler could have come across it? There is something frightening about this man's knowledge."

"I know. I cannot think how he could know it either. But he does. I'm convinced he is not making it up or deliberately lying to me. He is so matter of fact about it."

"Almost as if he had access to every record of the day," added the general, "as if he has read everything on the matter in my own library, though he puts a different gloss on it, but also as if he had also read accounts no longer existing, to my knowledge."

"You know he said he would tell me the rest of the tale next time we meet," Kate proffered this token of her trust in the general, "maybe we'll get more clues as to how he knows then? Should I ask him directly, do you think? Should I tell him I have told you the tale?"

"No, I don't think that would be wise. He might just clam up, and then we'll never find out." The general paused, took a sip of his drink, and continued, "This whole thing is just too much to take in. You, entering my house by a door that doesn't exist, meeting a woman who by all accounts may have existed and could have been held there, and all told by a man whom nobody knows."

"Well, sir, I'll try to get Shabby Tattler to tell me everything, and then maybe we can figure out a way of explaining it all?" Kate looked at the general.

"Right you are, then. I'm going up to London tomorrow to take these to an old friend of mine at the British Museum. You, in the mean time, see if you can find this Shabby Tattler fellow. Oh, and don't call me 'sir', will you? I think we know one another a little too well for that. Perry will be fine."

"Right. Perry," Kate giggled. It sounded too absurd a name to call anyone living. "I'll be going then, Perry."

With that Kate rose and opened the study door and left.

27

Gabriel

"Ha! You thought you could sneak in and out without being caught, did you?"

"Let me go!" Kate wriggled and squirmed to escape Gabriel's grip. He had pounced on her in the long corridor from the general's study and hauled her into a small chamber. "It's not funny, Gabriel Tercel. It's not the right time for this sort of prank."

"Oh, sorry," Gabriel sounded surprised and hurt, "I was just…"

"Fooling around, yes, I know. But can't you ever be serious?" Kate looked angrily at him as she straightened her clothes. "Life isn't all fun and games, you know."

"I said I'm sorry. I didn't know you were in a bad mood." Gabriel shuffled uneasily. He had never seen her like this. He wondered what had been going on between her and his father. "He hasn't been annoying you, has he?"

"No, you have, Gabriel. I've got things on my mind at the moment. Serious matters I am trying to sort out in my head…"

"What, involving my dad? What's going on between you two? He hasn't been making a pass at you, has he?" Gabriel looked angry now, "I'll do him if he has."

"Don't be silly, Gabriel. It's nothing like that. He's been helping me with my A-level project on local history, that's all.

Some of us need to get exams and things, you know."

"Oh, I see. So why so tetchy, then?"

"Look Gabriel, just let it be, will you? I'm not in the mood right now for fooling about. I'll see you tomorrow or something."

"OK. But please accept my apology, Kate." Gabriel looked so downcast that Kate relented, as he knew she would. She smiled. "When can I see you then?" he chirped merrily, taking her by the arm solicitously and leading her to the front door.

"I don't know. I've got some work to do. I may come round tomorrow afternoon. But if you come and pester me while I'm working, I won't come at all."

"Terms accepted, Countess." Gabriel bowed and watched her as she walked out of the courtyard. "She's a doll," he thought, "she'll impress all my pals, not to mention my dad."

Gabriel laughed, pirouetted and minced exaggeratedly back into the entrance hall.

"Gabriel, a word, if you please." His father's voice came from the direction of the study.

"Oh, god, I hope he didn't see me." He muttered under his breath. "I'm coming, father," he shouted back.

"I'm going up to London to the British Museum tomorrow morning. I need you to drive me to the station. It is the chauffeur's day off."

"Ok, dad. British Museum?"

"Oh just some old manuscripts I want dating, that's all," the general turned his back on his son and gather up the two sheets of vellum and packed them into a large briefcase. "That'll be all, my boy."

"Yes, sir," Gabriel saluted and clicked his heels, turned smartly and marched out, banging the door behind him. "Why's the old sod always got it in for me?" he mused as he went upstairs to his own room and put some music on, louder than he really wanted to hear it.

28

The Diary (1)

Kate turned the key in the lock. She had returned to her house and fetched the key and run straight back to the East wing. She was determined to find out more about "Amelia Linnece" and her daughter "Grey Kate".

Closing the heavy door behind her, she felt her way up the spiral staircase in the dark. Reaching the door at the top, she carefully opened it a little way and peered into the great hall.

The scene was much as she remembered it. The tapestry still hung on its frame, but not highlighted by the light from the windows, since the hour was later. Of the room's mysterious occupant, Kate could see no sign.

She quietly entered and pushed the door to, not quite closing it, but close enough so that her entry would not be noticed. She crept quietly, hugging the eastern wall, crossing the pools of light cast by the high western windows quickly, until she reached the far end.

There were two doors at this end of the hall, as there were at the southern end, through one of which she had entered. She guessed that the other one at that end led into the main body of the house. She chose to explore the door nearest to her first. Tiptoeing up to it, she lifted the wooden latch slowly, trying not to click it noisily.

She peered around it carefully. She could see immediately that this must be the lady's bedchamber. At the far end of the room, a large four-poster oak framed bed was hung about with heavy curtains, pulled aside on one side. Two large chests stood along one wall, while a closet was set into the outside wall with a wooden door. Kate presumed this must be her privy. On a nearby table stood a large china basin and ewer, next to which stood what looked like a crude bar of soap and some linen towels. A couple of simple chairs completed the furnishings.

Amelia Linnece, if that was the name of this lady, was not here. Kate quickly walked around the room, taking everything in and trying the bed. There was a quilted mattress on top of which lay another, feather-stuffed, mattress. Across the head of the bed was a long bolster upon which several feather filled pillows lay. The bed had two sheets and quilts on top, with a fine bedspread covering all. Kate sat on it and then lay down. She found herself sinking into it so that it formed a sort of nest about her.

Hearing a noise coming from the room next door, she quickly jumped up, feeling a little guilty at her frivolity, and raced to the door. She made her way to the next door and quietly opened it.

The lady was there, sitting at a writing desk with an open book before her. She was bowed over as she wrote on its pages with a quill, periodically dusting and blowing the pages as she went. Kate quickly glanced around the room. It was similarly sparsely furnished. A fire burned in a small hearth before her. The walls were wood panelled to half their height. The windows were the same as in the hall, high and small. The lady's desk was in the brightest part of the room, but even so she had to light her writing by using a stout candle set in a holder on a stand next to the desk.

Kate tiptoed lightly towards the hunched figure, keeping out of her line of sight. She wanted to see what the woman was writing with such concentration. She reached her and leaned over her shoulder, taking care not to breathe on her.

She stared at the page being written upon, and then tried to read the left side, already complete.

"…cannot allow of much hope for her return. I fear for my sanity. I believe I dreamed it all, conjuring my hopes into being out sheer desperation for their fulfilment. Oh, how the days drag on in endless succession with no hope of rescue. How did I conjure this apparition of my daughter, so familiar to me and yet so strange in her apparel? She wore trousers like the peasants wear, and yet wholly different from these. It is as if she had miraculously returned from some foreign land. And her hair, cut so…"

Here was confirmation that the Kate Linnece of the story told by Shabby Tattler was indeed the daughter, not sister, of Amelia. But how could that man know what was hidden from nearly all at the time? Kate peered further to try to read the right-hand page, but in doing so touched the left shoulder of the writer. The woman let out a small gurgled cry and jumped in her seat, dropping her pen and looking round. The terror in her eyes quickly melted into tears of joy as the lady, realising that she had been discovered, not by her dreaded persecutor, Sir Gabriel, but by her beloved 'daughter'.

She stood suddenly, knocking the seat over, and embraced Kate, kissing her passionately, clasping her tightly to herself, so that Kate, overwhelmed by this exhibition of affection, also found herself crying. For a few moments the two stood in weeping embrace, the silence only broken by intermittent sobs.

The woman broke free from this embrace and holding Kate at arms length studied her with an expression of joy mixed with disbelief. She took Kate's hand and beckoned her to draw up a second chair. Pulling out a piece of that same vellum which the old general was about to take to London, she scribbled a few words: "Darling Katie. Thank God! I thought you must be Sir Gabriel, come to spy upon me, or Black Martin, his clerk. But it is you. I can't believe you are real. I thought I must have dreamed you to appear before me. But you are here. Again. Please let me touch you again?"

She handed the note to Kate who read it through. Putting it down, Kate asked her: "Tell me, Amelia, why is it that you are dumb? Have you always been like this?"

Amelia took the note and added: "No I was not always dumb. Once I had the most beautiful singing voice in the county. It was my singing that first attracted that bastard Gabriel to me. He heard me in the woods, picking flowers. He came to me and declared his love for me. I said that was impossible; he was married to my older sister, Phyllis. But he took me and forced himself upon me there and then. From this rape I became pregnant. I refused to say who the father was, for Phyllis's sake. Our family covered it up and pretended that our mother was in confinement, that she was poorly and that I was keeping her company. When the baby was born nine months later she claimed she was the mother, your mother, Katie my love. I had to pretend I was your older sister, to save the reputation of our family. So now you know."

Kate looked at the tears and sorrow of this woman who thought she was her mother, put her hands on her shoulders and drew her close until their lips met.

They hugged one another for a long time, until the up welling emotions of both were assuaged and a feeling of wellbeing and trust in the other's impossible existence surged through Kate.

Suddenly she cared no longer that what she was experiencing was absurd and could never be explained, for she knew here was a reality beyond all doubt: her mother, Amelia, was here, in front of her. Though struck dumb and unable to communicate through the spoken word, the charge between them was as real and potent as that so familiar to her throughout her life with her own mother.

Somehow, two moments in time had become conjoined

so that the relationships between two mothers and their daughters had become intertwined to create somehow, one mother, one child, in two different eras. But that this was her mother she did not doubt.

Then, as these thoughts and feelings churned through her, the realisation suddenly came to her that she, Kate, could somehow influence the outcome of her mother's plight. Could she somehow rescue her? But how could she, without bringing her into her own universe and time? For as soon as she walked out through the door at the foot of the stairs, she knew she would set foot in her own century. And how could she bring Amelia into her world without precipitating the most dreadful consequences? Her father would recognise his own wife impossibly returned from the dead but struck dumb.

But she, Amelia, would not recognise her, Kate's, own father as he who had fathered her own darling 'Katie'. It would be impossible. Kate realised that she would have to find some other way of freeing her mother. But how much time did she have? Kate realised she must find Shabby Tattler and wring from him the rest of the story in every detail to discover at which point in the story she was entering at this moment. Perhaps each successive visit brought her 'mother' closer to her own fate.

Kate freed herself from their embrace and said: "Mother, darling, if I am to rescue you I must go now and find some means of doing so. You must let me go and I will try to work out a way of freeing you so that you will not be immediately recaptured."

Amelia nodded submissively, turned and picked up her diary and, beckoning Kate to follow her, led the way into the hall. She walked to a spot near the door Kate had entered by and, handing Kate the book, pulled at a ring in a stone at the back of a niche that had probably once held a small statue. The stone moved and slid forward onto the base of the niche, revealing a dark cavity beyond. Taking the volume from Kate's hands, Amelia slid it into the cavity and pushed the stone back.

She turned to Kate and smiled, putting up her forefinger over her lips in a gesture of silence. She led her back into her writing room and wrote on that piece of vellum "Gabriel's father showed that place to me when I was a little girl. He used to leave me secret messages in it and trinkets. I think he wished he had had a daughter, so adopted me as such. When he died, my secret hidey-hole was forgotten until Gabriel imprisoned me here. I was able to get the empty volume from Phyp Spadger, who was in love with me, and I have kept it secret ever since. Gabriel suspects I may be keeping a journal, but he has never been able to find it. In it is written everything that has happened to me. Take this note with you. Burn it. Your loving Amelia"

Kate took the note, read it, rolled it carefully and put it into her coat pocket. She kissed Amelia before turning for the door. As she left she looked back. Amelia raised her right hand and gave a flicker of her fingertips. Kate waved back, shut the door, locked it and hastened downstairs.

She locked the outside door and walked off in the direction of the woods. How could she find Shabby Tattler again? He seemed to turn up at the most unlikely moments, and yet, always in time to launch her on the next phase of this weird adventure.

At least she knew there was a diary, kept by the Elizabethan Amelia, and she knew where it was hidden. It would be impossible to get access to it while in the room with Amelia. "But what if," thought Kate suddenly, "I were to go to the house itself by the normal route and search the east wing as it is today, then surely I could find the place where the alcove is, or was, and dig into the wall and try to uncover it. It might have survived the fire, hidden away behind the stone. After all, it was placed at the far end of the great hall from the seat of the fire in the bedroom. If it survived, it must be possible to find it as it was at the time of the fire. So effectively I would be able to read everything she wrote right up to the moment of the fire. The only question is, how on earth can I get in and find it and dig it out without being discovered?"

She decided to pay a call on Rob. It was time let him in on her scheme. She decided that, however hare-brained her plan would seem to him, she could persuade him to go along with it, just to get even with young master Gabriel. She could tell he was eaten up with envy at the way Gabriel had so easily 'seduced' her, as he saw it.

How reading the diary would help her to rescue Amelia, she had not considered. She just knew that obtain it she must, to get a complete understanding of the whole affair from Amelia's own pen. Maybe then she wouldn't need Shabby Tattler to finish the tale, or his help to unravel the problem.

Kate skipped cheerfully along towards Rob's cottage, planning her little subterfuge to enlist his help. She felt very pleased with herself, as if it had become a game from which no harm could come.

29

Robert

Robert sat on the edge of his bed swinging his legs. He was completely bemused. Kate had just left. She was in a state of excitement bordering on hysteria, it seemed to him. She had just told him a story so preposterous and made a proposal so insane that he did not know what to think.

She had described to him her two meetings with the woman claiming to be her mother from another time, shown him the great black key for a door in the East wing he had never seen, and let him read this second letter from 'Amelia' describing her rape and the birth of her, 'Katie' as a result of it. She had told him of the Elizabethan diary and its whereabouts in the East wing and actually asked him to help her find it, dig it out and steal it!

He shook his head in disbelief. He had agreed! How could he have agreed to such madness? How could he have made a binding pact with her to do such a thing? They would be caught. Then what? How to explain they were not stealing anything from the house today, but only an artefact from the distant past that almost certainly didn't exist. He could see the old general or his butler catching them red-handed with a mallet and chisel, prying away the plaster from the wall as if digging for treasure.

But he had agreed. He had promised he would find a means of getting into the house unseen and help her do this thing. Why had he agreed, he asked himself. But he knew the answer.

To be her accomplice, her intimate and exclusive aider-and-abetter in crime, was to get one over that arrogant turd Gabriel. But to take this thing out of the house from under his very nose? He had to devise a distraction to get Gabriel away for long enough to get in and out. Kate had told him that tomorrow was the day off for the butler and chauffeur, and that she knew the old general was going up to London. But Gabriel wasn't. He was only going to give the old man a lift to the station, less than ten miles away. He would back in less than forty minutes. Not long enough to get in, find the spot, dig out the diary, if there was a diary, and cover up the hole so that no one would notice, at least, not for a while. He, Robert Ruddock, was going to have to find a way to lure Gabriel away from the house for at least an hour and a half, preferably two.

But then, thought Robert, whatever happened, it would be worth it. Kate had intimated that she would be his, unconditionally. For that he would do almost anything short of killing someone.

He took a swig of brown ale. It was warm. But then he liked it warm. You can taste it, sweet and nutty, he thought, like a woman's tongue in your mouth in the midst of a passionate kiss." He leaned back, imagining bliss.

"Bring the car round, will you, Rob, there's a good lad." Gabriel stood in the door to the stables where Robert was preparing feed for the pheasants.

"Right you are, sir," replied Robert in a jolly obliging manner, "the Rolls, is it sir, or the Range Rover?"

"Range Rover. Dad only likes James to drive the Rolls. Family heirloom, he calls it. Anyway the Range Rover is much more my style." Gabriel laughed as he handed Robert the keys. "Bring it round to the front door in five minutes will you. I've got to drive the general to the station at Horseworth.

"Oh, sir. I've just had a thought. I know its not my place to ask, but…"

"No. Go ahead. What is it?"

"Well sir, you know young Kate Pegler from down the village? Well she caught a train this morning early to Hengiston to do some shopping for her dad. She asked me if I would drive up there to save her catching a train back with her shopping. She said she didn't think that there was a convenient train and that it would save her carrying her stuff home. It's a long walk. The thing is, I've got a lot on here, helping my dad. I just thought that if you were driving halfway there already to drop your dad off, you might be able to…"

"…drive on and pick Kate up? I reckon I could probably just about manage that." Gabriel grinned widely, thinking what a fool Robert was, putting his duty before the chance to take Kate for a ride. "When were you going to pick her up, and where?"

"Well, that's just it. She said she would definitely be finished by midday, so would I mind meeting her under the market cross at about half twelve? I said I would, but if you could manage, then I'd be awfully obliged. I'd lose nearly a whole morning's work otherwise."

"We wouldn't want that, now, would we?" Gabriel looked suitably solicitous, "Of course I'll do it. Only too happy to. Consider it done. I'll have a look around while I'm waiting, and maybe have a pint in the George to kill time."

"Thank you sir. I'll just go and get the Range Rover." Robert walked out smiling to himself. "Looks so smug, he does. Thinks he's got one over me, the mug."

"Kate? You ready?" Robert stood outside her cottage. It was ten o'clock. He was feeling pretty pleased with himself.

178

He had sent Gabriel on a fool's errand that would keep him away for at least two hours after he dropped his father off at the station.

Kate opened the door and came out with a backpack on. "I've got a small mallet and two stone chisels, some instant plaster and a trowel, a brush and dustpan and a couple of pedal bin liners in here. Oh, and a torch."

"Hmm. You seem to have thought of everything," replied Robert, "now all we have to do is get in and find the spot."

"I'm certain I can locate it. I know how many windows along the wall it is. I carefully noted it as I was leaving last night." Kate smiled and linked arms with her co-conspirator. "This is exciting."

"Yeah. I just hope we don't get caught."

"Nobody to catch us, unless one of your yard men tittle-tattles."

"I'll just tell them I'm mending something in the house."

They walked hurriedly towards the house yards. They made their way through these and in through the servants' entrance, close to the East wing. Up the back stairs and along the hall to the sixth window. Looking around, Robert opened the door to the room that now occupied this part of the old great hall.

They went inside. It was an old store room. It was dusty and there were cobwebs over the windows. "That's lucky," Robert said, "Nobody's going to check in here for ages by the looks of it. So we can just repair the plaster roughly and hide the rubbish under something."

They picked a path through the dusty furniture placed haphazardly about the room. Kate looked around for a minute, and then felt her way along the wall, stopping every few feet to check her bearings. "Here. I think it is here somewhere. You see that slight depression in the plaster. I think this may be it. Shine the torch on it from a sharp angle, so I can see the outlines."

Robert moved close to the wall then pointed the torch along its length.

"There. See?" Kate exclaimed, "I can see outline of the alcove. Shine the torch up a bit."

Robert pointed the torch up a fraction. They could both see the curve of the top of the niche. He shone it at the base. "I'll put the torch on this table," he said, "then I can chip away at the plaster and whatever is behind. You catch all the bits of plaster and bag them. Ok?"

"Ok."

Robert took out the tools and began hammering at the chisel. "Wait! Let me put this over it." Kate said, taking out a tea towel and wrapping it over the chisel handle. "There! Now you can bang harder."

Working hard, Robert soon had most of the lower plaster out. Behind this layer he found a wattle and daub infill. "That's lucky. It's not bricked up." He bashed away and soon ripped out a section of the wattle. "We'll keep this and put it back to plaster over when we've finished" he said, handing the section to Kate. "Look, there's nothing behind it. Get the torch."

Kate fetched the torch and shone it into the hole. They could see the semi-circular shape of the alcove's base. "This is it! We've found it." She gripped Robert's forearm tightly. "Look, see? There's the ring in that stone at the back. All we have to do is pull the stone out and hopefully…"

Robert grabbed the ring and tugged. It didn't move. He put his foot on the rim of the alcove and heaved. Nothing. "Damn. Maybe they mortared it in."

"Let me see. No, they didn't. See? It's just dirt accumulated in the cracks around it." She pulled out a penknife and scraped away at the joints around the stone. A thick cloud of black dust fell out as she did so. "Soot, I guess, from the fire. I hope the diary isn't burnt."

But then her scraping freed a lighter powdery dust beneath

the sooty layer. "Great. The soot must have sealed the crack. Try pulling again, now."

Robert grasped the ring in both hands and with his foot on the sill, heaved again. "It's moving. I can feel it." He tugged again. Suddenly the stone shot forward, sliding easily now. Robert pulled it aside.

Heart beating fast, Kate shone the torch into the cavity. There it was. The diary. Almost pristine. Untouched by fire. The heat must have failed to penetrate through the stone. Kate turned and hugged Robert tightly, "I told you so! Now do you believe me? I told you it was all true, and here it is: proof!"

"Incredible. You were right. I can't believe it. It's impossible. Yet here it is. Just as you said it would be." Robert burst out laughing. "Crazy!"

Kate reached in and carefully picked it out of the hole. "A little dusty that's all!"
She carried it to the table, put it down and slowly opened the cover. On the first page was simply written: "The diary of Amelia Linnece: my imprisonment by Sir Gabriel de Tiercel."

"Wow!" Robert's eyes were agog. "Look at that writing, it's so beautiful."

"Right, come on, we'll have plenty of time to look at it later. Let's get this mess put right," Kate's voice was trembling, urgent. She was frightened now that they might lose everything. Robert responded by pushing the stone back a bit, to support the wattle frame, laying that carefully over it till it was wedged into place, and then getting out the tub of instant plaster and starting to plaster the surface.

Kate swept the floor of all the bits of plaster and dust as Robert worked on the surface of the alcove. She put the book into a bin liner and the rest of the dust into another. She hid the dustbin liner in one of the cupboards standing nearby and returned to help Robert finish off the plastering with the other trowel.

181

It took them fully ten minutes to make a reasonable job of it. "Well, I think that'll do. It ain't perfect..."

"But it's good enough. Come on, let's go." Kate put the tools back in the pack and gave it to Robert. "You carry it. If anyone asks, you can say you were just doing a job in the house and stopped to show me out. Not that anyone is likely to ask."

Before they left, Robert pushed a large bureau in front of the freshly plastered section of wall. "There, that should keep anyone from noticing."

They rapidly returned along the corridor and down the stairs to the servants' entrance. "Now Kate. Don't forget. You've got to back me up. Tell Gabriel that there was a train after all, and that you caught it. Tell him you thought it was only me coming to pick you up, so you weren't that bothered. You knew I wouldn't mind, because you know I would do anything for you. That'll help soften the blow. He'll think you don't care for me. Tell him if you'd known it was he coming, you'd certainly have waited. That'll please him. Then he won't come after me accusing me of leading him on a wild goose chase."

"Right. Don't worry. I know how to handle him," replied Kate. "Give me the bag, and I'll be off. You'd better get back to your work before he gets back." She stood on tiptoe and gave him a kiss. "There, now off you go. I'm going back through the woods or he might catch me in the drive and then I'll never be able to explain how I got there. Damn! I forgot. I said I would come over this afternoon to meet him if he stopped pestering me yesterday. Hell."

"You said you would come over? To meet him? To do what? I thought..." Robert looked annoyed and hurt.

"I only said it to get rid of him yesterday. Still, after this morning's little catastrophe as far as he is concerned, I think I ought to go. Or he might start getting awkward. I'd better butter him up a bit."

182

"You could come over to apologise to me for not being there," suggested Robert. "It's the least I deserve, after being so horribly let down this morning."

Kate laughed: "I could let him see me apologising and you being ever so reasonable about it. It might make him a bit jealous that you are getting a moral advantage over me, since he knows it wasn't you that suffered all the waiting."

They both burst out laughing. "Hurry!" said Robert suddenly, "I think I can hear the car."

He watched as Kate sped across the East lawn to the edge of the woods. She ran into the woods and vanished. Heart still beating fast, Robert returned to the stables and resumed the filling of his bags. Then he walked over to the workers' eating room and got out his sandwiches and thermos.

He heard the sound of the Range Rover approaching. It screeched into the cobbled courtyard and skidded to a halt.

"Robert! Robert Ruddock! Where are you?"

It was Gabriel, and not in a good mood, thought Robert as he strolled into the sunlight clutching a sandwich. "Here I am. What's up?"

"What's up? You Jerk! You had me waiting around there for nearly an hour and she never showed up. That's what's up. What bloody game do you think you're playing, you bloody idiot?"

"What do you mean, she never showed? She told me..."

"She wasn't there. Didn't turn up. Comprendez vous? Cochon!" Gabriel was almost dancing around in his fury. "Why didn't she? Eh?"

"I've no idea, sir. Maybe she did catch the train, after all. Why don't you go and ask her? I've been here all day. Maybe she didn't think it was worth waiting about because she thought I was picking her up? I don't know."

"You're right. It's not your fault. Sorry." Gabriel screwed his face up, realising that to any impartial eye his tantrum must look rather foolish. "It's just so bloody annoying,

183

wasting time like that. But you're right; she didn't know it was me. So I can hardly go bursting round there and blaming her, can I?"

"I suppose not, sir. I suppose she may explain why she wasn't there to me later," suggested Robert.

"Yes, well. Don't go telling her that I went instead of you, ok? Just pretend it was you. I don't want her thinking I wasted a morning hanging around for someone who didn't show. Just keep it to yourself, eh? There's a good lad. I'll see dad gives you a bonus this week, for extra duties performed, you know..."

"Yes, sir," Robert smiled, "thank you sir."

"Oh, and wash the Range Rover before you put it away, will you? There's a good lad." Gabriel tossed Robert the keys, turned on his heel and strode across the court into the house.

"Wasting time! What does he do with time other than waste it? That's what I'd like to know," Robert growled as he climbed into the car to drive it to the standpipe.

30

Gabriel

Gabriel sat by the window in the hall. He was still in a stew about being kept waiting all that time and having to return empty-handed. He had dreamed up a little plan to take Kate out for a spin in the Range Rover, possibly to a country pub he knew on the river. It had rowing- and outboard-motor boats. He had in mind a beer and picnic sandwich on the river.

She had foiled that with her rush to go home by train. Still she was due to come over this afternoon. She had promised. That should annoy Robert Ruddock. He would make sure he would see them go out together. "That's it. I'll make him fetch the Range Rover again, having just had to clean it, and he can watch us drive off."

He smiled to himself. "I hope she comes soon. Then there will still be time for my river trip. No girl can resist a river picnic."

Just then he heard a voice calling. He looked out into the courtyard. It was Kate. "What was that she was calling? Robert! Of course, she thought it was he who had been kept waiting." He listened as Robert came out to greet her.

"Hi, Rob. I'm so sorry if you were kept waiting at the market cross. But I finished early and came back on the 11.50 train. Will you forgive me?" She took his hand in hers.

Robert looked annoyed and reluctant, but let her plead a

little longer before relenting, "Oh, alright. But it wasn't very thoughtful of you, was it. Dragging a man all the way over there and then making him wait for nothing. All that time too"

"God, The little liar! It wasn't him. I am the one she should be apologising to. The little bastard." Suddenly Gabriel remembered instructing Robert to do just this. He had promised him a bonus to do it. And here he was, milking it for all the sympathy he could get.

"Do you forgive me? Truly?" Kate looked earnestly into Robert's eyes. They were holding both hands together now.

"I do," Robert replied simply. Damn! Kate was leaning forward now and kissing him on the lips!

This was too much for Gabriel. He leaped up and strode to the front door and opened it. "Oh there you are at last, Kate. I thought I heard something." He bounced down the steps gaily and said, "I thought we could go for a spin. I know a great pub down by the river. I'm going to take you on a little boat trip and picnic. I've rung ahead and they are preparing it now."

He walked briskly up to the pair of them and, turning to Robert, said: "Oh Robert, I'm glad you're here too. You're just fellow I want. Go and fetch the Range Rover for me, will you, there's a good lad." Gabriel tossed him the keys, watching his expression as Robert's face turned from triumph to humiliation.

Robert spun on his heel and stomped off.

"You shouldn't be so abrupt, you know, Gabriel," admonished Kate, glancing after Robert.

"Why on earth not? He's only a servant, after all. They need to be kept in check, you know." Gabriel smiled.

"Well if you must know, he's a school-friend of mine, and I won't stand by and watch him being humiliated. Not by you, not by anyone." Kate stared at him crossly.

"Oh, terribly sorry. I didn't realise you and he were still…"

"We're not. But that's not the point. I don't agree with it, that's all."

"Ok. I promise. I won't do it again. I don't know what comes over me at times. I think it must be the old general's genes coming through, ordering people about like that." Gabriel smiled his sweetest smile, "I won't do it again. Now will you do me the honour of accompanying me in an expedition to the upper reaches of the great grey green greasy Limpopo River, my angelic girl?"

Kate smiled at last, "Well, Ok. But only if you behave yourself."

"I am behaved! Consider me fully behaved. And if I behave in any other wise you may be-havin' me any way you want." Gabriel stood to attention and saluted smartly just as Robert rounded the corner into the courtyard.

Robert slewed the Range Rover to a halt inches from Gabriel. Gabriel did not flinch a muscle. He stood rigidly to attention, saluting, and winked at Kate. She had to admire that, at least, in him.

Robert jumped out and stormed off into the barn, leaving the engine running.

"Well, then, off we go," cried Gabriel, as they drove down the grand driveway.

"Is my picnic hamper all set, innkeeper, my good man?"

"Don't be rude," snapped Kate, "You can't talk to people like that nowadays, they get upset."

"I can't? They do?" Gabriel's eyebrows leapt up in mock-surprise. "Innkeeper, old fellow, do you hear that? I can't call you innkeeper any more, apparently. It's the end of a long friendship then, my good man. We've had some good times together Innkeeper, haven't we, old boy? But there it is. I am under orders to behave. And behave I shall. I shall have to call you Landlord, from now on, like any other common publican. No acknowledging your superior inn keeping, and your hospitable hostelry shall be known henceforth simply as a Pub. I am sad, dear boy, but there it is. Barman! Is my scoff and booze ready, yet?"

"Ok, ok, point made," Kate smiled wanly at the innkeeper, who was ruddy faced and roaring with laughter.

"That's alright, miss, master Gabriel here and I go back a long ways. Since he were a young absconder from school. E's got a room of is own out back, he has. Gabriel's lock-up we call it. He's a regular, and I don't mind what he calls me, as long as it's to me face."

"I see, I apologise," said Kate, "it was none of my business."

"But this is!" Gabriel yelled from the boat. "Come on, or we'll never get to Niagara before dark."

Kate sighed, and shrugged her shoulders at the landlord before climbing into the small clinker-built rowing boat. "I thought you said they had motors?"

"Motors? They're for cissies. I'm an oarsman, as I am about to demonstrate."

Gabriel pushed away from the bank, gained midstream and pulled powerfully and smoothly on the oars and the boat glided swiftly and almost silently up stream.

"You see? This is much more romantic than a smelly old outboard chugging away," said Gabriel, as he rowed, "look, it doesn't disturb the swans even, and the swish swish of the oars is quite charming, don't you think?"

"Yes, I do, actually. Where did you learn to row? You row amazingly fast."

"Ah! Wherein lies the secret?" Gabriel laughed. "Two secrets, actually. Firstly, I learned to row at school, and here it is, just round this bend. Hence my skill and my familiarity with yon hostelry from a young age."

"Honestly! So that's why you were able to be so familiar?"

"Yes. And my second secret is this. I can row so fast upriver because I'm rowing with the current! It's a tidal river, you see, for another six miles. So it's all a matter of timing: I go upriver on the incoming tide, picnic on the head of the tide, and row back down on the outgoing tide. Est-ce mon secret, peut-être?"

"No wonder you were in such a hurry to go then. You can only impress by your cunning. I bet you don't tell most of your girls this secret of your prowess." She laughed, imagining him as the manly oarsman with a swooning girl on each arm.

They came to a landing place: a meadow sloping gently down to the river's edge. On either side of the little niche in the bank into which Gabriel's boat's prow seemed to lodge precisely, a lawn bordered on either side by a row of huge weeping willows.

"It's perfect!"

"Of course it is. It's taken me years to get it to this. The ideal picnic spot in the sun, away from everyone. And if you feel like something a little more intimate, my willow curtain cave has all that you might desire."

They disembarked and Gabriel prepared his feast while Kate wandered along the bank. She walked under the first willow's canopy. It was cool here, and very private.

She sat on the bank and gazed out through the willow fronds at the sun glinting on the river. A couple of swans glided silently by, looking her up and down.

"Shhh!" Kate started. She imagined that another swan must be stood close behind her. Had she barged in on their mating ground? She looked round quickly. Nothing.

Then she saw a white graceful head and neck emerge from behind the willow's thick gnarled trunk, followed by... "Gabriel! What are you doing?"

Gabriel emerged, dancing balletically in a white leotard. He pirouetted and pranced and finally leaped high in the air and collapsed in the pose of the dying swan next to her.

She burst out laughing, and said, "Where on earth did you

get that outfit?"

"It suits me, doesn't it?" He asked, looking worried.

"Well, yes. Of course it does. You've got quite a figure…"

"Beautiful, some say," started Gabriel, cocking his head modestly, "but then who am I to judge?" He flounced off, exaggerating his movements so that Kate couldn't help laughing.

"Lunch is served," he called as he reached the rug on which he had laid everything out. Kate got up and followed him. She sat down and started eating.

"It strikes me," she said, pausing to chew, "that you have got everything here off a little too pat."

"Two pats? There's not a cow in sight. I don't know how it happened. I went before I came out. Didn't you?" an expression of mock horror came across his face, "because I'm afraid I forgot the loo-roll."

Laughing Kate said, "Can't you take anything seriously?"

"Yes. Money. But only when I haven't got it." He looked at her questioningly. "But to answer your statement. Yes I do have it off pat. But then most girls don't notice that. They take it for granted that it was devised especially for them. Such is vanity. But it does make life easier for a seducer, on the whole."

"And I'm the exception?"

"Yes, dammit. You are. And I love you for it. There! I said it, I said it!" He jumped up and danced about like a marionette, "how dare you say it, you uppity puppet?"

His disjointed movements were so pathetic, Kate got up and joined him in his silly dance and gradually his marionette arms ceased their jerking about and his lolling head straightened up and his movements became liquid as he slid into her arms and they danced the dance of lovers in timeless embrace, their bodies and their lips conjoined in slow bliss.

"Bloody hell! I forgot. I've got to pick up the old man from the 4.30 train. God, I'm sorry, but we must go." Gabriel rushed to the rug and grabbed its corners and picked it up, crashing the plates and glasses and food containers together. He dropped it into the enormous hamper provided by the pub. The blanket was oozing liquid: beer, pickles, juices from the tomatoes and other salad vegetables. A mess.

He stuffed them all in and threw the hamper into the middle of the boat. "Jump in, Kate," he yelled.

She obeyed, amused at this sudden transformation from seducer and consummate lover to nervous subservient son eager to please his father.

Nothing was said as he rowed furiously downstream till they reached the inn. He leaped out and ran to the Range Rover. "Quick. I've got to drop you off first."

"There isn't time. You'll have to take me with you, I'm sure the general won't mind. He likes me." Kate replied calmly.

"You're right. Let's go!"

31

The official history

The next time Kate visited the house she was greeted at the front door by the General, dressed most peculiarly. A tattered beret askew on his head, he wore a threadbare smock, bespattered with paints of all colours. His bright and comical grin was so at odds with the staid old soldier of her previous encounters that it made him look almost clownish.

He burst out laughing at her perplexity, "You really look quite stupid, you know dear."

"Oh, I 'm sorry." Kate blushed, "But what on earth are you dressed like that for?"

"It's my painter's garb. You know, I told you I painted – or used to – well here I am, painting again. And all thanks to you."

"What do you mean?"

"I can only paint when inspired," explained Sir Peregrine, "and it is so long since last I held a brush in earnest. Thank you, my dear." The General smiled gently.

"I don't understand. Why thank me? What are you painting?"

"That you must wait to see," the General's eyes twinkled enigmatically, "I never let anyone see my work before it is finished."

Seeing her disappointment, he added: "Come, follow me. I've something interesting to show you."

Kate, unable to resist such an invitation, followed him down the passage.

Offering Kate a seat in his study, the General walked over to the bookcase and, opening his hidden cabinet, poured himself a whiskey, "I thought you ought to know the outcome of my meeting at the British Museum. I should be hearing in a couple of weeks whether a positive conclusion can be drawn concerning the identity of the two letters and their author. But I can tell you that Professor Fulk was of the opinion that both were of the same age and that any differences in the scripts were indiscernible, near as dammit!"

"But that would mean the letter I saw with my own eyes being written for me, with the ink that I saw being dried with powder, was actually from the time of Queen Elizabeth? Impossible!" Kate paused, before continuing: "There's something very strange and scary happening here."

General Tercel looked thoughtful: "I don't know how or why, but you do seem to be deeply entangled in some mysterious goings-on relating to the persons involved in the events of that time. I think under the circumstances, it is only fair to let you know what I know. Then, when we discover for certain whether your manuscript letter exactly matches that of Amelia Linnece from this library, then we can decide how to pursue the matter further. Though how it could possibly be as old if you saw it written as you say, is beyond me"

"According to our official records, compiled during his lifetime by, or at the instigation of Sir Gabriel de Tiercel, and afterward by the guardian of his young successor, the massacre was perpetrated by Falco Basard, his lieutenant, Gormer Scart, and their gang of smugglers.

"Falco Basard's gang was tolerated in the district because he rendered certain services to Sir Gabriel, almost certainly in the realms of the exporting of munitions and the importing

of contraband to bolster Sir Gabriel's income. In fact, Falco
Basard eventually became a sort of right hand man to Sir
Gabriel, a position he started to abuse.

"The foundation of his wealth was, after all, the
manufacture of cannon from Wealden iron ore smelted in
the new, super-efficient by the standards of the time, blast
furnaces whose technology had recently been imported from
the forests of the Ardennes in northern France. Each blast
furnace, whose chamber was force-fed air by a number of
great bellows pumping in sequence, compressed by a rotating
wheel powered by horses or water, had mixed iron ore and
charcoal poured into it at the top, and produced, at the
much higher temperatures, liquefied iron which flowed out
in channels from the base. Each furnace could produce as
much iron as twenty to thirty bloomeries, as the old hand-fed
furnaces were called. Their liquid iron poured directly into
moulds, and heavy cannon, much needed for the ongoing
wars, could be cast in a single mould, making the old banded
iron weapons all but redundant."

"The fuel for all this new manufacture on a scale unheard
of hitherto was the wood of the great Wealden Forest, a
substantial parcel of which his family owned. This was
a precursor of the great industrial revolution you were
taught about at school. The Weald, so prettily forested
now, became at that time a great wasteland. The Wealden
forest was literally consumed by the iron and glass works.
The devastation was comprehensive. Roads became all but
impassable due to the continuous traffic of this new industry.
But fortunes were made by those who controlled it."

"You must realise, Kate, that nearly all the nobility and
gentry were corrupt by today's standards, and pursued every
avenue open to them to rob their enemies, the exchequer
or even their fellows. Sir Gabriel was known to have, as
a quartermaster of the army in the Netherlands in Queen
Elizabeth's campaign against the Spanish to aid her fellow

Protestants, the Dutch, garnered for himself a substantial slice of every contract for supplies and weapons. The government paid for five cannon for every four delivered, and so on, so that those in charge became very rich, including Sir Gabriel.

"Often the excess was sold into the next batch of five, or even to the enemy, to further increase the profit. There was scant regard paid to the moral implications of supplying those who were butchering your own troops, especially when dead men continued in service for many months, drawing pay that of course went straight into their commanders' wallets.

"Now when Sir Gabriel brought over the German, White Whiskey John, the Wurchangel, or Destroying Angel, as he was known, together with his deputy, Black Martin, and the extremist Parson Mew, his two sons, Crocker and Sprat Mew, and his giant, Saith Fool, it was for two reasons. Firstly it was to deal with Falco Basard who, according to his diaries, had been getting above himself and threatening blackmail, and secondly to bring his recalcitrant villagers to heel. They were, as country folk often are, slow to adapt to new circumstances and were, in his view, recusants, or dogged adherents to the catholic faith, so out of fashion for a forward-looking young would-be protestant noble as Sir Gabriel.

"Their so called discovery of Falco Basard in the act of massacring the recusant villagers and his own neighbour, Sir William Linnece and his family, gave Sir Gabriel the perfect excuse to do away with Falco and his gang. It appears from what you were told that they might have been framed or set up by Whiskey John, who assumed the reins and became Sir Gabriel's steward, running his affairs.

"Local legend has it that the girl, Kate Linnece and Robin, son of the huntsman for the Linneces, escaped the massacre, though there was no confirmation in the official histories where she is listed among the dead. Indeed her gravestone lies beside those of Sir William and Rosie, his wife, and Amelia.

"Further, local folklore also speaks of a mysterious prisoner in the East wing of the house. To an extent this was borne out by the fact that five bodies, including those of two women, were found after the great fire there. It is known for certain that Sir Gabriel, his wife, Phyllis, and their son, Raphe, disappeared that night. No one could account for the fourth body, that of a woman, or the fifth, walled up and desiccated, not burnt, or for the fact that the child's bones were jumbled up and the skull separated from them.

"However, I get ahead of myself. A year or so after the massacre, a child was born who was fostered out. No one knew of its existence at the time apart from Sir Gabriel and his intimates. It wasn't until his will was read after his own death that the boy's existence became public knowledge and his identity known, because the child, Daniel, was named as sole heir to the Linnece estates as the second son of Gabriel who had assumed the title. Raphe was named in the same will as heir to his own Fugglesham estate.

"This is very strange, because no mother was named, and if he had been Phyllis's son, there would have been no reason to hide him away. But if he had been a son of Gabriel and Amelia – if she had been that mysterious prisoner – then it would make a sort of perverse sense. She was a Linnece, and he, as her son, therefore could inherit those estates. The terms of the will would then slot neatly into place in the jigsaw whose missing pieces bedevil this period in our family's history.

"A couple of years before Sir Gabriel's death, however, both Michael, Gabriel's younger brother, and White Whiskey John met their ends violently and at the same time. Again, confusion reigns. Michael, according to Sir Gabriel's account, had been plotting with White Whiskey John to replace him. He had evidence for this, as he had for Michael having previously plotted with Falco Basard to do the same.

"Now it appears these two had a falling out and Whiskey John murdered him horribly while out hunting. Sir Gabriel caught him red-handed, literally, with blood on his gloves, and had him hastily tried and executed. A little too hastily, some say.

"At this time the Mews and Saith Fool disappear from the scene. We only know this because records state a new parson was brought in for the funeral of Michael, which was odd. Black Martin appears to have assumed the role of steward after Whiskey John's execution. He kept the records until Sir Gabriel's death when, after installing the young Daniel, he handed over the stewardship to the guardian of young Daniel de Tiercel and disappeared.

"As you can see, it's all very confusing. Lots of strands all twisting this way and that, not weaving a comprehensible pattern at all. All loose ends. The upshot of it is this. We, today's Tercels, are all descended from the named heir, Daniel de Tiercel. He inherited the Linnece estates as stated in Sir Gabriel's will, but also all the de Tiercel lands and property by virtue of the fact that Raphe was dead and he was the only surviving member of both families.

"Hence our family's vast wealth, nurtured and handed down over fourteen generations. We have had our ups and downs, of course, but nothing to compare with the upheavals of those years."

The general rose and went to his drinks cabinet to pour himself another whiskey. "Would you like one, dear?"

"Er, no thank you, General. It's too early for me." Kate's thoughts were racing. She stood up and said, "General, would you mind awfully if I went home. You have said so much already and I am having difficulty taking it all in. My head is aching a bit. May I go, please, and come back once I have sorted it all out in my head. I don't mean to be rude, after your kindness, but..."

"Of course not, dear girl." The general came over to her and asked, "May I fetch you a paracetamol, or something?"

"Thank you, yes." Kate smiled at the old man: always so

thoughtful. She watched as he opened a drawer in his bureau and brought the pills and a glass of water. She drank them down.

"Tell you what, if you don't come visiting before then, I'll call on you once I know the results, eh?" The general ushered her to the door and she took her departure.

32

The Diary (2)

Kate plumped her pillows up and piled them at the head
of the bed. She sat on the bed, kicked off her shoes and
leaned back into the pillows. The diary was laid on the bed
beside her. She had carefully dusted it down in the kitchen
before making herself a sandwich and a cup of tea. She had
told her father she had a lot of work to do tonight and must
not be disturbed. She had lit a joss stick and was savouring
the woody aroma. In short she had prepared herself for the
revelations she was sure would come.

She picked up the leather-bound volume and opened it.

"Today I have acquired this volume through the good
offices of Phyp Spadger, servant to my master and gaoler, Sir
Gabriel de Tiercel, cursed be his name. He who procured this
for me is the only servant of this household who knows of my
existence, apart from Sir Gabriel's right-hand man, the evil
White Whiskey John, and his intimate, Black Martin. This
evil pair has taken over Sir Gabriel's wits, so that they control
his actions by their wiles. White Whiskey John it was who
first imprisoned me. White Whiskey John who cut out my
tongue that I might not speak nor cry out for succour.

"Here shall be written down all their sins that one day
they may be brought to justice by the discovery of this
document. Both the pair of them, White Whiskey John and

Black Martin, and my chief gaoler and torturer, who nightly abuses my body with his lust, Sir Gabriel de Tiercel. I place on record in his defence that Phyp Spadger, though assistant to these deeds, has redeemed himself somewhat by his actions in rendering me service in secret.

"I will start at the beginning, giving an account of how I come to be here in this state and what happened to those I love.

"My family are neighbours to Sir Gabriel; Linnece is our name and Runswick Abbey our home. My father is called Sir William Linnece, 'Sweet William' to us girls, and my mother, Rosie. Sir Gabriel married my elder sister, Phyllis, god bless her, but lusted after me in secret.

"Shortly after he had married my sister, Sir Gabriel came upon me in the woods, picking flowers. I was just fifteen at the time. He declared himself my loving servant but when I objected and tried to send him from me, saying that he was my sister's husband and could never have but my sisterly love, he jumped upon me and tore my clothing and forced himself upon me.

"I was so shamed I dared not tell anyone. So it came to pass that I grew large with child until my mother noticed and asked me who had fathered this offspring upon me. I could not, would not, tell, for the shaming of my dear sister and our family.

"My mother devised this ruse to conceal my growing belly: she took to her bed and declared herself with child and poorly with it and would allow none other than myself and my nana, her most trusted maidservant, to be in constant attendance upon her. Convinced it was her whimsy, my father allowed this to pass and no other person entered her chamber, nor did I ever leave it.

"Our victuals and water and clothing were left daily in the antechamber and I 'ministered unto her' in the eyes of the world, a devoted daughter. In truth it was the reverse. When

I went into confinement it was she and nana that midwifed me and safely brought my darling Katie into the world.

"I, full-breasted with milk, had to endure seeing my darling Katie breast-fed during daytime by a wet nurse, my mother saying that her nipples were too sore after the night's feeding. But in secret, at night, I gave her my breast and she suckled heartily and long, and I think she knew it was her mother feeding her, for she showed more contentment than when with the wet nurse.

"My mother made me promise never to tell a soul that I was Katie's mother, nor even Katie herself when she grew of age, lest our family's name become besmirched by such a revelation. Henceforth, Katie was to be my beloved youngest sister, and Rosie her dear mother. It pained me beyond endurance, both then and later, to have to live this lie, and I beg the forgiveness of our Lord nightly in my prayers.

"But I was young and unmarried and could not, in my station, have such a scandal reported about me. So I agreed and never did break that agreement till now. Shortly before the ghastly events I am about to relate, darling Katie herself guessed truly that I was her mother. But I kept my peace and denied it as best I could, though to my heartbreak she would not believe me but insisted that she was right.

"But now I must hasten to that dread day. I was twenty-two, and was betrothed to an ugly and fat old man, Lord Barnaby Stave-Carew. He was harmless enough and loved me to distraction. But then so did everyone. I was a beauty, acknowledged universal, my skin pearly, my eyes the blue of lapis lazuli, my hair raven and russet mixed so that it seemed burnished with the evening sun. But I had a taint about me. There were rumours afoot that I was cursed, that I had been in consort with the devil and had his mark upon me so that many fine young men who came were driven away.

"Who put about these tales and destroyed my prospects no one knows, but I believe it was my evil pursuer, Sir

201

Gabriel himself. He would have me for himself and could bear no other near me, as he proved beyond all doubt by his subsequent actions.

"At last, in despair of ever marrying me off, beauty second to none that they claimed me to be, they accepted the plea of Lord Stave-Carew, that man of such unlikely prospect were it not for these slights, to wed me and care for me. He was from a family of diminished wealth, but a Catholic lord; and our heirs, my mother pointed out, would inherit his title and wealth enough from our own family.

"Since the advent of our Queen, Elizabeth, brought in its train a proscribing of the Catholic faith of our ancestors in favour of the new Protestantism, espoused most fervently in our neighbourhood by that Sir Gabriel de Tiercel for his own advancement, my father took it upon himself to be a refuge for the persecuted.

"It was he who, on the driving out of the priest, Father Jack Straw, from the parish of Fugglesham, gave that good man shelter in a quiet part of our household and bade him continue to minister to us in the true manner. When it became too dangerous to openly worship, and there were carrion-birds in every corner of the land looking for corpses of the faithful to pick upon, we went from our chapel and sought a safer church in the heart of the woods.

"Here, each Sunday, we would gather with those of the true Faith from all the district, Fugglesham as well as Runswick, to worship unfettered. My father was a good man, and not especially religious. In truth, he was a believer in the rights of all to a better life.

"He saw the new religion as yet another means to suppress the common man and advance the ruthless. It was merely a pretext for one group among the privileged to usurp the power held by their peers. It benefited not the ordinary hard working man or woman who continued to be held in abject poverty and near-enslavement, and it was for these that my father, wealthy as he was, sought justice.

"It was during one of these forest masses that the thing happened. At first, above our singing, we heard a distant noise as of geese flying and honking and a rushing as of a wild wind, turned thunder. Suddenly there broke upon us a storm of horse and hound as an apocalypse. They tore amongst us, cutting and spearing, trampling and crushing our small congregation.

"At their head, the killer White Whiskey John, rode up to my father and, drawing two large pistols, shot him in the face so that it came away, showering us with blood and gore. As he fell, my mother went to support him, but that man drew a long gun and shot her in the chest, blowing a gaping hole therein. She collapsed to her knees. I can still see her eyes, looking at me in wonderment as I tried to support her, before he rode her down mercilessly.

"That evil man then snatched me up upon his horse and rode away with me. I cried to my daughter, Katie, to run. The last I saw of her was as Robin, her young companion, who came from I know not where, threw her to the ground and dragged her into the shelter of the woods away from the massacre.

"I was taken to a wooden hut hidden deep in the forest and there imprisoned for days. It was crude but well made, with a bed and a table and chair, a blazing hearth and a garderobe. But I was chained as a dog is, to a ring on the wall, so that I could move from bed to table but no further. Its windows were too high to see out of, and the hearth was out of reach, chained as I was."

"My God!" Kate stopped reading. "That's the same hut where I was taken poorly. It must be. It must have survived all these years because built so sturdily as a prison."

Kate recalled now vividly the feeling of claustrophobia, of being trapped in the hut that day. Convinced she was right, she continued reading.

"I cursed that man and said to him, Sir Gabriel will punish you, but he laughed and later I discovered why. I was brought one night to Fugglesham Court and secreted in this East wing that was Sir Gabriel's study and laboratory so that no one went there. Here I was permanently imprisoned and here I remain unto this day.

"Sir Gabriel de Tiercel, cursed be his name, husband to my sister, was prime mover in that he ordered the massacre of my whole family and my husband-to-be, along with all our household intimates and those of the hamlet of Fugglesham, in order that he might enjoy my body in submission to his lust in secret for as long as he will, and power over the estates of my father through his wife, my sister.

"Whether Katie, my darling daughter, survived, I know not, though I do believe so. It is my belief and fervent hope that young master Robin hid her, then took her from there to a secret place far from the clutches of Sir Gabriel and his henchmen, where she might grow up to avenge me and mine.

"Each day is a drudge, but terrible in anticipation of my nightly humiliation at the hands of Sir Gabriel. He comes to me each evening after his supper, reeking of wine and ale, and forces himself upon me. There are few nights I am spared. Then he goes, as he gloatingly tells me, to re-enact this lust upon my sister, all the more thrilling for her ignorance of my existence and her belief in his love and good faith.

"A few months after these events I became large with child, but even then I was permitted the grace of no female company, nor even, after my nine months were ended, in my confinement and travail did they permit me a midwife. Whiskey John, foul whoremonger, presumed himself so confident in his own midwifery skills that it was he who doctored me and it came about that, in a fit of agony I passed out. He, foul-mouth fiend, failed me.

"My babe was a boy, still-born. He was taken away for burial in un-consecrated ground, sent into Limbo by that beast, un-christened. His name was to have been Daniel, 'God is my judge', born into a lions' den. He would have been my saviour, but that Wurchangel, 'Destroying Angel' killed him at birth. It is all too convenient: my little angel destroyed.

"Gabriel seemed too little put out by the news of my babe's death. Could he have ordered that too, at the instigation of White Whiskey John? He has not the brains to have conceived these acts, but has the 'courage' to carry them out, being led like a bull with a ring in its nose by this demonic German and his Black henchman.

"One day, months later, in revenge for his destruction of my babe, I told him that I would sing for him at last. He was overjoyed, thinking that at last I had accepted my lot and would cooperate henceforth. But I told him that I would sing until the walls shook and the doors resounded with my voice and my sister would be aware of whose voice it was that sang and know I was alive. I told him he would be undone and I freed. He took a fit, gagged me and called his henchman, White Whiskey John, and they conferred awhile. I could not hear all but I heard the Destroying Angel say to him that it would make no difference to his enjoyment of me save the one pleasure, but that, if this expedient be not carried out, that I would surely be discovered and he, Sir Gabriel, would indeed be undone.

"They went away but returned soon with Black Martin and Phyp Spadger which two men sat me down upon a chair and bound me to it and held my head back and prized open my mouth. White Whiskey John, with a pair tongs that he heated in the fire, came and seized my tongue and wrenched it out of my head and scorched the stump of it to quench the bleeding, saying, 'there. It is done. No more will this lark sing or utter condemnation of your acts, Sir Gabriel.'

"I screamed without voice or sense, in a fashion

incomprehensible, and then fainted. Before I passed out I saw Sir Gabriel's eyes. They were wide with terror, as if only then did he realise the full horror of what he had brought about.

"I only slowly recovered from that wound, not eating for days afterward and then being force fed simple gruel until my strength recovered in spite of my will. Phyp Spadger too, repented of his role, for he was enamoured of me and endeavoured to help me. As I have said, he it was who has enabled me to write this.

To him I turned now and begged him to carry for me a secret note to my sister, Phyllis. At first he dared not, but after I caught him peeking at me, through a peep-hole in the wall of my chamber, as I dressed and engaged in my toilet, and threatened him with exposure, he agreed to so act as go-between.

"This brings me to the present. I have today written to Phyllis my sister, telling of my miserable existence here and where I am hid. Phyp Spadger took this note after I agreed I would continue to let him be privy to my most intimate acts from henceforth.

"He is caught! Black Martin, who has been spying upon him for some time, it seems and knows of his peeping habit, caught him even as he carried my letter. Sir Gabriel was beside himself with anger and would have run him through before me, but White Whiskey John conceived a diabolical plan to wall him up in the little chamber from which he spied, 'to let him expire after a lingering internment, watching his heart's desire in her most intimate acts, without hope or succour else.'

"Black Martin has performed this deed. I heard him tell Sir Gabriel that he inserted a thick glass into the peep-hole so that no sound could carry and then placed Phyp Spadger on a stool so that his head was to the peep-hole and trussed him so he could not move from hence and walled up the chamber tight only leaving an air-hole to enable him to live longer.

He gave him a plentiful supply of water and one hand free enough to pass jug to lip to further prolong his life, so that he should only die after a long time of starvation. They all laughed at this cruel refinement of Phyp Spadger's torture. These two men had much knowledge of war and siege and the means by which men live and die.

"I have to live now in the knowledge my only hope of getting a message to my sister is gone. I have no means to kill myself."

Kate put the book down and lay looking at the ceiling, trying to take all this in. The woman she had met, twice now, had suffered beyond endurance. She tried to imagine what it must have been like, being raped day after day, with no hope of ever escaping, even into death. To have lost her newborn son and not know whether her daughter lived? It was unbearable.

She rose from the bed and went downstairs to make herself some tea. Her father appeared at the sitting-room door and asked: "Are you alright, Kate, darling? You look a bit tired to me."

"No, I'm fine. Really, I am. I've just got a heavy workload on at the moment."

"Well, you know it can always wait till morning. Rest will revive you and then you can go hard at it again without exhausting yourself."

"Yes, goodnight dad." Kate smiled at his concern. If he only knew what burden she laboured under, he would have a fit, she thought.

Upstairs, she drank the tea before resuming. She read on for many pages of unrelenting misery before coming upon the following entry:

"Today the very best of news. I am in a state of pure joy and euphoria. Sir Gabriel came to me in a black humour. He announced in a fury that White Whiskey John is dead! He told me that Whiskey John had killed his brother, Michael, while out hunting, had been caught with his blood on his hands and been summarily executed. His head, he said, has been impaled on a staff at the gates as a warning to other murderers and thieves.

"Not since I have been imprisoned here have I heard better news. He, who murdered my family, imprisoned me and cut out my tongue, is dead, killed by his own master. One of my chief enemies is dead, and I do rejoice in it. I pity poor Michael, of course. The innocent fool was always the weakling of the family."

Kate read on. This was the only note of cheer in Amelia's diary for some months onward.

"I have conceived a means to convey a message to my sister. I have persuaded Sir Gabriel that I must have some activity if I am to survive and not waste away. He is to provide me with the means to construct a tapestry.

"I played at that as a child in the workshop of my own nurse's family, Huguenot weavers, and learnt the rudiments there. My dear father, bless him, though a Catholic, could never stand idly by and not succour the persecuted, though they were of different faith.

"I persuaded Sir Gabriel that the satisfaction that that would give me could only improve my mood and health as his prisoner and mistress.

"I have embarking upon my planned work. Its theme is a fairy story that was a particular favourite of my sister and I: one that we saw depicted upon a tapestry in that workshop and that was subsequently hung in the home of a friend.

"I am halfway through my work. Sir Gabriel is delighted with my progress and the change in my demeanour. He is proud of my skill in this work. He does not suspect that such an innocent theme could carry anything of great import to my sister and has agreed that, when finished, he will take it to hang among those in his dining hall as though the work of those Huguenot weavers.

"I have today embroidered our family crest, hidden in the oak leaves in the foreground in the right hand corner. It is not coloured as such, but Phyllis will surely recognise it. That will convince her that I live.

"My work is done. Sir Gabriel has taken it and hung it. He is thrilled because I appeared pleased at his acceptance of it and I allowed him to love me and showed him tenderness in the doing of it.

"This waiting seems endless. Will Phyllis never look at the tapestry and glean its message? It is worse because I can do nothing. I am continuing to show some little tokens of affection to allay the suspicions of Sir Gabriel. Black Martin stares at me as if he suspects my motives. He is too clever to be fooled for long, but I cannot read his face. Sometimes I feel he is spying with mal-intent, while at others he seems to look at me with something akin to pity and affection. Could it be that he knows and yet betrays me not? If so, what is his purpose? Could he, who showed such fanatical cruelty, be turning from his former allegiance? But he gives nothing away. He is an enigma.

"Thank God! Today Phyllis entered my room. We embraced and kissed. I showed her my tongue less mouth and she cried and cried. I showed her this diary and she read my tale. She was beside herself. All these years has she spent loving her husband, Sir Gabriel, in innocence of his mighty sin in keeping me, her sister, as his captive concubine while making love to her all that time.

"She told me she had recognised the theme and style of the tapestry, but thought at first it must be a copy of one of that one we saw as children. Only when she noticed the crest did she realise that no one but me could have included this, since all members of our family were dead. She got Sir Gabriel drunk one night and made an impression in wax of his keys. Then she slipped into Horsworth to have new keys cut while ordering new dresses.

"She had to wait a further two weeks before he went to London, taking Black Martin with him. Then she came up and entered my room.

"We have made a pact. We agree we cannot continue to live under such shame. We agree that his acts are so abominable that nothing can cleanse the world of them or of our mutual shame in being the objects of his fearful crime: nothing short of death. The death of Sir Gabriel and all that is his.

"Phyllis is to go from here now and find her son by Sir Gabriel, Raphe, and bring him here. Here we will slaughter him and cut him to pieces. We will prepare a feast for Sir Gabriel tonight with a great spiced stew as its central course. The meat for this stew will be Raphe's flesh. His bones we will hide in the great chest in my writing room. His offal Phyllis will take and feed to Sir Gabriel's great hounds.

"It is done. Raphe's head Phyllis has put in the trunk in the hall ready for tonight. He put up a struggle and cried for mercy, but none did she show him. She is cold and hard as ice. Hatred burns in her. She slit his throat over the basin as one would a goat, having bludgeoned him into a stupor. Then in a blanket we gutted the poor wretch and severed his limbs. I skinned him and Phyllis cleaved the meat from the bone and placed these cuts into a leathern bag that she has now carried down to the kitchen. She has arranged for the cooks to be out. I am to clear up any mess and wipe away the blood. Phyllis took the basin's blood in the ewer and is tipping it I know not where. It was a prodigious amount from such a small body.

"When Sir Gabriel has feasted and drunk, he will come to me. I will receive him willingly and cling to him as if he were all my desire. All men are foolish in this regard, Sir Gabriel

210

most foolish among them.

"In his lust he will be pliable and when Phyllis enters the room with Raphe's severed head, he will look upon it, recognise it and yet not believe. He will cry out: 'where is Raphe? Where is my son?'

"Whereupon, she has told me, she will fling the head at him and retort: 'that which you seek is within you," before hurling her lantern upon the bed head and herself upon him with dagger drawn. I shall cling tight to him to prevent him rising. He will be embedded in my flesh and I shall hold him there as she strikes. I shall strike him also with this dagger Phyllis has left here with me. Between us we shall transfix him as the flames from the bed and its hangings consume us.

"Nothing will stop us from ending the line of de Tiercel as he has the line of Linnece. He shall die in the knowledge and torment that he has feasted upon and enjoyed the meat of his only beloved son. That shall be, albeit but for a few moments, or into eternity if there be such a state, our revenge. Thus shall we, in death, be avenged for our parents' deaths and my own living torment. I hope this diary may be found after my death so that my awful tale becomes known. I am sealing it in its nook in the wall in such hope."

Kate nearly choked as she read this. It was the last entry in the diary. It was appalling, incredible. The fire in the East wing that she had heard about was deliberately started by the two sisters, killing themselves, Sir Gabriel and Raphe, his son by Phyllis. What suffering and humiliation must she have endured to drive her to such an extreme act.

33

Kate

"Come along, Kate Pegler."

Kate started. It was Shabby Tattler, again appearing as if out of the blue. Standing silhouetted against the sun, he towered over her in the entrance to the bus-shelter. It was the morning after her reading of the diary and Kate was waiting for Robert, to tell him of its terrible contents.

"It is time but," Shabby Tattler continued as if he were reminding her of an appointment they had agreed upon.

"Time for what? And where to?" Kate looked up at his shadowed face. "Where have you been? I've looked for you, but nobody seems to know you. Where do you live?" She stood up and moved outside where she could see him without being blinded.

"Oh, here and there. Never you mind. I've got me own business to attend to. But just now you're my business. Things is movin' on rapid, like. You and Rob been findin' things you'd rather not, have you?"

"Well, yes. We have actually…"

"Stands to reason. 'Tis the right time. 'Twas bound to 'appen. You come along with me now; I've got a sight more to show you. If you be minded for it, that is."

Shabby Tattler strolled along jauntily in a careless matter of fact sort of way as if he were just passing the time of day. Kate couldn't figure him out at all.

"How come you know all this? How can you know so much detail about things that happened 400 years ago? Who are you?"

"I been about a bit, you know. Met a good few folks in my time, and bad, many! Now I reckon we'll go on down to that hut you discovered. We can make ourselves a brew up there, make ourselves comfortable, like."

"Why would we want to go there?" Kate looked at him suspiciously. "And why should I go with you anywhere, especially somewhere miles from anywhere like that? Any way, I can't go. I'm meeting Rob here soon."

"You'll come with me because you wants to know the answers to all them questions you keep askin' yourself. And because Robert Ruddock is meeting us down there. Because you must, and you know it."

Shabby Tattler led the way and Kate obediently followed. She knew he was right. Without him she had no idea what to do. He seemed to hold the keys to the whole mystery. "Strange, " she thought, "that Rob has agreed to meet him there without letting me know. Maybe because Shabby Tattler told him he's fetching me too."

They walked along the path that led to the hamlet Kate had discovered hidden in the woods. Kate recognised it and wondered whether he knew where it led.

Rounding a bend in the path through the woods, the clearing in which stood the hamlet came into sight. There were the villagers, dressed in the same queer garb, going about their chores, apparently. Kate looked at Shabby Tattler, trying to figure out if he could see what she was seeing, or whether he would walk through them.

He walked straight on into the main street, ignoring the activities around him. No one seemed to pay him any heed either. "Strange," thought Kate, "I was sure he would be able to see them."

But Shabby Tattler walked on through, not looking to right

or left, as if the village and its inhabitants were invisible to him. As they reached the far end of the clearing and entered the deep woods beyond, Kate looked back. Some of the villagers seemed to be stopping whatever it was they were doing and moving towards a point in the centre, near the house of Jack Herne, the headman.

As they rounded a bend in the path, she looked again. Sure enough, they were congregating and starting to walk towards her along the path she had just trodden. The hairs prickled on the back of her neck. They were following. She looked nervously at Shabby Tattler and said, "Excuse me, but the villagers seem to be following us."

But he appeared serenely undisturbed by this news and continued on at the same leisurely pace, ignoring her.

They continued on for a further ten minutes. Kate looked back at the end of every straight stretch of path, but never saw the villagers again. She wondered if she had imagined the whole thing. Maybe he didn't answer because there were no villagers to follow them.

They reached the hut without further incident. Rob was already there. Kate was mightily relieved that he was. At least it meant Shabby Tattler was not trying to hoodwink her in some way.

"Hi Rob, I'm glad you came."

"Hi. I've no idea why I'm here," replied Rob. "I only came because that Shabby Tattler feller said he was bringing you and I thought I had better keep an eye on you."

"Thanks." She touched his forearm nervously, as if to reassure herself that he really was here. "Why are we here, Mr Tattler?"

"Because it's on the way to where we're going. And because Rob knows it." Shabby Tattler smiled. "But I reckon we'll do without that tea. We'll just press on. There ain't much time."

As he was talking, Kate noticed Robert looking strangely distracted, looking all around him as searching for something.

"What is it, Rob?"

"I don't rightly know." Robert looked puzzled, cocking his head this way and that. "Do you hear it? As you arrived, I noticed the noise of birds singing…"

"So what? They always sing."

"No. Getting louder I mean. Then I saw birds flying. Not just here and there. But all in one direction, like they would if fleeing a forest fire." Robert looked at Kate and Shabby Tattler. "But it looks like it's passed. They've all gone now."

Suddenly Kate's ears pricked up. "You're right. They have gone. Listen!"

They all stood listen for a moment. "See?" added Kate, "There's no singing, except faintly over in that direction…" She pointed due West.

"Where we're goin', my dears," Shabby Tattler interjected. "You'll soon see why. Just follow me." He moved off down the path. Kate grabbed Robert's hand and the pair of them followed after, heading in the direction of the receding twittering of the birds.

Shortly they saw another clearing ahead and Shabby Tattler turned with his fingers to his lips to hush them, waited for them to catch up, and then pushed them gently forward in the small of their backs, whispering, "Now watch and listen. Keep quiet, whatever happens. You see that ancient oak, the one on your left there. Get yourselves next to that, keep out of sight behind the bushes there, and let you see what you will see."

"Why? What's happening?"

"Kate, listen!" Robert jerked her arm urgently.

"Ow!"

"Listen," Rob urged in a whisper. "There's no birdsong."

They both listened. Silence. "See, Kate? They've stopped. There are no birds, either." Rob looked at her, then asked, "What do you think, Mr Tattler, Sir?"

They looked round, expecting his answer, but he was gone.

Vanished. "What the hell? He's buggered off and left us out here." Robert looked around in anger and disgust. "What the hell's he playing at?"

Suddenly a big black crow swept past them into the clearing, brushing Kate's face with its wings as it passed, and flew away over the woods.

"Ugh! Where did that come from?" Kate shuddered.

"Look, Kate, listen!" Rob had turned his face back to the clearing and was looking surprised and frightened. From the silence there emerged a strange humming sound, getting louder. They crept forward until they gained the edge of the clearing.

Ahead of them stood a gathering of cloaked and hooded figures with their backs to the pair. In front of the crowd stood a priest beside a table and a large carved wooden cross. The humming he heard was the indistinct chanting of this grey congregation.

"I dreamed this!" Kate whispered, "I dreamed it on that first day you took me to the lake. It's them. And in my dream they turn to me and they're all dead! They're all cut up like they've been killed."

"Calm down," Let's just listen and wait." Robert put his arm round her shoulder.

The voices in the clearing seemed now to be engaged in responses. "What are they saying?" Kate looked at Robert.

From the throng came a low growling prayer: "'Ere be assembled all of us on this 'ere day of remembrance."

A shrill voice responded: "What day's that?"

"This thirteenth day of seven monath of thirtieth year of the reign of Queen Bess."

"What was that? Thirteenth day of the seventh month," said Kate, "the thirteenth of July…"

"But today's the twenty-fourth of July," Rob whispered.

"What for we be assembled on this 'ere day?"

"I know, it is the thirteenth – was the thirteenth, then –

216

today," Kate said, "because they were still using the old Julian calendar; eleven days behind our modern calendar…"

"To give thanks for them Wunners Caped, same's every year we dun it."

"Why for?"

"Them Wunners Caped, from out of our brudders –n– sisters, fadders –n– mudders, sons –n– darters…"

"I remember," Kate said urgently, "this year, 1588, Elizabeth's thirtieth as Queen, was the year of the Spanish Armada, when Catholics would be at their most persecuted."

"Them's Chosen Few, them is."

"Chosen are them Wunners Caped, an we's holdin' a promise against their a-turnin on day on this day of the year."

"Blessed be them Wunners, them Wunners Caped, 'cos they'll inerit the earth what we bled for."

"Can you understand them?" Robert turned to Kate.

"They seem to be saying, 'Blessed be the Wunners. Blessed be the Wunners' Caped?' Maybe they from a religious cult who all wear capes or something. Listen."

"Blessed be the Wunners Caped," chanted the crowd.

"For them'll turn again, an in their turnin' shall be us salvation an' the vengeance of the Lord," chanted the priest.

"An in their turning shall the Wunners' Caped be blessed, Amen."

Just then Kate and Robert became aware of a different sound in the distance, a low drumming noise and a strange noise like the rushing of wind and the cry of geese in flight seemed to surge right through them.

At that moment horsemen burst from the forest, roaring and flashing their swords in the air. The chanting had given way to a crescendo of screaming as the villagers tried to flee the onrushing horses. Kate saw the leading horseman, a powerful man in a black hood, disappear momentarily in a crash of smoke as he discharged a pair of pistols in the face of her father, Sir William, as he sought to wrap his arms in protection of his wife and daughters. His face seemed to explode as he cried out to the man to stop. A spray of blood and bone and brain engulfed his family as his headless torso, arms outspread, stood upright for a minute before collapsing forward onto his wife.

Kate felt a thud in her chest as if hit by a heavy missile, and she was thrown to the floor, breathless.

The horseman pulled a long gun out of a saddle holster and pointed it directly at the chest of Kate's mother, who was vainly trying to wipe her husband's gore from her eyes. There was another flash.

Her mother, Rose, stood, a look of disbelief in her face, as she felt her breast with her hands. A huge hole gaped through her chest. For an instant Kate could see right through her. Her mother's knees buckled and she collapsed, kneeling upright, looking up to heaven, as if praying.

Her older sister, Amelia, knelt, clinging to her bloodied mother as if trying to protect her from the massacre unfolding. Frozen like a pieta amidst the mayhem, they remained untouched by any weapon as people were cut down all around. The horseman reared his horse, rode her mother down, grabbed Amelia, throwing her roughly onto his horse, turned and galloped away through the trees.

Dazed, Kate was dragged backwards through the undergrowth and into a dark place. She thought this was the end and made to scream out, but a hand clamped firmly over her mouth, stifling the scream. She bit hard and turned her head to see her assailant. It was Rob.

"Quiet. Shh. Not a sound. Curl up here, beside me," he whispered urgently.

"Where are we?" she whimpered.

"Safe, for the moment. But you mustn't give us away," he continued, "We're in a hollow tree."

Kate shrunk to her smallest hiding size as she wriggled into Rob's protective arms and lay still, scarcely daring to breathe.

Rob pulled some bracken in to block the entrance of the hole, which was partially covered by a bush. Kate could see through a hole in the gnarled trunk the massacre unfolding.

Horsemen were everywhere hacking at the defenceless villagers who were running in all directions seeking escape. Hands, limbs, heads were hewn off. Men were split down the middle. Some villagers had surrounded a horseman and were trying to drag him from his horse. One man took hold of the rider's helmet-strap and was hauling him off his horse when another horseman ran him through with his sword, impaling him and the horseman's leg through the heavy saddle into the body of the horse. The horse reared, snatching the blade from the rescuer's hand, and galloped away with the two men pinioned to its side, crushing the men crowding round and tossing the two men about like rag-dolls until the blade slid out of the horse's side and the pair tumbled to the ground.

Then suddenly Sir Gabriel appeared and dismounted. He appeared confused.

"Kate! Kate, where are you?" he yelled.

Kate jumped up. Rob pulled her back and held her fast. "No. It's a trap. Keep quiet."

"Kate, where are you?" Sir Gabriel de Tiercel cried out again.

She struggled to get free of Rob's grip but he clamped his hand firmly over her mouth again. "It's a trap," he repeated, "Don't move."

"I'm afraid we've lost her, sir," Kate recognized Black Martin, "you'll have to go now, sir, to raise the Linnece household, with or without Kate. Or we'll never be able to overcome Falco Basard and all will be lost."

"But where is my darling Kate?" Sir Gabriel was distraught, "I must find her."

"You can't, sir, there isn't time. You must go and alert the Linnece troop. I will keep looking for her, sir. But I'm afraid someone may have killed her by accident. You must go now, sir. Or we're all done for."

"I'll go, but keep looking. Promise me you'll keep looking."
Sir Gabriel remounted his horse and galloped off towards
Kate's home.

"You see," whispered Rob, "Sir Gabriel's in on it. He is
part of it. He must have organized it."

"What? Killing Papa and Mama? Taking Amelia? He can't
be. Why would he?" Kate's whisper dissolved into tears.

"He is. I don't know why, but he just is."

The priest, Jack Straw, was grabbed by Parson Mew's two
sons and hauled to the great wooden cross. The giant, Saith
Fool, lifted him in the air, spreadeagled him over the cross
and the brothers drove two daggers through his wrists in
imitation of Christ. They ripped off his clothes and nailed
his feet together to the base, so that he was arched over the
wooden effigy of Christ. He was taunted and mocked and
spat upon, but did not scream or cry or plead with them.
He stared them in the eye, challenging them to the point
where they could endure his gaze no longer and Parson Mew
ran him through the side with a spear. He died slowly, but
without a word to satisfy their craving for a triumph over his
Faith.

Kate saw fat Lord Barnaby Stave-Carew throw off his
cloak and wave his arms in protestation, declaring himself
and his rank, before an amused audience of Falco Basard's
rough riders who slowly circled around him. He was puffing
and panting as he blustered, demanding to be released
immediately, on pain of outlawry.

One of the men rode forward and with the tip of his sword,
tore a rent in his doublet from neck to waist. Another then
ripped the garment from him, and with his dagger severed his
belt, so that his codpiece and hose fell away. Lord Barnaby
grabbed at his clothes to try and cover himself, whimpering
now, and pleading.

The first man plunged his sword into Sir Barnaby's huge belly and drew it sideways, opening a slit from hipbone to hipbone. A great yellow gash opened across him like an eye, staring at Kate, from which after a moment's pause spilt steaming grey tubes, followed by a gush of blood. Sir Barnaby desperately tried to catch his entrails and stuff them back into place. He was moaning now and crying. This only increased the men's excitement and determination to inflict complete humiliation on him. One urged Falco's mastiffs onto him. The first dog started towards him and tentatively licked a hanging piece of gut before wrenching it from Lord Barnaby's grasp and tugging at it, dragging more out with it. The others dogs joined in and Sir Barnaby stood in bewilderment as the dogs fought over his bowels, just like they did in their kennels with sheep-guts, until he was dragged to the ground. In a few moments the beasts had torn him apart amid howls of laughter from the men.

One group of horsemen now rode away. The others, led by Falco Basard, now turned their attention to the women. They were huddled in a group near the altar, screaming hysterically as, one by one, they were dragged away, pulled down and had their clothes torn from them. Soon nearly everyone in the clearing was on the floor, fighting, with the men trying to squash the women into the ground.

Kate saw a baby snatched from her mother's arms by the leg and swung like club at the mother's own head. She saw the skulls collide and the baby's burst apart before the man threw its body to the dogs. He ran his rapier through the woman's throat before leaping down, still holding his sword, pushing her onto her back and ramming the blade deep into the earth. Pinioned to the ground, she was stripped and the man jumped on her and they fought for while before the got up again, pulled his sword out and slashed her throat. The woman jerked around on the ground like a chicken, blood pouring out between her hands, before she collapsed and lay still.

Kate put her hand to her mouth and bit hard to keep from screaming. She had to keep quiet. One sound would betray their hiding place. Helpless, fascinated, she could not tear her eyes away from the horror unfolding before her.

"Oh my God, Rob," Kate clutched Rob's arm. Suddenly it dawned on her that she was seeing through Kate's eyes, all those years ago, "This is real! How do we get out of this?"

"I don't know."

She looked at Rob. He, too, was staring, wide-eyed, as if through the eyes of his namesake.

From their hiding place inside the tree they watched the unfolding of the massacre exactly as Shabby Tattler had told it, or rather, as he had very deliberately glossed over it; as if he knew that by bringing them here at this time they would witness this crux of his story as an undeniable reality. They saw Amelia Linnece snatched onto a horse and carried away. They saw the butchery and rape. They saw the crucifixion of the priest. They saw the murderers themselves massacred and their killers themselves dissolve into the woods. But where each body fell, the next time they looked, there was nothing there. Each body vanished somehow into thin air, and through the smoky haze of the slaughter Kate and Rob gradually came to realize that once again, they could hear the birdsong growing to a crescendo.

Looking out they saw the air above now filled with birds of every kind, flying frantically hither and thither, as if trapped in a huge cage. They climbed out of the hollowed oak and walked, hand-in-hand into the centre of the clearing and stood still.

The birds circled them now, swooping low over their heads as if inspecting them. Their cacophony increased until suddenly, as if on a signal, the birds dispersed in every direction, and the sound diminished with their departure.

Kate and Robert sat still for a while, completely overawed and confused by what they had just witnessed.

Kate shivered. Despite herself, tears welled up in her eyes with the sheer intensity of her despair at the loss of Amelia, of her own helplessness. She looked at Rob. He too looked dazed, overawed. She took his hand and he hugged her to him. They remained locked in this embrace as waves of emotion swept over them.

As the forest and its sounds returned to normality, they looked at one another. "My god! Incredible! What was that all about?" exclaimed Robert.

"I think I know," replied Kate. "I think we've just broken the curse. I think we've witnessed the last massacre of the faithful here in these woods. I think we are the 'Wunners Caped'. They were saying, 'blessed be the one's escaped, the one's who have escaped... the massacre.' We are those ones. We have returned. And it looks like they are being released from the curse of having to re-enact the massacre by our appearance here today."

"Jesus. That's just too much. You mean these weird people we've just seen turn into birds are supposed to be the villagers massacred in the sixteenth century? You're pulling my leg," said Robert.

"I wish I was," said Kate, "but you just saw the whole massacre, didn't you? You saw that rider kidnap Amelia. You saw the murderers massacred themselves. You saw all the dead people disappear and the birds reappearing didn't you? If they are not them, who are they?"

"I don't know," Robert paused, "what now?"

"Now, it appears, the rest of the legend will come to pass... And that means the end of the Tercels... at our hands. Unless we can find a way to stop it."

"Don't be silly. That's ridiculous. You mean we're supposed to murder the general and Gabriel. Much as I despise the spoiled brat, I wouldn't dream of doing that."

"What are we going to do, Rob?" Kate clung to Rob's arm, looking imploringly into his eyes. "And where's Shabby Tattler gone? He led us here. He must have known that today was the day of the massacre. So he led us here and forced us to witness the slaughter."

"I don't know where he is, but he's got a lot of explaining to do when we find him. But first, let's get out of these damned woods and go home. There's nothing more we can do here, that's for sure."

34

Hidden facets

Kate knew that she had to find Shabby Tattler again, and quickly. She had told Rob last night, after they got back from witnessing the massacre of ghosts, the dreadful tale of Amelia Linnece as recounted in her diary. But this itself left so many details unanswered: details to which she was certain only Shabby Tattler had access.

More and more it seemed certain to her that he must be some kind of spirit and no man at all; that he wielded some sort of demonic power over this whole tragic mess in which she found herself entangled.

She thought of enlisting the General's help in locating this elusive man, but decided that if he could be located, he certainly could not be coerced, so it was better to await his next epiphany, which she felt certain could not be far off.

The next day, as Kate wandered aimlessly about the General's study, awaiting his arrival, her glance happened upon a small booklet, lying on a high shelf. What caught her eye was not the title, "Daisy Chain", but the name below it on the book's spine: "P. G. Tercel".

She couldn't help but pick it up. "Peregrine," she thought, "write a book? Called Daisy-chain?"

"Surely it could not be about love?" She chuckled. "Many the things old general might be, but a romantic?" Perhaps this book would reveal hidden facets of his character: something of the man she had come to admire for not being quite what he projected to the outside world.

She sat down in an armchair facing the windows. She flipped to the first page and started reading:

"The pale oval of her face. The fall of her hair in two strands over half-closed lids, shading under dark lashes the water-green of her irises. In stolen glances, a flashing iridescence seemingly reflecting his own joy in beholding her.

The subtle curves of her lips quivering intermittently in half-smiles as if in some private pleasures recalled. The occasional dropping of her lower lip in tantalising self-forgetfulness.

Her hair, pulled back from her face by two clips, gradually released by the movements of her head and the jerking of the speeding train. Individual locks flopping forward in a gentle sliding into loose abandonment, periodically compelling her to reach behind her head, unclasp the clips and shake loose a swirling flame of lustrous hair before gathering it carefully on either side to clamp it once more in hard steel jaws.

This cycle of abandonment and self-control is reflected in the way she talks and laughs and is silent in succession. With no turn holding sway for long, her face bears mobile witness to her character, so fluid in its metamorphoses of mood, rippling her surfaces as succeeding waves make manifest on the shoreline of appearance the deeper ebb and flow of emotion under the influence of a changing moon.

The slow deliberations of this tussle with her hair reveal the smooth underside of her bare arms, whose hollow swoop leads his eye as in a sensuous big dipper to the upthrust mounds of her breasts, softly responsive to her every gesture."

"Wow!" thought Kate, "Who'd have thought it? Our overtly crusty old General – a sensualist!" She read on.

"Her sides, exposed in this lifting motion, curve inward and downward to a narrow waist and the smooth broadening of her hips.

It is with a tumescent guilt that he finds himself stroking her every declivity with such passionate imagination that it is as if..."

"I see you've discovered my secret."

Kate leaped out of the chair in alarm, dropping the book and tripping over the side-table in her haste to escape.

"Don't worry, my dear, " continued the General, bending over to pick her up off the floor. "I don't mind at all, really I don't."

Kate, flustered, half fell into his arms in her confusion and, as he drew her up to her full height, looked imploringly into his eyes. He was smiling broadly as he released her. "There. Are you all right? You look a little shaken."

"I didn't mean to..." she started, "I mean, I didn't..."

"I know what you mean," answered the General. "No need to explain. You were curious to discover whether this old grouch could possibly be a writer of sentimental nonsense."

He picked up the volume* and handed it back to her. "Take it. Read it. Let me know what you think. I'm curious, too. You may borrow it with one proviso. That you promise to let me know what you think of it."

"Thank you," Kate blushed. "Thank you, I will read it, carefully, I promise, and let you know."

Their eyes met and locked, momentarily, and a wave of intimacy passed between them. Kate had an inkling of the effect he might have had on women in his younger days.

He gracefully stood aside, indicating that she should leave now. She thanked him again and slipped past him and made her way out of the house.

35

The General's secret

Kate put the book down. The book was the tale of a man's accidental meeting with a younger woman, of their brief affair, and its termination in his own death.

She felt strangely conflicting emotions. She felt moved by the sentiments of the lover's poems to his beloved, while feeling vicariously hurt in the way the hero's wife must have been by his ignorance of her needs and by his selfish concern with his own emotions. What drove the man in this tale (the General?), she wondered, to act so? And, if so, why such an outcome? The quasi-mystical unification of all women in the persona of a Goddess, was it to justify his obsession in his own mind?

And what of the just-as-strange end piece, seemingly an autobiographical myth making of the desire to return to primitive origins? What was she to make of that?

Was any of this based in fact? Did the General have such an affair, or affairs, betraying his wife as depicted here? Or was this pure fantasy, a figment of his desires? Why did it end in his apparent death, or disappearance?

Kate knew that the General's wife had been killed in a car accident on holiday when their child was about the same age as those depicted in this fictional family. Had he written this as some sort of atonement, reversing the roles, and mythically making the death his own? Was this driven by a sense of guilt at his wife's death? Had he been having an affair prior to her death, which she had discovered, as the wife depicted here, and had he then, being the cause of his wife's death, then died himself, as here, emotionally and retreated into an abstraction, absorbed into an undying love for the Goddess behind all masks, behind all individuation? Kate's mind raced with ideas and theories; question after question.

Certainly the story portrayed the General's personality in a completely different dimension to the humdrum, if genial, old gentleman she had known till now. Kate determined to question him deeply on this matter. Somehow, she knew that it mattered, that she had been allowed to find the book, to read it, to unlock the secrets behind it.

"You're right. In many respects you are right." General Tercel smiled. Kate had just given him an account of her reaction to the book and all the questions it raised in her mind. "The end piece was, I suppose an interpretation of the fall from grace we all suffer in becoming who we are, and the yearning to return. I, too, was born on the edge of the ocean and spent my early childhood in the surf. In Malaya, as it was then, during the Emergency. My father was a soldier, sent out there to deal with the Chinese Communists who, after fighting with the British during the Japanese occupation, turned on us and launched a guerrilla war to drive us out. It was a war in all but name. Went on for twelve years, nearly.

We lived at Port Dickson, an army base on the west coast. Long white sandy beaches, mangrove swamps, Malay kampongs, or fishing villages, from which the local fishermen set forth in their sampans and returned with all sorts of fish, which they laid out to dry in the baking sun. Coconut palms fringing the beach provided our morning snacks in the little school, an unused barracks, I attended there. Swimming all afternoon after lessons. It was heaven for a little boy, apart from the sweltering humidity. But the sea made up for that.

Then at seven, I was packed off to England, just like that, to go to boarding school and live with my uncle and aunt, in loco parentis, during the holidays. That was a culture shock for me, I can tell you. I only saw my real parents once a year, during the long hols. Sometimes they came to England, other times I went to Malaya, then later to Kenya, where he was posted next.

I used to abscond into the woods – the school had four hundred acres of woodland, armed with my parang, a machete, or my Kukri and jungle saw to make myself little shelters; or with my blowpipe to pretend I was a Sakai, the indigenous people of Malaya. And always I got punished when I returned. I was beaten many times in my first term until I learned to be subtle in my absconding.

It seems strange now, I suppose, to people of your generation that a seven-year-old boy could be allowed such an arsenal at school. You would think there would be stabbings and suchlike, but there weren't. It never occurred to one to use such weapons when one got into fights. It was all fisticuffs and wrestling.

We did boxing at school, and rugger. The violence was organised and ritualised, you see. Sport was highly competitive and so aggression was channelled, I think probable to the good, overall. When I look at the nancy way schools treat children with their abhorrence of allowing them the experience of failure and disappointment in a formalised context so that they can learn to fight back and rise above it, I am not surprised that boys show such disdain and disrespect for their teachers.

They don't want to be mollycoddled. They want to face challenges, and when there aren't any in fields in which they might probably excel, those that aren't academic feel hurt and humiliated and ultimately rebel."

"But in that story," interrupted Kate, "it seems that you hated the tough regime, the bullying and discipline."

"And so I did. Things went too far the other way, then: all the beatings and so forth. But the experience did toughen me up. Made me learn to cope. At the cost of internalising all my regrets and sorrows."

"But is that better? Than today's world?" Kate looked at him questioningly, "I mean, should we still be aiming to breed generations of stiff upper lips but sick inside people?"

"No. Obviously the degree of machismo is no longer suitable. It is just that we have allowed the pendulum to swing too far in the other direction. But I digress. Once I get started I tend to forget what it was I started from, if you see what I mean. Too long alone, I suppose." The General chuckled. "But I do enjoy talking to you like this. It has been so long you know..."

"I enjoy it too," Kate smiled. "It's an education in itself. I didn't know such a world existed so recently. It's bit like having one's history books come alive, so to speak."

"A living fossil, you mean? Welcome to my Jurassic Park, my dear, where dinosaurs roam free..."

"Oh, I'm sorry. I didn't mean to offend..."

"No offence taken, my dear. None at all. It's quite funny, really, seeing yourself as others see you." General Tercel leaned forward and patted her on the knee. "But to return to my book. I'll start with your last question first, if I may. How did I get it published?

Vanity is the answer, and of course, having the means. You see, no publisher in this country would consider such a work. Comments like: "Too personal an approach to storytelling..." "Poetry doesn't sell..." "It doesn't fit any category of fiction..." That sort of thing. In France, maybe, some small press might have taken it on. So I did it myself. Distributed it among friends."

"And how was it received? Were they surprised?" asked Kate.

"Surprised? Oh, yes. Shocked, some of them. Took it all too

literally. Only too keen to, of course; read into it biographical insights. People love to speculate, especially into anything that might unearth a bit of scandal."

"But was it based in fact, at all? It seems so personal, so vivid…" Kate looked at him keenly. "I don't mean to pry, but…"

The General sighed, looked at her and slowly smiled, as if relieved of some great burden. "Yes, there was an affair. But it was not as depicted here. The individual fragments of emotion, poems, if you like, interspersed here, range throughout the period of my youth and young manhood. The story was a way of stringing them together into a fictional daisy-chain. You know: 'She loves me. She loves me not'. A necklace to adorn the throat of that Chimaera, the Eternal Woman, whom we men would all love to love."

General Tercel idly flicked through the pages with his fingers, as his eyes regarded the ceiling, in manner reminiscent of the bead-telling of a rosary, counting off and reliving the sins of his past, his atonements and prayers for forgiveness.

"She has forgiven me, I feel," he added quietly, as talking to himself alone. "You see I loved her deeply in my own wayward fashion. Still do."

The General looked at Kate. "I killed her, you know. It was my fault. I was drunk. I lay oblivious as she, unconscious, drowned. I could have saved her if I had not been drunk."

"I know," said Kate, "Gabriel told me roughly what happened. You don't need to go through it and torture yourself."

"But I do, you see. And I will, no doubt, until the end. It is my doom, so to speak, to relive the horror of my discovery when I woke that night." The General leaned back in his chair and let the book slide from his grasp into the nook by the chair's arm. He seemed smaller somehow, crushed.

"You see, if I had not had had the affair and if it had not been discovered, we would never have gone on that holiday at that time on our own, leaving the child, Gabriel, with his grandmother. It was a second beginning, a rebirth; a second honeymoon, if you like.

And I, in my elation, foolishly got drunk, and felt invincible as I drove the car from the restaurant to our villa. I had survived wars and conflicts for twenty years through my natural instincts, been decorated and reached the highest ranks of the military. I felt at that moment so self-confident I ignored her warnings. Yes, she tried to stop me. She told me I was not capable of controlling the car. What nonsense, I told her. Those were my last words to her, you know. What nonsense! If only I had listened."

The General became silent, sitting very still. Only his eyes betrayed the turmoil he was going through. Kate moved towards him, kneeling by his side and taking his rough gnarled hand in hers. She stroked his hair and gently pulled his head to her breast as tears rolled down his cheeks.

They remained locked in this silent embrace for several minutes. Then the General wrested free of her enfolding arms and laughed uneasily, saying, "I haven't shed a tear since that night, you know. I died there and then, emotionally. I vowed never to allow myself intimacy with another woman as long as I lived. You have freed me from that vow. I don't know why it is, but I feel at ease with you in a way I have not felt for a long, long time. Thank you."

Kate got to her feet and, without asking, went to the drinks cabinet and poured them both a drink. She handed the General his whiskey and watched him as he slowly sipped the golden liquid.

They sat together for a long while, exchanging glances but no words. No words, it seemed, were adequate to express the affection that passed between them. At length, Kate rose to her feet and said: "I'm going now."

The General saw her to the door. Before leaving, as she passed him, she stood on tiptoe and kissed him briefly on the

233

lips. "Your blouse is all wet, you know," he said.

They both smiled.

36

A clown's tale

Gabriel Tercel stepped outside and looked at the sunrise. He stretched himself languorously like a cat with an exaggerated yawn, as they do. "Such a beautiful morning," he thought to himself, "deserves an act of singular abandon, of wanton bravura."

He shook his long hair loose from the band holding his ponytail and ran his fingers through it as he pondered what he might do that would be so shocking and dramatic as to rival the rising sun's beauty.

He ran into the stable, unleashed his favourite black stallion, bridled him and led him out into the courtyard. Ignoring the saddle, Gabriel leaped onto the horse's back and dug his heels into his flanks, so that the startled horse reared and raced forward out of the yard and across the lawns of Fugglesham Court, churning great clods of damp grass into the air behind him.

Gabriel laughed as he clung to the galloping beast with his thighs, one hand holding the reins, waving his other hand madly in the air.

He kicked off his shoes as the horse sped along, leaned over and pulled each sock off, the better to feel the brute power of the animal under him. Then, ripping his shirt off, he flailed the air before flinging it away.

On a sudden inspiration, he reined the horse to a standstill and, still sitting on its back, undid his trousers and pulled them off, so that he was stark naked.

Yelping with delight, he goaded the horse forward, a slim white figure with black hair trailing behind, reflecting the flying mane of the black stallion careering across the meadows.

Kate, hearing the strange yelping, looked out of her bedroom window to see the small but instantly recognisable, if by his behaviour only, figure of Gabriel Tercel, naked astride his horse. "Oh, my god," she exclaimed, giggling at his panache, careless of all censure. "He's such an idiot!"

Gabriel steered his charger towards her cottage and, seeing her curtains move, galloped right under her window, waving wildly at her shocked face and then away across the field towards the distant river.

She watched, fascinated, as his form grew smaller, the horse moving at a furious pace across the landscape, the sound of his laughter diminishing.

Suddenly she saw the horse skid to a stop, its head down and hindquarters rear up. Gabriel's body was flung like little pink rag-doll over its head with a yelp, and she heard a muted splash. He must have been thrown into the river, she thought.

Dressing as fast as she could, she ran out of the house and towards the spot where she had seen him fall. As she approached, she saw the horse, riderless, munching grass a little down stream of the place, as if nothing at all had happened.

Of Gabriel there was no sign. She waded out into the river until it reached her chest. Looking down into the cold, clear water, she could see the pebbles on the bottom and the water-grasses waving in the current like hair, but no sign of Gabriel.

She worked her way downstream, searching among the reeds at the edge of the water. A rising tide of panic pulsed through her now chilling frame as she pushed ever more urgently through the shallows. He would be dead by now, drowned, she knew it, all because he was trying to show off to her.

Rounding a bend in the river, she saw him, washed up against the shingle on the outer reach, amongst the grasses and reeds in the shallows there. Her vision of his body, white as alabaster, his face up towards the sun, eyes and mouth open but inanimate, his hands on either side held as in supplication, his long hair flowing, mingling with the soft water-grasses, was of a male Ophelia.

She rushed towards him and, putting one arm under his neck and the other about his chest and under his armpit, pulled him towards her and started to drag him to the shore.

His head hung loosely back, lolling awkwardly as she moved forward in small jerks. Despairing of gaining solid ground in time, she pulled his head towards her and put her mouth to his, blowing hard down his throat. He stirred. Taking a deep breath, she again put her lips to his. At that moment, his eyes opened and his lips became languid, actively moving to kiss her as his arms embraced her.

Kate's muffled scream as she tore loose turned to a shout of anger, "How dare you! How dare you frighten me like that! I thought you were dead, or dying at least." She collapsed and sat down in the stream in shock and burst into tears.

Gabriel reached to embrace her but she beat him off with her fists, "You're a beast. You're a selfish insensitive beast!"

"Oh, Kate, I'm so sorry. I didn't mean to hurt you. I don't know what came over me." He pleaded with her, allowing her to pummel his chest in her anger. "But when the horse threw me and I felt the cold water surge over me, I thought for an instant, I'm a goner. But then I surfaced, unhurt, and a feeling of beautiful well-being washed through me and I knew, I just knew you would come for me and my whole body cried out to be still and awaiting your coming, to rescue me, just as you did, and embrace me, as you did, and put your warm lips to mine, just as you did. It was a blissful feeling, a blissful moment."

He knelt beside her and as her lashing out became more muted, slowly embraced her ever more tenderly until at last she relented and fell into his arms and allowed him to kiss her. After the fear and the shock her need for this tenderness overwhelmed her and she returned his kiss with a passion.

As she recovered she suddenly felt the cold of the water, and pulled away from him, saying: "come on, we've got to get out or we'll freeze to death."

At that moment she looked at him and woke to realisation that he was wholly naked. "Here, take this." She took off her jacket and put it round his shoulders as he stood there up to his knees in water, shivering.

They climbed onto the bank and made their way to his horse. He leaped up and pulled her up in front of him and they trotted off towards the House.

"I think you had better go via my cottage. You can drop me off there and I'll give you a set of my father's clothes. You can't go home looking like that."

As she handed him the clothes and watched him dress, she couldn't help but think how absolutely beautiful his body was, so delicately formed and yet so lithe and muscular, he could have been a Greek God.

"Thank you, Kate. I mean it. And you have rescued me, in a manner of speaking, from myself. Shown me something I didn't know existed, through my feelings for you."

Gabriel Tercel rode away slowly, looking back often at Kate standing silent by her front door, until a bend in the road took him out of sight.

37

The portrait

Kate opened the door to the General's bedroom. She knew she shouldn't be poking around in such a place, but something was drawing her here, into his inner sanctum. She felt a powerful desire to get close to this strange old man, to know him more intimately.

Creeping in guiltily, as if she might get caught like a schoolgirl prying into the headmistress's study, she cast her eyes around. The curtains were half drawn and a dusty gloom pervaded the room. She walked over and opened them wide, a little surprised at her sudden bravado.

The furniture in the room was old, sparse, but obviously all of good quality. The walls were hung with paintings and old photographs. By the bed was a very subtly lit photographic portrait of the General's wife in her prime, taken beside one of the great windows in the dining hall. It was a work of great beauty, and Kate wondered whether the General had taken it himself or had hired a professional.

Looking around the other pictures of family and home and even of the General himself, she supposed, as a young army officer, astride a horse somewhere in Africa, it seemed, she felt comforted in the very ordinariness of the General's choice. In the middle of the furthest wall, facing the bed was a small curtain on a wooden curtain pole, beckoning her as if just waiting to be unveiled. She walked over and carefully pulled it aside.

Behind the curtain was an arched alcove, a bit like the one in the East Wing where she had seen the ghostly Amelia secrete her diaries. In it hung a painted portrait, but she could not make it out in the shadow. Finding a switch on the wall beside the curtain, she turned it on.

She let out a little scream. There before her was a perfect painting of the woman of the East Wing: the beautiful face of her own mother. "It's her! He's seen her too!"

The woman was sitting in much the same attitude as when Kate had first seen her in the East Wing, sideways on, bathed in a single beam of light from high up, much as the tapestry had been then.

Her small delicate hands were folded in her lap. She wore a velvet gown of deep maroon with a collar of a deeper, almost violet, ultramarine, upon which lay the loose curls of her long dark auburn hair, burnished with flecks of dark gold in the sunlight. Her face was turned slightly towards the onlooker, with her lips curved in a half-smile, but the expression about her eyes, looking straight out at Kate, was one of despair, of sadness and longing... of pure affection.

In its dimly-lit setting of half-suggested forms, and its subject, mesmerically attracting the full empathy of the viewer, this painting was a work out of time, with a transcendent beauty that carried within it a music that transported Kate into her childhood and her mother's arms once more.

"You really shouldn't be in here, you know."

Kate started. The General walked up behind her and put his hand upon her shoulder.

She looked up at him, slightly fearful that he might be about to take advantage of her compromising position. But he was staring now at the portrait with such intensity she could only interpret as with a passion.

"How did you get that picture? I mean, where did you find it? Is it a historical portrait of one your ancestors? Why is it hanging there, opposite your bed?"

"That's a long story. You wouldn't understand. But no, it is not an historical portrait." The General looked at her in curiously detached way, as if sizing her up, judging just what he might and might not reveal to her. "In fact, I painted it myself, and if I say so myself, it is not at all a bad likeness."

"But that's my mother! I mean, that's the woman in the room; the ghost-woman I told you about. You've seen her too!"

"I don't know about your mother, but I saw the lady in this picture in a dream, once, a strange and wonderful dream, the details of which I won't bore you with, but when I woke to the cold light of day her face haunted me so vividly I knew I had to paint her, to keep the image of her beauty before me."

"Then that proves it! That proves there is a ghost, the Lady of the room I told you about. You must have been drawn to her in your sleep as I was when awake. Her cry for life must have driven you to paint her as you did."

"I don't know. I suppose, in a curious way, that what you say is true. You know that day when you saw me, as you described me, dressed so ludicrously?"

"I never said that!" Kate protested, the image of the General in his beret and paint-bespattered smock leaping into her gaze. She covered her mouth to hide the grin creeping across her cheeks, "I..."

"No, no. But your eyes said that." The General laughed. "You really are a giveaway, you know. However, to return to that day: I told you I had started painting again, thanks to you. Well, this portrait is the painting to which I referred. I only finished it a week ago. It is just as well you didn't poke it with your fingers or you might have smudged it."

"I don't understand," Kate started.

"Listen, then. I started this painting many years ago, but

somehow I could never capture the essence of that vision, and eventually, discouraged, I just gave it up. But recently, since meeting you, I suddenly felt inspired to finish that portrait. Because, you see, after our conversations I suddenly saw that vision of beauty again unclouded by the conflicting emotions following her first visitation and she appeared as fresh as if she were standing before me. And so I was able to complete my work, finding my powers of depiction had returned with a vengeance. Hence the little tale about inspiration I told you then. Does that make any sense to you?"

"Yes, I suppose it does, in a curious way. I certainly think you have succeeded in capturing her perfectly. I wish I had the talent to do so," Kate mused, as she looked again at the portrait. "Can I come back to see it again, soon? You see, it does remind me of my mother, so…"

"Of course, of course." The General smiled with deep satisfaction. "But I think you have seen enough for one day. It's time you left my bedroom before someone sees us here together. Tongues wag, don't you know."

"Oh, gosh, I mean, yes, let's get out quick," Kate stumbled past him and fled the room, followed more sedately by the old man, chuckling to himself.

Kate sat silently, her hands locked together over her knees, staring out of the window, her mind in some other place.

When she came to, Kate realised she was alone here, at the top of the house. The sun was setting at the far end of the long gallery, its rays streaking down the floor towards her, almost reaching her feet. How had her feet carried her here after her encounter with the portrait in the General's bedroom?

She stood up. And suddenly doubled up: her feet had pins and needles so sharp she had to sit down again and massage her calves. The house was eerily quiet. There was a little door, a little over five feet tall, in the oak panelling to her right, under the sloping panelling of the roof. It reminded her of the doors Alice had encountered in Wonderland. The curious feeling suddenly came over her that through it she must go. She looked around, as if for the table with the magic shrinking potion, or even a key. She tried the handle. It was a bit stiff, but with a wrench she managed to turn it and the little door creaked open. She remembered that, according to Gabriel, it had been used by his grandmother a long time ago to come up here from her quarters somewhere down below. She had used it daily, taking her exercise by walking the length of the gallery, back and forth, winter and summer, until well into her nineties. She must have been very petite or bent, perhaps, by old age to pass easily through it, Kate thought, as she bent forward.

She peered into the space beyond. Lit by the window of a small gable, a narrow staircase descended in a square spiral, which sounded so suitably Alice-like as to make Kate smile as she ducked through and closed the door behind her.

She descended, trying not to creak the stairs or trip over in the growing gloom. She wondered onto what room this stair might open. Perhaps even a door to a secret garden in a completely different place? This house, after all, had a peculiar logic in which Lewis Carroll might have been at home; except for it's being so threatening and doom-ridden.

At the bottom she came upon another door, of normal size this time, again unlocked. She quickly opened it and stepped through; a little afraid it too, might lead into one of the rooms in the East Wing that no longer existed.

She found her self at the end of a short, rather dingy, passage running west along the north side of the main house. It looked unused and not a little dilapidated, compared with the other, more public corridors in that house. She walked to its end, opened the door and found herself in the main hall of the first floor.

Kate returned and opened the first of the doors she had

passed. It opened onto a room she had not yet visited on her official tours of the house. It was oak-panelled and had a large south-facing window. There was a huge four-poster bed against one wall covered by an old tapestry, and the room was dusty and had an air of dereliction, as if the old General had just let it go. She supposed that, with so many rooms and so few occupants, he couldn't really keep all of it up to scratch.

On the opposite wall to the bed was a small window. Peeking through it, Kate found herself looking out into the Great Dining Hall from the East end. So she must be above the central passage on the ground floor.

On the further side of this room, she found another slightly smaller room, with a window at its end. She recognised this as being above the central Southern Porch.

Returning to the passage, she made her way back towards where she had entered it, and opened the next door on the right. It led into a similarly oak-panelled room with a large window reaching to the floor, its curtains drawn shut. As she cast her eyes around this also apparently unused bedroom, she noticed on the wall to her right that one of the oak panels didn't quite seem to fit. Hoping to find another secret panel such as those in the General's study, she walked over to it and pushed at it. It moved a little. Gripping an edge that jutted out slightly with her fingertips, she pulled gingerly at it.

It came away and the whole panel swung open, only to reveal a plastered wall behind it. Before she had time to register her disappointment at this, Kate noticed that there was some graffiti scrawled on the plaster. Too dark to read, she hastened away to open the curtains and returned to scrutinise the script.

"When Adam delved and Eve span. Who was then the Gentleman?"

"Who could have written this?" Kate thought to herself, as she closed the panel again. "One of those who carved and erected the oak panelling, a disgruntled craftsman," she guessed, "one who knew no lord of the house would ever discover it in his own lifetime, at least. Maybe scrawled as a sort of curse upon the wealthy. But why does it sound familiar to me?"

Suddenly she recalled the tale of Shabby Tattler. "That's where I heard it! It was in the words of the preacher John Ball and the responses of his congregation that I heard it."

A shiver ran through her as she tried to reconcile the fact that all those who were there at the sermons were slaughtered, and yet here was this text, hidden for generations behind the panelling. Was it a curse on the house, and if so, how did it get there? And how could whoever wrote it have known its significance, unless someone did survive the massacre and return later, disguised perhaps as a wood-craftsman, to lay his hidden curse upon the lords of this manor?

Thoughts raced through her head. Robin Ruddock survived the massacre, according to legend. Could he have returned? He was a woodsman's son. Perhaps he became a carpenter and returned unrecognised to lay his curse.

But what of Shabby Tattler? How did he come to know of the words of the sermon, re-iterated there on that wall? How could he possibly know what was said, unless he was making up the whole story? But if so, and the words came from another source, how then did they come to be here also, but hidden away? It was surely too much of a coincidence. It was as if shards of solid evidence, like an archaeologist's fragmented artefacts, were being unearthed, piece by piece, enabling her, Kate, to join together shapes and patterns to form a coherent structure, rather like a complete pot, on which was depicted a mythical story whose content corroborated what he, Shabby Tattler, could not possibly know, unless he had seen it in its original entirety. Unless he himself was something more than human, a being able to reach through the ages and speak to those who participated in these events, or even a being who was himself there, then, at that time, and yet could appear before her here and now; a shadowed being of impossible longevity with an omniscience that was almost – dare she think it – god-like. Not in the sense of the great Gods of modernity, but in the sense of their pantheistic precursors, members of a race of gods or beings whose universe ran parallel to that of man, but with an enduring power and knowledge far in excess of man's.

So her thoughts ran as she made her way hastily towards the back door by the great kitchens and out through the courtyard towards her own home in the gathering twilight.

38

The grave

"I don't know how to say this, Mother," Kate whispered, her forehead resting upon Amelia's headstone, "I know you are resting here below my feet… I know it's impossible but I have met you in another time."

She stared hard at the ground, as if willing herself to see through it into her mother's grave to somehow confirm her presence, solidly interred in that cold prison, unable to rise and pass, like the morning mists, through the trees and across the wild brooks to the foothills of the downs upon where stood the great house in which she was imprisoned as a living being in that other time.

"…Yet you are there, Mother. And there, too, your name is Amelia. And that Amelia also calls me 'my darling Katie', just as you used to. So you were her, and she is you, if you see what I mean…" Suddenly Kate stopped, shuddering as a cold wind blew through her.

She tried to recall what was familiar about this situation, about her words. Shaking her head, she dismissed her qualms and continued her story, "and that Amelia has been seen by others too. At least, by the current owner of the house, General Tercel. He has painted her portrait, you know."

Kate looked up into the sky, "And it's so real, Mother. It is as if he has brought you back to me. I hope you will forgive me for saying this, but I am strangely glad of that ghost, however awful its plight is, because without it he could never have captured your likeness as he has, so beautifully."

Kate looked around to make sure she had not been talking aloud, that no witness had heard her. "I think I must be going mad. I don't know what to think any more. Its crazy." She shivered and stood up. "Ignore my stupid talk. I miss you so much I think I must have conjured your spirit somehow in that ghost. But what of the old man, Shabby Tattler? Who conjured him? He frightens me with his knowledge of things that happened so long ago which then prove to be true. Oh, Mother, if you hear me, down there, protect me. Let some normality return to my life, please."

Kate stepped back and, briefly glancing across the brooks towards the woods behind which lay the Hall and her home, turned and walked towards her bicycle, which leaned against the gate.

"So this be where your mother lies, God rest her soul."

Kate looked back. Silhouetted against her mother's grave was the unmistakable back of Shabby Tattler, looking down at the gravestone. He did not look round.

Kate trembled, "How... how did you find me here?"

"Not a case of findin'. I been 'ere awhile, restin' down by that great oak there. A graveyard's a waitin' room of memories, for them what 'as ears ter hear. A concourse of the livin' and the dead." He turned and smiled at her as he ambled slowly across the graveyard towards her.

"Come with me, young Kate, across to that there great oak, under which we'll take our ease an I'll tell the rest of that story, from the massacre to the fire. You deserve to hear it from my lips, now, I reckon, an' a-piece it together, like."

THE SECOND TALE OF SHABBY TATTLER

"Black Martin, evil ruthless man though he were, had himself a conscience. He were deep, that man, a thinker. Not like White Whiskey John, who were cunning, clever, for his own advantage. No. Martin saw his self as a man to change the world for the better. He believed with a passion in justice for the common man, but he believed that the end justified the means, any means. The sacrifice of anyone for the sake of the common weal as he saw it in some perfect future.

"Trouble was, what he saw, he see-sawed, so to speak. He swung from this to that as he found fault with each faith; but while he held each, he held it with a fervour that brooked no opposition. He were a man of good intention but foul deed."

"How can you say that? You know what he did." Kate exclaimed, "He tortured, murdered and was my mother's, I mean Amelia's, jailor right up to the fire. How can you say he was good, or..."

"His were a different age than this 'un," replied Shabby Tattler, looking kindly at Kate, "you can't judge his actions by your own mores, my dear. People was all cruel and ruthless back then. They didn't know better. By today's ken they was all crooks, so just you let me be gettin' on with me tale, startin' with him, eh?"

39

Black Martin

Arriving at Runswick Abbey, Black Martin, his men,
and the Linnece fighters hastily brought the bodies of the
Linneces to their chambers to be made presentable. He sent
the Linnece men to Fugglesham Court to escort the only
surviving Linnece family member, Phyllis, against attack by
any remnant of Falco Basard's gang.

Holding the family servants at bay until he had made
their bodies less frightening, as he put it, he had dressed the
corpses in the apparel of young Kate and Amelia, disarranged
the materials and smeared them with gore. Then, bandaging
the worst of their wounds, he allowed the Linnece household
servants to enter to help finish the cleaning up.

By the time Phyllis arrived with her entourage, the corpses
had all been laid out in as respectable a fashion as could be
achieved. Phyllis, in a state of cold dread, was helped from
her horse and led by Black Martin up the stairs to the laying
out chamber.

"I warn you Ma'am, you will be shocked by what you see,"
Black Martin said as they approached the chamber, "Are you
sure you can stand it?"

"I will not believe what my own eyes do not confirm,"
retorted Phyllis, "There are evil men about, and not just in
the woods." She shot him a penetrating glance as she said
this, but Martin did not flinch or betray any emotion.

"As you will, Ma'am," he replied, opening the door. Phyllis walked slowly towards the pallet upon which lay her parents and two sisters. She stood in the middle of the room and slowly turned her head from one end of the line of bodies to the other.

Martin watched closely for a sign, a twitch or gesture presaging sudden breakdown. He was amazed. Apart from a slight movement of her fingers tightening their grip on the front of her dress, and a deepening of her frown, Phyllis stood impassive.

"Uncover their faces!" The barking of that sudden order made Martin himself start. "Uncover them, I say. I will see the worst these fiends have wreaked upon my kin. Do it, now." She turned on him and glared with Martin could only take to be a naked hatred.

"As you wish." He lifted the cloth covering Sir William's head. Under it a layer of bandaging held together what remained of his face.

"Go on."

" But Ma'am, this is enough, surely," pleaded Martin, "You don't know what a mess…"

"If you don't, I will." She stood erect, quivering with rage.

Martin carefully unwrapped the damp parcel that had been Sir William's head, and as he did so, it collapsed further and only the gaping shattered remains of his jaw protruded from the bloody pulp.

Phyllis gasped and clutched her throat. "My God, they did this?" She trembled and an awful groan issued from her throat, her skirts billowing outward like a cloud of dust as she suddenly collapsed backwards. Her head hit the floor with a hard dull thud, and her skirts gently settled around her.

"Hell's teeth," growled Black Martin, as he rushed over to her prone form, lifting her head and shoulders and cradling them in his arms. "I hope to God she hasn't killed herself with her curiosity. Sir Gabriel will go mad." Loudly, he shouted: "In here! Her ladyship's collapsed! Hurry!"

The ladies of her chamber came bustling in, all flustered and chattering. "Silence! Just help me put her on a litter and fetch smelling salts and water!"

They laid her down and Martin splashed her with cold water while feeling the back of her skull. "At least she hasn't cracked her skull. Now, wake up, Milady!"

He wafted a powerful nosegay under her nose until she started to quiver and stir. Eventually she opened her eyes, and as she recollected herself she began to weep. Her ladies comforted her as Martin rose, walked over to Sir William, and re-covered his visage. "Ma'am, I am sorry, but I could not do other than obey your instruction."

Phyllis slowly gathered her composure and quietly asked: "And the others, Amelia, Kate, my mother, what of them?'

"Your mother, Ma'am, was shot in the chest, but young Kate and Phyllis are much as Sir William is in his wounds. I beg you to look no further, for your own sake." Martin looked her in the eye with as much honest concern as he could muster, and it passed, for she subsided and acquiesced to his request, saying, merely, "Enough, let them rest."

40

The wagoner

As the first birds began to twitter, before even the eastern sky grew light, Robin stirred and looked around. For a moment he was confused, until he remembered where they were.

"Kate, wake up. We've got to move quickly, before someone comes along." He shook Kate until she lifted her head from his lap.

"What's happening? Where are we?" She blinked several times, trying to see his face more clearly in this almost-night. "It's still dark, why must we get up?"

"Because we... Move! I can hear a wagon coming." He grabbed her roughly, hauled her to her feet, dragged her into the hedgerow on one side of the track and flung her down behind it, flopping down beside her and covering her mouth.

The sound of horses' hooves clopping and of wheels creaking grew louder. They could hear a man's voice, first chattering then humming to himself as the wagon drew closer. Robin peered through the hedge. It was an open cart, piled high with hay, and a solitary man, cloaked like them, was talking away to himself as if keeping himself company.

"Naw, that's not right. You got that wrong, Tom Nouf, you did. It don't go like that at all, it don't, " he said.

"So, how do it go then, you old fool, if not like that, then?" said he, answering.

"It were more like this," replied he. And Tom Nouf began to whistle tunelessly ditty that vaguely resembled the humming before.

"That were nothin' like it," cried Tom indignantly. "Mine were better, mine were. Yours is like a bleedin' cat's meowl."

"And yours is a cow in labour, more like," retorted Tom. He rolled his head back and laughed.

"Truth is, neither of you'll ever earn a piece of pie, singing or whistling."

"Who's that?"

Up jumped Robin from the hedge and sauntered over to the front of the wagon, which Tom Nouf had pulled up in his surprise. "Can't a man argue with his self in peace of a morning without some scamp interrupting?" he shouted down. "Who are you?"

"I'm by-and-by," said Robin, calmly taking the horse's rein, "and you're in my road."

"I'm not in your road, you little scallywag," said Tom Nouf, "so you just be gettin' out of my road."

"What road is this then?" replied Robin. "A main road? No. A highway? No. A bye-way? Yes. And Who am I? By-and-by. So it's my way – bye-way – see?"

Kate had crept through the bush until she could see both Robin and the carter as they exchanged banter in the growing light.

"I don't know about no bye-way belonging to nobody hereabouts, seein' as it stretches from Horseworth, across these here Downs, all the way to Glattin' Harbour what lies right down there yonder. But you got lies coming out o' your tongue-wag longer than that that road itself!" Tom Nouf chuckled, "What's your name, boy? And how come you're out here in this wilderness at this robbers' hour without a gun or knife, eh?"

"I say, I'll tell you, by-and-by," said Robin, "Take it or leave it."

"Done! I like a man who keeps close till he knows what's what and who to trust. I'll wager I'll like you, by-an'-by. Hop up." Tom Nouf roared with laughter at his wit and held out a hand. "You'll do for company, anyways. I've had enough o' Nouf's company for one night."

"Wait Tom, I've got a friend, here. Come out, Elfling!" Robin said this so loud Kate jumped. As she clambered out, she saw Robin put his finger to his lips and frown hard at her. She guessed he meant her not to tell her name, as he had done.

"Well, well, well," said Tom Nouf, "a pretty party we've got here. What you called, little one?"

"An elf," said Kate, looking up at the hooded man.

"An Elf? Well, I'm a Nouf! Tom Nouf. So I guess that'll do just fine," said Tom Nouf, winking as he leaned down to pull her up onto the bench beside him. "Up you come, too, master By-an'-by, an' we'll be takin' our leave o' this place. I got a long way ahead."

"Where are you going?" asked Robin.

"Carslake Manor, not far from Glattin' Harbour," he replied, "and you?"

"Littleduncton, by the sea," said Robin, jabbing Kate in the ribs as she started. "We're going to my grandma's there."

"Littleduncton's a long ways off, it is," said old Tom, "but Glattin' Harbour's on the right road. So if you don't mind listenin' to my banter for a while, I'll get you there, by-and-by."

"I'm hungry," said Kate suddenly. She had smelt the yeasty smell of bread wafting from the bag at her feet.

"Really?" said Tom Nouf, giving her a sideways glance, "I thought elves never went hungry, what with their magic bread and such."

"Some do," began Kate.

"Especially on Fridays," interrupted Robin, "because Thursdays are fast-days for elves. So by Friday morning they're really hungry, because they mustn't eat till the first rays of the sun come over the hill, like now, look!"

Just then, sure enough, the first rays peeped over and bathed them in yellow, like buttercups under the chin.

"Well I never," said Old Tom, "you're never too old to learn somethin' new. For what do they fast on Thursdays, then?"

"So they've got more room on Fridays," said Robin, as if it were the most natural thing to say.

"For a fry-up, you mean, " laughed Tom Nouf, "talkin' of which, I haven't eaten since sundown. We'll stop, now the sun's up and it's a getting' warmer, and set ourselves a little fry. What do you say to that, then, eh?"

"Yes, yes," they cried in unison.

"Right-o, then. Reckon we'll pull over there, up agin' them trees in that patch of sun."

The carter stopped by a patch of long grass to feed the horse and Kate and Robin leaped off. "Here, take these, an' I'll get me old pan of grease out" Old Tom passed down his satchel and reached down between his legs and pulled out a large flat skillet and handed it carefully to Robin.

Jumping off the wagon, Tom Nouf, went round the back and returned with an armful of twigs, logs of various thicknesses and some bark tinder. He skilfully stacked these and lit the tinder with a flint. Soon the flames rose through the little pyramid.

He grabbed a strange metal contraption with a square grille with four rods attached at the corners. These he jammed into the earth so that the grille sat over the flames. " Good, eh? " he said, grinning, "Me own invention that. Right we'll put my pan on that to heat. Here, elfish, you cop these eggs carefully, and you, By-an'-by, cop these rashers. I'll pop me mushrooms on first, then you put in me bacon. While they're fryin', by-an'-by, stick these slices of bread on these skewers here and hold 'em up to the flames."

Within minutes the smell of bacon and mushrooms and singeing toast filled the air: "It's time to crack eggs!" announced Tom, and he took them from Kate, one each, and cracked them on the edge of the pan with one hand and dropped them in without breaking the great golden yolks."

"Wow! They're the biggest, reddest yolks I've ever seen," cried Kate.

"And the tastiest, I'll warrant," said Old Tom, "They're from my brother's farm down in Glattin'."

"Oh," exclaimed Kate, looking alarmed. "You mean you're from Glatting Harbour?"

"And why not?" asked Tom Nouf. "Got to be from somewhere and that's as good as any, I reckon."

"Oh, yes, yes, " said Robin, "What's it like there? This Glatting place?"

"Good enough for some of us what likes water. Here, take this," replied Tom Nouf handing out two dishes with egg, bacon and mushrooms. "Give the littl'un a piece of that toast and get cracking, then."

"But there's no knife and fork..." started Kate, "Ow!"

"Sorry," said Robin, frowning hard at her. "Just do as I do," he whispered.

Kate watched as Robin squashed his egg onto the toast so that the yolk soaked into it, then put his two mushrooms on one side and the bacon on top and folded it over into a sandwich and, grasping it in both hands, rammed the end of it into his mouth.

"Oh," Kate followed suit as best she could. Her yolk burst and spilled onto the platter and as she folded the toast over a mushroom slid out and landed in the yolk.

"What a mess, miss, and no mistake!" laughed old Tom Nouf. "You'd think you'd never eaten food before."

"In fairyland," cut in Robin quickly, "where we come from, we don't eat like this. We eat like Royalty – with a knife and a fork – don't we, little Elf?"

"Yes, and with plates and spoons and cups and everything, in Fairyland," added Kate.

"You should come and visit sometime, Tom," said Robin, "good folks are always welcome."

"I wouldn't know the way," said old Tom. "Is it North, South, East or West of here, this Fairyland of yours."

"Yes!" said Robin and Kate together. They looked at each other and laughed.

"Well I guess it must be then," said Tom smiling, "If you both says so. But how do you get there?"

"That's a secret, " said Robin. "Which I'll tell you if you can get us to Glatting safely."

"Deal," said, Tom, "now shake on it. And no fooling, mind. I always wanted to pay my respects to the Queen o' Faerie. She must be beautiful, is she?"

"Oh yes," replied Kate, "beautifuller than the sunset and the sunrise and the moon altogether."

"That's beautiful enough for me. I'm goin', definite." With that Tom Nouf gave himself over to the feed, stuffing his cheeks till he looked like a toad, finally wiping the platter clean with the toast. He paused looking up at the sky.

"Time to move on," said Tom, getting up and smothering the fire. "You put them platters and vittles back the bag, boy. I'll tidy up around here."

As they came round the wagon, Robin suddenly dashed over to the base of a tree and bent over. He turned and Kate saw a red flash for a second as he slipped something under his cloak.

"What's that?" asked Kate.

"Shh. You'll see, soon enough," Robin pushed her up onto the seat ahead of him.

Soon they were back on the main track meandering down the slope towards the river valley and the sea.

"You never told us," said Robin, "about Glatting, I mean."

"What was I sayin'? Oh yes. Then again, if you don't like

water, I can't think of a worse place. On the edge of the great marshes and full of reeds it is. And in the flood time it gets cut right off, except by boat, it does."

"Sounds nice. Do you think you could take us there, after you go to the manor? I think we'd like to have a look at it, on our way, of course." Robin was trying to think of a way of asking without arousing suspicion.

"I suppose. But what about your grandma in Littleduncton? Won't she be expecting you?"

"Oh, she won't mind. She expects us when she sees us. She's not our real grandma. She's a wise-woman. That's why we go. We take her messages from the Queen of Fairyland." As Robin wove his tale, Kate looked at him in awe. "We may seem like children to you, Tom," he added, "but we're quite grown up, you know. Only Kings and Queens grow taller."

"Really? Well I never," said Tom Nouf, stroking his chin. "Bein' elves an' all I suppose you could disappear in a trice if need be, eh?"

"Well, yes..." began Robin.

"Cos I reckon now'd be a good time for it," continued old Tom casually.

"Why?" asked Kate.

"Cos there's a rider comin' up behind us and he's comin' fast. Either he's bein' pursued or he's the one doin' the pursuing, as if he was lookin' for something, or someone."

"Where? I can't see anyone," said Robin.

"I heard him first, then I saw him as we went over that last ridge. He was just cresting the ridge behind, so I reckon he'll be in sight in a minute or so." Tom Nouf turned to them as he pulled up the wagon. "Now hop it, quick, into them bushes yonder, and don't come out till I whistle, see. Git!"

Frightened by his urgency, Robin and Kate leaped up and scrambled up the short bank and into the hedgerow. They turned to see the carter start his wagon and creak slowly away down the road.

"Why'd he get rid of us, just like that?" asked Kate, "just as we were getting to be friends." She started to sniffle.

"Quiet!' whispered Robin, "someone's coming."

A clatter of hooves was followed by the appearance of a dark figure on a horse over the horizon and within a minute he was upon them, thundering past, cloak flying.

The horseman drew up beside the wagon and Kate heard a shout. The cart stopped. She could hear voices. One urgent, one drawling. Then the horseman leaped off his mount and walked slowly round the cart. He drew something and started poking into the hay-bales.

"He's stabbing the bales, " whispered Robin, "trying to find us. I recognised his cape. It's Black Martin. White Whiskey John must have sent him after us."

"Why? No one knows we're here, do they?"

"Maybe someone saw two children coming this way and he's following their trail. I don't know."

The horseman and carter exchanged a few more words and then the horseman remounted and galloped on.

The wagon didn't move. There was no sound from Tom Nouf for what seemed an eternity to Kate. "Why isn't he calling us, like he said?"

"He's waiting, like us, for the horseman, Black Martin to get well out of earshot. Don't worry, he'll whistle soon."

They waited and waited. Kate could hear the buzz of insects close by, the twittering of birds, even the rustle of leaves and the swish of the long grasses in the warm breeze. Down the track the air was shimmering on the horizon over which the horseman came come. It was getting hot.

Suddenly she heard the singing of a skylark high overhead. "Look, look, a lark," she cried, "I can see it, can't you?"

"Yes, yes," muttered Robin, intently only on hearing Tom Nouf's whistle.

Just then it came. Three soft trills followed by a pause and then another three.

"That's it! Let's go," cried Robin, dragging Kate out of the hedgerow. "Come on, run!" he cried as he scampered ahead.

Kate ran as fast as she could. It seemed a long way to the wagon when running in the heat, and when she reached it, panting, Robin was already up on the bench with old Tom, chattering away. He turned and pulled her up and old Tom started the cart creaking on its way once again.

"It's lucky for you that you two are elves," laughed Tom, "cos that there man was huntin' for two children just about your description. Says they were scivvies, absconded in the night. Offered a reward for them, he did. Two groats apiece. Useful monies, eh?"

Tom smiled down at them, "but never you mind. I didn't like the look on his face. So I kept me peace and let him search me wagon. He poked here and there with his sword till he was satisfied and left."

"Thank you, mister Tom," said Robin, "you saved our bacon."

"And you ate mine!" Tom chuckled. "So I reckoned I wasn't goin' to give mine away to easy. Now listen. I don't need to know your names or where you're truly from. I can see that man means no good by them two children he's after, so I'll keep you safe, by-an'-by. And the safest place for you now is inside that pile of hay. He's been right through it so if we meet him again he won't think to look in there. In you go now."

"Thank you, Tom," said Robin, "and we are going to Glatting Harbour too."

The two children climbed back and crawled into the hay, making a den in the centre.

"I knew you were goin' there," replied Tom, "you're not too good at your lies, yet. I could see by the way the elf's eyes lit up when I said the name that she recognised it. Now, just you two keep quiet as mice and we'll steer clear o' trouble, if we come across that man again. Right?"

41

Glatting Harbour

The sun was up high in the sky when old Tom Nouf and his load grumbled into the high street of Glatting Harbour.

"Here we are then, Glattin' Harbour!" Tom cried aloud. Several people in the street looked round to see who had shouted.

"Talkin' to yourself were ye?" asked one old crone. Kate could see her silhouette bent almost double, leaning on a long stick. "First sign, you know."

"I know, I know," replied old Tom, "and how are you Sal?"

"Mother Pickersaille to you, young Tom," snapped the crone.

"Well then, how are you and all your little ones, and their little ones, and…"

"That's enough of your lip, Tom Nouf. I've done my share and I've a right to some respect from the likes of you carter-folk. All that talkin' to yourself ain't improved your manners none. Still, maybe you'll have someone new to blab all you tales to now. There's a stranger in the village, knockin' on doors."

"Stranger? What's he look like?" said Tom Nouf, his voice suddenly sounding serious.

"Why, got somethin' to hide have you? Been smugglin' again?" Sally Pickersaille laughed. "He's tallish. Couldn't see his face too well on account of his hood. Black cloak with a blue lining. Silk, most like. Big horse. Roan, with a white flash. Man walks as if he were floating across the ground, graceful, like."

"That's him. That's the man passed me way back there. Stopped me and poked about me wagon with his sword. Says he was lookin' for two runaway kids."

"That's the man." Sally Pickersaille came closer to the cart and said in a confidential tone. "Offering a reward, he is. Two groats for each of 'em. Tide me over a winter, that would."

"You wouldn't do that, now, would you Sally Pickersaille? Turn one of us over to them. You'd be driven out of the village and then where's your winter, eh?" Tom Nouf's voice sounded threatening.

"No, no. Of course I wouldn't," Sally Pickersaille said quickly, "I were only supposing…"

"Supposing what?" A familiar sing-song voice from beside the wagon made old Tom jump in his seat, creaking the wagon.

"Supposing what we could buy with your four groats if we found your two runaways, that's what." His voice was defiant, challenging even. "Not a lot. What's your best offer, Mister…"

"Black Martin, and if you brought me news of them both, all tucked up safe and sound, I could go to a shilling."

Kate squirmed. Was old Tom going to sell them for a shilling? Didn't he know who she was? Of course not. But a shilling! Robin could see her fretting and put his hand on her shoulder and his finger to his lip. She quietened down.

"In that case, master Martin, we'll keep a weather eye out for 'em, won't we mistress Pickersaille?"

"That we will. But what makes you think they've run this way?" asked Sally Pickersaille. "This here's a dead-end. Nowhere to go but water. So they'd have to come to us for a boat, wouldn't they? An' then we'd have 'em!"

263

"Good, good. If you capture them, hold onto them and send me a message. Addressed to me only, mind, at the Bell Weather in Yarnfold. And don't tell them anything but this: 'Black Martin is needed urgently at the Cat's Paw.' That'll tell me without giving away where or what. You understand? You deliver me this and you'll get your shilling, maybe more. Oh, and a warning: I'll kill any man or woman found sheltering them."

Black Martin glided past them like a ghost and on down the street to the inn where his horse was tethered. He mounted and cantered back, past the pair by the wagon, "Don't forget, now," his voice tailed away in the wind as he spurred his horse into a gallop.

"Well, well, well," sighed mistress Pickersaille, "that's a man in a hurry for somethin', and no mistake. And don't you worry, Old Tom, your secret's safe enough with me."

"Secret? I ain't got not secret, ma Pickersaille. We were just supposin', weren't we?"

"We were, we were," she winked. "Get along with you, now."

"Yes, mother. I don't suppose you'll be needin' any nice fresh straw for your bed, then, eh?" Tom geed the horse and it plodded on.

"Just you mind you bring it round, same as always, cheeky Tom," the old woman called after him as the wagon crept down the road.

"You can come out now," Tom called back, "we're all friends here."

Kate and Robin crawled out and sat beside him. Kate rubbed her shins and Robin kicked his legs up and down, drumming on the foot-board. They smiled at each other and Kate put her hand on old Tom's.

"Thank you, Tom," said Robin, "We'll remember you to the Queen of Fairyland when we get there. She'll give you a reward I'll warrant."

"Hold your horses," said Tom Nouf, as he pulled the cart up and turned it into an alley beside the inn. He jumped down and secured the horse to a post beside a water trough. The horse immediately stooped its head to drink.

"A promise is a promise, ain't it?" he asked, laughing, as he fetched a nose-bag full of hay and drew it over the horse's head, once it had finished drinking. "And you made a promise, and no mistake."

"A promise, did we? What promise was that?" asked Robin.

Kate nudged him: "You know, the one about taking him to Fairyland."

"Oh, that promise." Robin thought for a minute, then said, "Is there a old birch tree hereabouts?"

"Yes, but what'd you want with that?" Old Tom looked puzzled.

"Take us there," said Robin. Kate looked at him. He winked. "And we'll need a cloth too."

Old Tom Nouf led the way as they crossed the village street and walked down another alley at the end of which, close to the water, stood an ancient birch, its bark white mottled with greeny grey, its leaves pale green, rustling serenely in the breeze.

Beyond it, a narrow stretch of open water glistened. Tall reeds filled the horizon as far as they could see beyond that. "Is that where?" began Kate.

"Not now," interrupted Robin, "now we've got to take Tom to Fairyland, right Tom?"

"Er, right," said Tom. He looked around nervously. "Are you serious? I thought it was a game we was playin', back there."

"A game? No, Tom Nouf," said Robin gravely, "Fairyland's no game. Now you just open your mouth and bite on this."

He held out the red thing Kate had seen him pick up. It was a red and white spotted mushroom.

"I... I don't know. Them mushroom's poisonous, ain't they?" stuttered Tom.

"Only for them who're not meant to eat them," said Robin. "They get their just deserts for trying to enter unbidden. They get nightmares and tummy cramps, and serve them right. Now you just follow my instructions to the letter and we'll get you there."

He broke a piece off the mushroom and put it between Tom's lips. "Don't bite, now. Or chew. You mustn't swallow. If you swallow, you won't come back."

Tom Nouf's eyes started and he nearly dropped the piece as his lips quivered. "I'm not sure as I want to go, right now, " he blurted, "later, perhaps."

"Nonsense. Now, I'm putting a blindfold on you, so that you can't see the way. No mortal can know the where the gates of Fairy lie. Now then, that's it." He took Tom's hand and sat him against the tree. "Can you see?"

"I can't see nothin', " replied Tom.

"Now, we've all got to sit quiet and count to fifty, in our heads," said Robin.

"Mmmm" said Tom. "Mmmm!"

Robin took his bandage off, and the piece out his mouth. "What is it? You've got to keep quite silent."

"But I can't count, not beyond ten," moaned old Tom.

"Is that all?" scolded Robin, jamming the piece back between his lips and tying the blindfold tight again. "Just count to ten, again and again, till you get there. Don't worry, you'll know you've got there because suddenly you'll be able to see again, in spite of the blindfold. And don't forget to call the Queen of Fairyland, 'Your Majesty' or she'll send you straight back with no reward."

"Mmnn," old Tom Nouf mumbled gently.

"Right, off we go!" Robin took Kate's hand and held his finger over his mouth and led her tiptoeing away across the grass towards the village. Looking back they could see old

Tom's head nodding slowly as he counted, paused, then counted again.

They rounded the corner, crept up the alley into the high street and then ran and skipped and danced, laughing, all the way to Robin's grandmother, old Skitty Bilcock, who lived in the very last cottage in the street where it met the river's edge.

"Do you think he's alright?" asked Kate as she put the first scone to her mouth.

Skitty Bilcock had made scones with strawberry jam in honour of Robin's arrival, unexpected though it was. She had also brought out an old cake, "I was saving this for my birthday, but this better than that, so here we go," she had said as she cut it into huge wedges.

"Who?" asked grandma Bilcock.

"Er, old Tom Nouf," said Robin, turning pink, "we, er, played a trick on him."

"You did, you mean," said Kate, "and I think it was mean. Blindfolding him, and leaving him like that, after all he did for us."

"What? Blindfolded? Old Tom? Where" grandma sounded alarmed.

"Down by the river near the old birch tree," admitted Robin.

"With a mushroom in his mouth," added Kate. "What if he ate it, Robin, what them?"

"What do mean, a mushroom? What sort of mushroom?" She looked hard at Robin.

"The red sort, with white spots on," said Robin, "only a bit of one, and I told him not to chew or swallow it."

"That's cruel. Get down from this table at once young Robin," Granma Bilcock clipped him round the ear with a resounding crack, "and go and fetch him here. He might be poisoned."

Robin jumped down and ran out of the house, holding

his red ear. He ran all the way to the tree, thinking old Tom might be lying on the ground, foaming at the mouth, if he had forgotten not to chew.

Old Tom Nouf was still sitting, nodding his head slowly as Robin rounded the bend.

"Phew! Old Tom! Old Tom! Don't chew! I'm coming. I'm sorry." He undid the bandage and pulled the mushroom piece out of old Tom's mouth as he blinked repeatedly as if dazed.

"Where am I? Are we there then?" He looked around. "It don't seem no different. Where's the Queen?"

"There isn't no Queen. There isn't no Fairyland. It was all a joke," said Robin. "I'm sorry, I'm sorry old Tom. I should never have done it. Come to tea with grandma Bilcock. We've got scones and jam, and cake, lots of cake, fruit cake!" he shouted.

"Grandma Bilcock? Skitty Bilcock, you mean? She's your granma? Well I never. Take me there. Cake? Fruit cake? Grandma Bilcock's cakes are famous, from one end of the High Street t'other!" Tom Nouf laughed, seeing the expression of pure surprise on Robin's face. "Take me there quick, boy, before it all gets eaten."

"This takes some beatin', this does." Old Tom Nouf wiped his mouth with the back of his sleeve. "I'd exchange a slice of your cake for a day in Fairyland any day of the week, Skitty Bilcock, me dear."

"You're too kind, Tom Nouf, and that's a fact," grandma Bilcock beamed around the room.

"Except Fridays!" added Tom Nouf, winking at the two children.

"Fridays? Why Fridays?" asked Skitty Bilcock.

"We know, don't we?" he said. "You'll tell her, by-and-by, won't you?" He looked at Robin.

"I want to know now," said Skitty, putting her fists on her hips and staring at Robin, "What's all this by-and-by business? Tell me now."

"Well, it like this…" began Robin, and he told Skitty Bilcock the whole story of their meeting up on the track and pretending to be elves and of the man chasing them and their promise to reward old Tom.

"Well, eat my biscuits!" exclaimed Skitty as he finished, "What a yarn!"

"Nor have you told me your true names, yet, neither of you." said old Tom. "I think I earned that now, don't you?"

"Of course," said Robin, "I'm Robin, Robin Ruddock. And this is… Kate. Kate… I can't tell you her other name, on account of…"

"I think I understand, boy," said Tom Nouf, "on account of that man what was chasin' after you, eh? Best left out, I reckon. Less known, less to tell when time comes. And it will come, young Robin, young Kate, it will come that he will return to this village, cos trustin' people to keep a secret is like a havin' a sieve for keeping water in. And then what? I reckon I knows as much as I wants to know on this matter. I'm just glad I was there to help you, that's all."

"Thank you, mister Tom, thank you," said Kate, "we'll never forget you."

"Best be gettin' off now. Got my horse t'attend to afore I have a drink at the inn."

"Mind you don't get drunk, Old Tom," said Skitty, "we don't want you loose-tonguing your day's adventures in there now, do we?"

"Don't worry Skitty, I'm mum. Bye Kate, bye Robin, till we meet again."

"Bye Old Tom," they chorused as he slammed the door behind him.

42

The meeting house

At the gathering of family elders that night in Took's barn, Robin and Kate were tucked away in the hayloft, out of sight of the assembled folk.

"That's old Bumble Clabitter, my great uncle and with him Jill Blitter, on old Tom's right. Bumble's the head of the clan here. Everybody does what he tells them. Jill's not often to be seen here, I told you. And that's Collier Jack over there on Tom's left, and that's Red Took, beside him. And Sally Pickersaille you know already is there with our Skitty."

Kate giggled, "You're right, Collier Jack and Red Took are a funny pair. Was it Jill Blitter you said we would stay with? She looks nice; nice and quiet."

"Yes, if we go to hers we will be as safe as can be, especially with Bumble watching over us. No one will ever find us there. And if they do, there aren't many who can fight our boys in the reed beds and come out alive. Listen!"

The meeting had begun. Tom Nouf spoke first: "I brought 'em 'ere safe, and I met that Black Martin twice. He don't mince words and he don't take no nonsense. His threat's no mean threat. He'd run you through soon as look at you, if you stood in his way."

"So what're we goin' to do with them?" It was Red Took. "We can't keep them in the village. Not everyone here's to be trusted, outside of our family, I mean. And there's outlanders, passin' through. They might tell if they saw them runnin' around the village."

"No, we got to send 'em away," added Collier Jack, "leastways, out of sight of the curious."

"He's right," said Skitty Bilcock, "I'd love to have 'em here at mine, but it's too dangerous. Word would soon get back to that Martin Black."

"Black Martin," corrected old Bumble Clabitter. "Our question's been answered…"

He paused. "Answered?" chorused the gathering.

"Yup. By young Robin Ruddock himself. He said to me, he said, 'why don't we go stay with Jill Blitter out in them marshes. Nobody knows where she lives, on account of she keeps moving house, hither and thither, " he says. And I agree. Jill's the gal, ain't you Jill?"

All eyes looked at Jill. "Well I don't know," she started, "I'm not used to company, and my house is…"

"Neither here nor there!" interrupted Tom Nouf. Laughter burst out around the assembly, Tom's loudest.

"He likes jokes," whispered Robin, "and his own best of all."

"…too small." Jill firmly finished her sentence.

"Well, build it bigger, then. You build two or three a year anyways," said Red Took.

"And we'll give you a hand," added Collier Jack.

"And we'll all give a share of the food," said Bumble Clabitter, "won't we?"

There was silence for a moment. "Nobody's given a thought to feeding us, not from their own larders," chuckled Robin to Kate.

"You mean, they won't?" Kate's eyes widened.

"Don't worry, old Bumble will see to it they do, and anyway there's lots of fish and fowl out there."

Kate rubbed her tummy, "I like fish."

"And slithery eels and slimy snails and frogs and toads

271

too," added Robin, eyeing Kate, "but you'll get used to them."

"Urgh! I couldn't eat them," Kate squirmed. "Never."

"And crickets and grasshoppers, fried to a crisp, and beetles boiled till they burst – pop! All over you." Robin was enjoying this.

Kate looked at him and scowled, "I'm not going."

"Only joking, silly girl," he said.

"Elf," she retorted.

"Elf, then. Peace?"

By now the meeting had agreed that all present should contribute a share towards Jill Blitter's keep, as long as she cared for them. After the others had dispersed, only Tom Nouf remained with Jill Blitter and old Bumble Clabitter.

"You can come down, now," called Bumble. "I only wanted you out of sight in case some nosey poked into our meeting. You follow Jill now. She'll look after you."

"Thank you, Jill," they both said together, "we won't be any bother."

"I'll decide that, young 'uns, once I've had you around for a bit," said Jill, as she marched along the back of the houses, to avoid the high street, towards her boat.

"Either of you punt?" she asked as they clambered on board the flat-bottomed boat. "No? You will, soon enough."

She pushed the punt off, leaped lightly aboard as it slipped from the shore and poled away into the darkness.

The punt glided across the open water towards the reed-beds, with only the plopping of her pole to betray them. Jill's boat had a pointed bow that sliced through the reeds. bending them aside so that they swung back after they had passed, leaving no trail of flattened reeds to mark their passage.

Soon they arrived at her thatched 'cottage'. It was no higher than the reeds, which stood six feet tall, and floated on a raft of logs and twine, anchored to the marsh-bed by eight long posts thrust deep into the mud and tied at their tops to the structure of the house. The doorway was arched, with a rude wattled door attached to one side.

Inside there was a hole in the roof in the centre of the only room, with a flat stone hearth directly below it. Straddling this was a pair of tripods holding a spit-iron with kettle-hooks hanging from it. There were pots and pans and dishes and cups hanging or shelved along one wall over a large trunk. On the other three sides were rugs and a large furry skin at the end furthest from the door.

As Kate and Robin took all this in, Jill went outside and returned with an armful of reed-stems. "Lift up them rugs on the right," she ordered and, as they did so, released the bundle so that it rolled out across that side, providing a slight platform.

"Lay the rug on it, dears," she said. "That's your bed."

"Both of us?" asked Kate in surprise.

"Of Course. How big d'you think you are?"

"It'll be fine," Robin chipped in, "It'll be great, won't it Kate?"

Kate nodded.

Kate nudged Robin in the back. He grunted and rolled onto his back and then started to snore. She nudged him in the side, harder.

"Ugh!" Robin awoke. "What is it?"

"You're snoring," whispered Kate, "and you're squashing me into the wall."

"Sorry." Robin rolled back onto his side, facing the centre of the room.

"Robin?"

"Yes, what now?"

"I can see the moon... through the smoke hole," started Kate.

"Good, now go to sleep."

"But the moon's wide awake, looking down on us," she

said. "Do you think it is looking down on Amelia too, wherever she is?"

"Yes, probably."

"And she might be looking up at the moon, just like us."

"Just like you. I'm not looking," growled Robin.

There was no answer from Kate and Robin settled down to concentrate on going to sleep. Then a small mouse-like snuffling crept across the covers and settled into the back of his neck, breathing hot on his skin.

"Oh, I'm sorry," he turned over and crooked his arm around Kate's shoulders as they, as if in response to his gesture, started to shake.

After a while her sobbing ceased and she whispered, "They're all dead aren't they?"

"All except Amelia," he said, "we saw her, didn't we, being carried off."

"And I'm going to find her, however long it takes," Kate whispered, "I promised the moon, so every time she shines down on us she will remind me of my promise."

"I know, but for now we have to hide and keep quiet and be very very careful that we are not found out. Or you won't get the chance to find her later."

43

Black Martin

Black Martin clattered into the gold-cobbled courtyard of Fugglesham as the last rays of the sun were beaten back by the advancing shadows of the low West wall, and threw his reins to Whiskey John's boy, Joe Ben, muttering, "Bed him down for the night."

He followed the boy as he led the horse through the first arch towards the stable court and turned right under the arch and opened the door that led to Whiskey John's office.

"Well?" Whiskey John's curt greeting with it's implied lack of respect irritated Black Martin intensely. He was beginning to see through this ruthless and wily opportunist and thought to himself, I can play a longer game than you Master John.

"Nothing." Black Martin's equally curt and uninformative answer irritated Whiskey John just as much, Black Martin could see. He paused to refresh himself from a jug by the window before continuing: "I followed a trail – false, as it happens – all the way across the Downs and over as far a hamlet in the marshes called Glatting Harbour.

A shepherd swore he had seen two fairies dancing up on the Downs in the moonlight, near the dewpond, so I thought his fairies might have been young Kate and a companion. I followed that route, meeting a waggoner who had seen nothing and on down to the Harbour, where I let it be known there is a reward, not too handsome lest someone get suspicious, for two runaway servant children, and a severe punishment for anyone harbouring them.

The villagers seemed quite keen to claim it, so I told them, if they did find them, to hold onto them and leave me a message at the Bell Weather in Yarnfold."

"A message? Won't that give the game away?" Whiskey John stood up suddenly, knocking his stool back with a clatter. "Sir Gabriel must not find out, or we'll have double trouble, looking after her as well. I want her dead."

"Don't worry, the message I instructed them to leave, reads, 'Black Martin is needed urgently at the Cat's Paw.' That doesn't tell anyone anything, now, does it?"

"Well done, master Martin, you have a spark of wit about you, after all." Whiskey John clapped Black Martin a friendly blow across the shoulder, jerking him across the room.

"But we can't let it rest. You must keep searching. I can't trust anyone else with this mission, you understand?"

"Perfectly master John," echoed Martin, "but, now, I'm for bed."

For the next four days Black Martin searched, each day following a different route, each day giving the same coded message to those he met, each day getting no closer to the answer of whether Kate had survived and, if so, how and whither she had escaped.

He pieced together the patterns of her life before the massacre through the Linnece servant girl he had befriended earlier, learning of the peculiar intimacy she had enjoyed with a servant-boy who had, it seemed, acted as a companion and young guardian.

The suspicion gradually rose in his mind that should that boy have rescued Kate from the massacre, he appeared to have had the commonsense to know that her life would be in danger and possibly also the skill to lead her out of harm's way. But where?

44

Amelia Linnece

"It is time." White Whiskey John jerked Amelia up into standing position and, grabbing her leather belt, turned her to one side. He unlocked the belt and let it drop to her feet.

"Time for what? What are you going to do to me?" Amelia felt her waist through her dress. Her skin hurt, chafed by the heavy leather and the chain hanging from it. It felt so small, so familiar had the thickness of the belt become.

"You're being moved, come on," he grabbed her wrist and dragged her through the door of her woodland prison.

"Where to? Aagh! It's blinding," she shielded her eyes with her right hand as he, ignoring her protest, dragged her behind him towards a waiting wagon.

Black Martin stood beside it holding a cloth in his hands. As they approached he came behind her and looped it over her head, covering her mouth. Whiskey John held her steady as Martin tied it tightly. "There, that should keep her mum."

The pair bundled her into the back of the covered wagon and threw bales of straw over her till she could scarcely breathe and couldn't move. They closed the tarpaulin and tied it down.

She heard them move to the front of the wagon and clamber aboard. With a crack of a whip the wagon lurched forward and creaked its way along the rutted path. Each bump pressed the straw bales onto her chest till she thought she would choke.

Tipping this way and that, the wagon's wheels groaned and squelched along for a long time before their tone changed to a clattering which she took to mean they had at last left the forest and hit an open highway.

She guessed it must have been approaching nightfall, though she could see nothing under the heavy black fabric of the wagon's roof. Suddenly the wagon creaked to a halt, and she could hear the horses snorting for the first time.

"You wait here awhile, Martin," it was Whiskey John's voice. "I'll go and…"

"Are you there? Have you got her?" Another voice, further off. "Bring her out." It was Gabriel's! No wonder Whiskey John was so cocky when she had confronted him on that first day. He knew of course that Sir Gabriel was a party to it; had ordered it even. Who else? He must have killed Kate, Rosie and Sir William and all the villagers to kidnap her and inherit everything. But how could he keep her near him and not be discovered? Phyllis would find out, surely?

Suddenly the weights that pressed down on her were lifted and she was dragged out. It was still dark. It was night. Of course, she was being secreted somewhere at dead of night. Three shadowy figures flitted about her, brushing her down.

Suddenly she found herself crushed in an embrace. "My love, my love, never shall… Aagh!"

Her knee jerked up and impacted with something soft. The embrace was released and the figure crumpled to the ground and writhed around in a compact ball.

"Ha, she's got spirit, your wench, that I'll grant." It was Black Martin's sing-song voice chuckling.

"Aaah, aah… get her… inside," Sir Gabriel's gasping command was followed by a shove in the back and two hands gripping her forearms as Whiskey John steered her roughly towards a dark recess in the wall ahead.

Amelia was pushed into it, up a narrow spiral stone

278

staircase and through a doorway into a vast cavern lit only by high lanceolate windows through the upper panes of which filtered a weak moonless light.

A clanking following up the stairs behind, told Amelia they meant to bind her here, too. She struggled vainly to be free from John's grip as he steered her across a large hall and through a small door at the further end.

Amelia was held as Black Martin buckled the belt about her waist, clicked the lock shut and clattered the chain as he played it out across the room to a ring in the wall.

So it begins again, she thought, but where now? In Fugglesham Hall? But if so, where? Where could be secure from discovery by her sister, Phyllis, or some servant?

As she sat down on the edge of this new bed beside which they had placed her, she thought, at least there is no sign of Sir Gabriel. I must have hurt him well. I wonder how he will explain it to Phyllis?

Amelia lay back on the bed, feeling a trickle of satisfaction run along her spine at the thought of his agony, oblivious to the movements of the two men around her bed as they performed their duties and then let her alone. She smiled for the first time since that evil day.

45

Kate Linnece

"Wake up, wake up!" Kate shook Robin, who just rolled over to face the wall, grumbling. "She's gone! Jill Blitter's gone!" She jerked the blanket off Robin and stood up with it.

"Oi, give it back," growled Robin at first, turning back and half sitting, resting on his elbows, "Gone, you say?"

"Yes, there's no sign of her – or her boat," said Kate, "we're stuck here on this heap till she, or someone else, comes for us. Oh, what if Black Martin comes, while she's away? What if she's betrayed us?"

She gave a little squeak as the idea took hold. Black Martin swooping down on their little hideout and snatching them up and tying them, back to back, and poling to shore and throwing them up onto his huge horse and thundering away to hand them into the merciless clutches of hideous White Whisky John... Jill Blitter clacking her coins together...

"Don't be daft," Robin Ruddock grabbed her by the shoulders and gave her a firm shake, looking into her eyes, "Black Martin has no idea where we are. Jill's probably gone fishing for our breakfast. You'll see."

"Really? Do you think she'll catch a big one? Big enough for all of us?"

"Of course she will," Robin replied, "that's how she makes a living: fishing and reed-cutting."

Kate sat silent for a moment, then whispered, "Shh, shh..."

"What?"

"Shh… Can't you hear it? It's a boat, swishing. It must be her!" Kate leaped up and rushed outside.

"Stop," cried Robin. "Listen, hide over here, behind the hut… just in case."

The reeds parted and Jill Blitter's silhouette with its long nose could be seen clearly in the moonlight as her boat clunked into the log raft. "Come on out from there and give me a hand. I can see you eye-whites, all goggly in the moonlight. You'll have to hide better'n that."

They rushed round the side of the hut to where her boat lay. "Catch hold on that, will you, Kate, and loop it round the stay like I showed you. And you, Robin, take hold of these baskets."

The baskets were full of fish of all sizes and crabs and other wriggling squirming things. Kate shuddered.

"Where did you catch so much so quickly," asked Robin as he struggled to land one basket.

"Tidal nets, my dear," replied Jill, "the river here's tidal for miles and miles upstream, so we lay our fish-traps and wait for the river to fill'em. It's a powerful tide, and there's plenty of fish. You just need to know where to place the trap-mouth."

Robin and Kate both hauled the next basket onto Jill's raft. "We'll have a bite to eat, I reckon, before we get down to work."

She blew up the embers of her hearth till there was a good glow and skewered three smaller fish and hung them just over the glowing fire. She squatted next to the rod and turned it every now and again as the kettle hung next to them began to steam.

"Once we've done with eating I'll teach you how to gut 'em and slit 'em and salt em for hanging to smoke-dry over this fire while we go out in my punt and you'll learn all about trapping and fishing."

281

46

A cousin

Kate and Robin settled into their new life as marsh-dwellers, trapping fish to sell fresh or smoked, and helping with the annual reed harvest, undertaken by all the villagers under the instruction of old Bumble Clabitter, each winter when the weather was dry and the reeds at their hardest.

They moved house with Jill Blitter every year to take advantage of the shelter of the tallest reed-beds due for the next harvest, polling her clumsy raft along the channels till they reached a suitable entry-point; not too dense but not too open either.

Several times they got word of Black Martin returning, but no one gave them away and they began to feel at ease.

Then one hot summer's day as Kate and Robin were hanging fish up to dry in the sun on a small natural island in the reedbed, they heard Jill's whistling call, summoning them.

"That's odd," said Robin. "It's nowhere near suppertime. I wonder why she's calling us now?"

"I don't know, but it must be important," answered Kate, running to the small skiff old Red Took had fashioned for them, "Come on."

Robin leapt in and took the oars and the skiff leapt forward in short jerks as he pulled away into the channel that led to Jill's 'island'.

As they rounded a bend in the channel bringing the hut into

view, Kate, sitting in the stern looking forward, cried, "Look, there's a gathering. There's Jill and Old Bumble and Red Took and Skitty Bilcock and Tom Nouf and they're all chattering their heads off, it looks like. Something exciting must be happening, or going to…"

She broke off as the sound of their argument carried across the waters to her ears.

"Well, I don't know. Who is he, eh?" said Jill Blitter.

"Come outer nowhere, he did," added Skitty Bilcock.

"But he's right well-dressed," argued Red Took, "did you see them boots all shiny and right up to his thighs?"

"Don't mean nothing," replied Jill, "could be a 'postor. Posin' as such."

"As what?" shouted Kate, jumping from the skiff.

"Who?" said Robin, shipping his oars and stepping out, dragging the skiff up onto the raft. "Who's posing? Why did you call us, Auntie Jill?"

They all turned to the pair of children and stared for a moment as if the children had sprung, unsummoned, out of the blue.

"Oh, a stranger," said Bumble Clabitter, "at the inn. Came lookin' for you. Said he heard rumour of two young-uns hereabouts and wanted to know if you was Linnece-kin."

Kate's heart skipped. "Linnece-kin?"

"Yes. Said he is a cousin to your William Linnece and had heard tell of their terrible death and your rumoured escape and bein' pursued by Black Martin. That man came askin' over in Cockington where he lives, and he recognised him and put two and two together, so he said. Guessed them rumours must be true, so came a searchin' hisself."

"I don't reckon we should trust him," said Skitty, "he might be in league with Black Martin, tryin' ter throw us a wry 'un."

"But what about his bag 'o gold, then? What he said was for them two, to help 'em escape and set up far off out of harm's way with distant kin?" said Red Took.

"That gold were real enough. And he weren't trying to bribe us, neither. Not like Black Martin." Bumble Clabitter nodded sagely. "I reckon that does it for me. A wicked man would straightway try bribery, I reckon."

"Yes," agreed Jill Blitter. "You're probably right. So should we take them to him?"

"Hey, what about us?" interrupted Robin. "What if we don't want to go?"

"Don't reckon you got much choice in the matter, children," said Bumble. If this man's heard about you then it won't be long before idle gossip reaches Black Martin, too. You're safe here no more."

"No, you got ter go with this man," added Red Took, "or we're all in danger. We'll just have ter trust 'im."

"Tell yer what, I'll go with you, to keep an eye on you, like," said Tom Nouf, "an keep yer company too, eh?"

"Oh, yes, will you?" Kate and Robin chirped together. "We'd feel much safer if you came," added Kate, taking his hand. "Will you really come?"

"Course I will," he laughed. "I like a good long journey, especially when it cost me nothing."

"That's settled, then," said Bumble Clabitter. "But you Tom, go ahead with Tooky here to secure his agreement before we show him the young-uns."

With that the first boat set off back to Glatting Harbour while Kate Linnece and Robin Ruddock made their farewells to old Jill.

Tears in her eyes, Jill fetched into her old trunk and pulled out a gift for each of the children.

For Robin she had made a felt hunting hat, with a woven ring into which were set five beautifully feathered fish hooks "one fer each season, like I taught you, Robin. I was saving it for yer birthday but today's as good as any."

For Kate she had woven a straw doll with a yellow cloth

dress with seashell buttons and pink cloth head, hands and feet, complete with little strap-shoes, and carrying a large spiral shell. "And when you're lonely, young Kate, put that to your ear to remind you of me."

Kate hugged and kissed her for as long as they let her until Bumble pulled her away and ushered her into Robin's skiff for the journey to the village.

As they rowed away, Bumble called: "When you get there, go straight to Skitty's house till we call you, right?"

A few minutes later, Bumble's boat appeared astern of them, Tom Nouf pulling hard on his oars. "Reckon we'll take you, young Robin," he cried as he rapidly gained on the little skiff.

"Not if I can help it," shouted Robin, whispering to Kate, "watch." As the other boat pulled alongside Robin leaned into the bottom of the skiff and something flew across the water.

"Aargh!" Tom Nouf yelled, as he dodged back, oar missing the water, and tipping him over backwards with his feet in the air.

The skiff sped forwards as Tom tried to regain his seat and his rhythm, arriving at the jetty well ahead.

Robin leaped out, dragging Kate behind him, laughing, as Tom followed suit, clutching the great-clawed crab Robin had thrown at him, shouting, "I'll get you, I'll get you soon enough."

47

The inn

"Come in, come in, the pair of you." It was old Bumble Clabitter.

Kate and Robin peered round the door into the dark room with its shafts of light through which white curls of smoke danced. They could just make out the figures of their friends, Bumble, Red Took, Skitty Bilcock, Tom Nouf the carter, and Jill Blitter cast against the glow from the hearth. All were standing in a half-circle around a seated figure beside the fire. The figure, very upright on its stool, was robed like a monk and its red beard and moustache together with heavy-rimmed spectacles gave it the appearance of a perched owl-like bird.

"So this is young Kate Linnece," a mild soothing voice came from the owl, "Come here my dear, into the light where I can see you."

Robin pushed her gently into the firelight, keeping close and holding her hand.

"There now, I can recognise you, young Kate, even after all these years. You have you mother's bearing."

Before Kate could ask, he answered: "I am your mother's brother, Henry Cattrick, though I am known generally as Brother Placidus. I, like you, am on the run, so to speak, and have been so ever since my order was proscribed. Your family has served many of my brothers with shelter in this time of troubles, though I have steered clear of Runswick Abbey for fear the family connection, once discovered, could prove their undoing.

"I have not seen you since you were a toddler – this high," he added, patting his knee, "but word reached me recently of our family's disaster and of your fortunate escape to this haven in the marshes. I came at once to lend what aid I could and have learned, from your doughty friends here, of the constant threat you face from that evil man, Gabriel de Tiercel, and his wicked henchmen.

"We have resolved that I should take you to a much safer place in the West Country…"

Kate jumped and clung tight to Robin. The monk smiled, continuing, "…accompanied by young Robin, of course, and your friend, Tom Nouf, whose trade as a carter will arouse no suspicion in travelling so far. You will be called his children as we travel. We have brought together some Wealden iron goods and glassware to carry west as legitimate traders.

"I have some family there under whose protection you will fall. I will provide them with the money to keep you well. They are kind, trustworthy folk who can keep you, while not in the manner to which you were accustomed, in comfort and provide you with an education. He is a yeoman farmer called Sam Arkell. What say you?"

Kate looked at Robin. "And what of Robin, when we get there?"

"He will, to all intents, become your brother," answered the stranger, "if you agree, that is."

"Oh yes, yes!" Kate hugged Robin. "We can be together as brother and sister, truly, Robin, can't we?"

Robin laughed: "I suppose we can, if you insist."

At this titters spread among the adults, relieved to be free of the constant burden of sheltering fugitives.

The strange monk rose to his feet and walked over to the pair, placing his hands on their shoulders, "May you, Kate Linnece, be blessed with the peace you deserve, and may you,

Robin Ruddock, protect and guide her as you have done so well hitherto."

Kate looked up into the stranger's eyes, bulging behind his round spectacles. "You do look so like an owl, uncle Henry," she said, "but elves and owls are kin, you know."

"How so?" the stranger asked.

"We are both creatures of the night," she giggled.

"How true, how true," the stranger stroked his chin, "then we're friends, I take it."

"Oh, yes," the pair answered together, looked at each other, and laughed.

48

Black Martin's confession

"And now we come to the Black Martin and his deeds," said Shabby Tattler. "Which I will relate if you're not too tired of all this?" He looked at Kate and winked his good eye. "I thought not. Well, Black Martin, before he went to his Maker, made a confession, he did. In a monastery in Flanders where he lived out his old age, returned to the Catholic fold after all that."

"Why?" asked Kate, "and how do you know?"

"Why? I guess he was just sick o' the whole business of changing the world cos no good ever come of it," replied Shabby Tattler, "and he took himself off to a quiet cloister to contemplate his sins."

"And how, you ask? Well, this confession of his were all writ down, copied word fer word. Archived in that little sanctuary for hundreds of years. Still there, I don't doubt."

Shabby Tattler smiled at the eager frustration he saw in her eyes. "But we got ter get ter the point. This is Martin's confession, close as I can recall."

"I confess that, yes, at first I was a party to the evil deeds of Sir Gabriel de Tiercel, deeds whose chief conjurer and executioner was White Whiskey John, for Sir Gabriel had not the wit to dream up such refinements of torture for his victims.

The lady Amelia bore a child after her first year of captivity, a child brought forth by John and spirited away as 'still-born' as she lay drugged. This child, a boy named Daniel, was brought by me to those who were to foster Sir Gabriel's love-child, out of sight but not so far out of mind that Sir Gabriel could not oversee his upbringing.

Amelia, in her anguish, believing both her children lost, threatened Sir Gabriel that she would sing until the roof-tiles rattled and the windows shivered and shattered into splinters so that her beloved sister and Gabriel's wife, Phyllis, would hear and understand at last the state to which her sister had been brought.

That evil John, seeing Sir Gabriel malleable in his panic and confusion, proposed his hideous solution and bent us, Phyp Spadger and I, to the task of execution: to wit, prizing open her jaw and, with red-hot pincers, tearing out her tongue at its root.

Though I have seen this performed in war on spies or traitors, I never thought to see such punishment inflicted upon one so fair and innocent.

Phyp Spadger was torn, too, I could see and when, months later, he turned, was found carrying a letter from Amelia to her sister, I knew he too must be silenced or all of us suffer. He had, it seemed, been caught out by Amelia, spying upon her in her chamber from a secret compartment, an old walled up fireplace reached by a stair in that wall's thickness up which he crept every night.

She had laid upon him an oath of silence and a letter to be carried to her sister in return for her silence and a promise to permit his nightly pleasure.

I don't recall whose plan it was to seal him in that walled up chamber but seal him we did for our own preservation with a thick glass placed in his small viewing hole and the wall at the stair's head all bricked up and plastered over, so that not a breath of wind or sound would ever enter or leave again and him upon a chair strapped with his chin to the eye-hole and one hand free, sufficient to reach the jug of water placed to sustain him longer till every ounce of air be used up and he suffocated or died of starvation.

These many foul acts weighed heavy and against my principles, for now it seemed they served no higher purpose than the fulfillment of Sir Gabriel's fleshly desires and John's lust for power. I began to see through that man White Whiskey John.

His incandescent faith, like that of some Messiah, had led me here in his footsteps with huge hopes for a world renewed. Gradually I saw that man's true intent, his greed and ruthless pursuit of no greater goal than self-advancement and I began to hate him for this betrayal.

My purpose in quitting Flanders and espousing the Protestant cause had been so twisted by his evil intent that, even when ridding us of recusant Catholics, I had become embroiled in an infamy from which there was no escape.

But I was tied to his fate as surely as our meek prisoner, for White Whiskey John he laid traps all about with which to snare. With his snare for gross Michael, of which he often boasted that the man was his with that ill-fated signature, he coupled that man to me in conspiracy as he had before with Falco Basard, and thus he had me also bound to loyalty.

My first act of defiance, that gave me much satisfaction in its secret execution, was in garbing myself as a Catholic monk, replete with scholarly spectacles, and leading those I had discovered to a safe haven in the west. Yes, I Brother Placidus, used Gabriel's money to succour his own daughter, Kate, and her companion, Robin, but out of reach of his withering hand and safe from Whiskey John's murderous intent.

I returned to Fugglesham Court, telling Sir Gabriel and John that I had indeed found them or, rather, certain trace of them in a marsh village on the other side of the Downs.

I told them that Kate had died of marsh-fever the previous winter and that the young lad who befriended her had run away God alone knows where. I gave Sir Gabriel a tattered remnant of her dress that he recognised on the instant and gripped in his clenched fist so tight and white I thought the knucklebones would burst right out of his skin.

And so it was with great relief I later heard of the sudden death of Michael at the hands, as it was reported, of White Whiskey John and may no play to defend my mentor, though I suspected Sir Gabriel himself of the deed: a suspicion later proven to be the case.

His mind had been so unhinged over the years by the constant insinuations of poisonous conspiracy into his ear by that same Whiskey John that, and this is my guess, when he suspected him of same (what drove him to that suspicion I cannot even guess, but am glad of it) he acted with a ferocious determination to rid himself of both common conspirator (his brother, Michael) and chief poisoner of his mind (White John).

I had seen their separation develop. I saw grow his regret for the hurt he had caused his own dear lady and his resentment for its instigator. I did nothing and, when Whiskey John was expeditiously tried and executed before any outside law officer could intervene, was appointed in his stead.

"You ask me how Michael de Tiercel came to be murdered and by whom? Well I'll tell you. May I say first that I took no part. I will, however, here reconstruct, with the information gleaned from Gabriel's diary, that of Whiskey John and my own knowledge, the events leading up to the death of Michael and its aftermath.

Overweening as he was, White Whiskey John lorded it over Michael, gloating in the fleshy one's humiliation so that their intimacy, to all appearance, grew. At every opportunity he would seek him out to tease that coward as a cat a cornered mouse, and revelling in the public face of their relationship as Michael, despite his hatred, forbore expressing his true feelings and affected a quiet and respectful demeanour.

All this Gabriel saw and concluded the truth's opposite: that this distancing in public, in his presence, coupled with their oftentimes sequestering in some dark corner of Michael's apartments for long periods, indicated an unhealthy intimacy between them, reminiscent of that once between Michael and Falco Basard.

At the same time as his revulsion for the heinous mutilation inflicted upon Amelia grew so did his casting of all blame for its conception and execution upon White Whiskey John, exploiting his weakness of the moment into a deed irreversible, of which he was reminded every night thereafter.

"One morning Sir Gabriel was out riding alone, as he tells it, when he met, deep in the forest, the "Sisters", two old crones, useless old widows long outcast from the village to fend for themselves or die.

"Who are you?" he demanded, "and who gave you permission to live here in my forest?"

"Permission? Your forest?" cried the first crone, whose small wrinkled face, with its crooked nose and large dark eyes opened wide to reveal the whites all round, framed by wild grey and white hair sharp sticking out in every direction reminded Sir Gabriel of nothing so much as an owl caught in the glare of a lamp. "This forest was here afore ye and will succeed ye and ye've no power o'er it nor us two here, yet we've a power o'er ye. So speaks Jenny Yewlet."

"What do you mean, you've a power over me?" laughed Sir Gabriel, "I could skewer the two of you in a trice!"

"Not so, for ye've come here for a purpose, says I, Madge Woolert, a purpose unknown to ye till now," the second crone croaked.

"Fer your Fate ye've come and I'm going to spin it out to

you," cackled the first.

"My Fate? What do you old hags know about Fate?" Sir Gabriel de Tiercel stiffened in his saddle, revulsion shivering up his spine.

"Stand down from your saddle, mister. Show me your hand, your cack-hand," ordered Madge Woolert, "face up."

Sir Gabriel dismounted and held out his hand in spite of himself. She took his wrist firmly in her left hand and said, "Open it out."

Puzzled, he obeyed, and she began to stroke it with the tips of the fingers of her right hand, murmuring something indecipherable to him. Suddenly she dug her nails into his palm and drew them towards her as in a clawing motion, gouging four great weals into the flesh, bursting it open so that blood welled up into a pool in the centre of his palm.

Jenny Yewlet held out her apron and Madge Woolert turned Sir Gabriel's palm over so the blood spattered onto it. Then she slapped his palm down onto the apron and the two pressed it hard onto the cloth.

"There! 'Tis done." Cried Jenny Yewlet as Sir Gabriel winced and swore. "'Tis time to read, but."

Sir Gabriel, he looked on as the pair stared at the bloodied rag of an apron. As he stared at the cloth, his eyes drawn to it by their concentrated attention, he began to imagine that he saw, emerging from the smudging and spattered drops, a figure that looked like a hooded female, with a smaller figure beside.

"The Madonna and Child?" he asked, his voice cracking, a sudden fear breaking out in sweat upon his brow that he had offended some hidden power in his persecution of the Catholics and their Madonna. Before his thoughts had time to coalesce around this notion, his attention was drawn to the crones staring him hard in the eye.

Speaking with one ugly and dissonant voice, they said: "Beware! That which is dearest to you will be taken from you by that which is nearest to you."

Bewildered by this remark and with the bloody image of the Madonna and child burned into his retinas, Sir Gabriel dizzily remounted, left the little clearing and let his horse carry him back to a part of the forest known to him and so back home.

"Brooding on this over the next few months, Gabriel concluded that this Madonna and child were none other than his beloved Amelia and her son by him, whom he loved. His suspicions focussed on actions of his brother, Michael, and his apparent growing friendship with White Whiskey John.

He concluded with certainty now that his brother, nearest of kin, was in league with Whiskey John, intending to kill his dearly loved son, Daniel, whose identity was known only to him, White Whiskey John and me.

He feared that under John's influence, his brother might even be planning to kill him in order to usurp his estate, consolidating John's power through his influence over the weakling Michael. Here is his solution to and the climax of the matter, as revealed by his own diary and including my own witness, here dramatised by me:

"Come, Michael," Gabriel clapped his brother on the shoulder, surprising him with his warmth, "to the hunt. We must cleanse you of this indigence of purpose that keeps you from realizing your destiny. You need a manly quarry against which to pit your wits and your strength."

Michael, eyes bulging and swivelling from side to side, broke into a sweat as he struggled to gauge his brother's meaning.

Gabriel continued jovially, "A boar hunt, my dear brother, will test your mettle. That great baggage of petty worries with which you so amply gird yourself," poking Michael in the belly, "will all be soon left behind. The excitement of the chase will quick revive that virtue you once had, excelling all huntsmen in your pursuit to the kill."

Michael tittered, and cast his eyes down. "Come now, Michael, modesty becomes you not. I remember well that day when we were young that I, thrown by horse, fell into the path of a charging boar, and you, magnificently, leaped from yours, dagger in hand upon the hog's back with your left hand grasping his snout and your right reaching right under to slit his throat from ear to ear, so that he stumbled and collapsed, snorting blood and stinking breath into my nostrils. I will never forget that smell, my brother, the smell of my death, so close upon me."

Michael, laughing, replied, "You are right, brother, to remind me of what I once was and what I will be again, God willing. Let us go together to face our bristling enemy's fiercest onslaught and bring him to his knees."

"Whiskey John, you shall ride with us at the front," Gabriel shouted as they entered the courtyard where all the huntsmen and lackeys were gathered about, "the beaters to the flanks and the rest of you horsemen behind us on either side, for today is St. Michael's day, and his will be the honour of taking the kill."

As a cheer rang across the yard, Gabriel turned to Michael and whispered, "You thought I had forgot, did you not? But this day will mark your destiny."

Michael rode out of the courtyard, followed by Sir Gabriel and Whiskey John and the rest of the riders in two columns. The men on foot quickly overtook the column of horse and spread out in a fan as they broached the woods, to form two horns to drive any creatures encountered towards the centre.

They rode on slowly for half an hour before the cry went upon on the right flank and suddenly a boar in galloped into view and, seeing the horsemen, stopped dead.

"Gabriel glanced at Michael, smiled and struck his horse's rump with his crop, "Away, Michael, he's all yours!"

Michael spurred his horse towards the boar which, turning,

296

ran noisily into the undergrowth, reappearing in a clearing some twenty yards away. The chase was on. Sir Gabriel and White John followed close behind as Michael, suddenly heedless of all care, charged wildly through the trees, swerving to left and right as he determined to prove himself worthy of this honour bestowed upon him.

Soon leaving the others far behind the three drove on through the woods. Soon Gabriel slowed his horse, calling to White Whiskey John, "John, these reins are chafing my hands. I forgot to bring my gauntlets. Lend me yours, my good man"

Whiskey John pulled off his gloves and grudgingly handed them to Gabriel, Gabriel said, "I have just remembered, John, a shipment of goods is due to be delivered this noon to our storehouse over in Hangar Wood. You must go to meet it and take account of the goods or the rogues will filch some for certain. Quick, go now. Afterward return straight to the house and report to me the proceeds of this consignment. I must ride fast to catch Michael before he claims the boar."

Gabriel had not ridden far in Michael's direction before coming to a tiny glade in the centre of which stood Michael's horse, grazing quietly. As he drew alongside they could see Michael leaning against a tree, panting and perspiring with exhaustion. It was as if the fury had departed him as quickly as it had taken him. Gabriel could see his distress.

"Well, brother," Gabriel greeted Michael as he walked his horse towards him, "your appetite seems to be greater than you can stomach."

Groaning, "Where's Whiskey John?" Michael craned his neck to look up at Gabriel, silhouetted against the midday sun. Momentarily blinded by a glint of metal against the black shadow overhanging him, he received without flinching the slashing blow that severed his windpipe.

His head lolled backward and a strange sigh bubbled from the stump of his neck as his knees buckled and he sat with his back against the trunk.

Gabriel jumped down from his horse, axe in hand, and dealt his brother's body blow upon furious blow, hacking at him as if at any moment the mangled heap might rise up to deny him.

"So sacrificed, lies the fatted calf," growled Gabriel as he paused, exhausted by his own exertions, then plunged his gloved hands into the bloodied mass, flung off the cape in which he had wrapped himself, threw the gauntlets into the cape along with the great axe, rolled them up and placed them into a leather saddlebag, wrapped an identical cloak about him, mounted his horse and rode rapidly back.

Soon he came upon the main body of horse, "Have you seen my brother Michael or Whiskey John?" he called, "My horse stumbled and I was left behind. Michael was so eager for that boar he refused to stop."

"No, my Lord, neither have we seen," replied the chief of them. "They have not passed this way."

"Some of you follow on after them, then, and the rest return with me to Fugglesham Court. My arse is as sore as a tupped ewe's."

The men burst out laughing at this unaccustomed ribaldry from their master's lips and the party returned home in good spirits, despite their denial of a share in the spoils.

"Gabriel's diary is most detailed, almost triumphal, in his depiction of these events. So the story continued.

"At the Hall, Gabriel darted up the stairs to his room with his leather satchel, checked his clothing for bloodstains and, finding none and waited until the passage leading from his chamber to that of White Whiskey John was clear.

He glided rapidly to John's chamber, opened his closet, unwrapped his bundle and smeared the bloody gauntlets over a jerkin and breeches he found there. He stuffed the gloves and bloodied axe into a cloak and tucked them away at the back of the cupboard.

Returning to his own rooms, he washed and then sat down with a glass of wine to await Whiskey John's report.

Whiskey John returned to the house, unaware of events, and mounted the stairs to his master's solar to report the day's gains.

"You were right to have called me to witness the delivery, Sir Gabriel, for when I arrived I saw the waggoner delivering hitching up to depart and, upon inspection of the back of his cart, found two barrels of Spanish wine and several hams that I took to be ours about to depart with him. An oversight, he said it was. I gave him a sound beating and now we are an ox and cart the richer."

"You killed him?" Gabriel jumped up.

"Don't worry, Sir, I buried him deep so no one will find him, and anyway who's going to admit they knew where he was going?"

"Sit down, John, and take a cup," relied Gabriel, "You're a good and trusty man, indispensable."

"Thank you Sir, I try to take account of every eventuality," White Whiskey John grinned as he raised his cup.

"You do, you do," laughed Gabriel, "and I'll probably rue the day you don't."

At that moment a great hubbub rose from the courtyard at the rear of the house, and Gabriel rose and walked to the door, across the passage into a back room and stared down into the yard through a window there.

"There seems a devil of a commotion going on down there." He opened the casement and leaned out. "By God, what is all the fuss about?"

All eyes turned towards the window as if a herd of sheep had caught sight of their herder. A voice rang out, "It's Michael, Sir!" "He's dead, Sir!" "Cut to pieces!" "Throat slit open like a beast, Sir!" "We found him, Sir, half propped against a tree." "Looks like an axe, Sir, by the shape of the wounds."

Sir Gabriel roared, "My brother!" and leaped back, shouldering Whiskey John aside as he ran to the stairs and down into the court.

"My God, I'll have the dog that did this to my brother," he cried as he uncovered the remains, collapsed to his knees and roared, "I'll have the dog hung, drawn and quartered, by Heaven! Find the culprit. Search everywhere. Search the village. Search the servants' quarters. Search every room in the house."

He threw the cloak back over his brother's body. "With wounds like these, there will be blood. And the axe: I want that axe found if we have to round up every woodcutter in ten miles."

I, Black Martin, having been left behind that morning, was now at my master's side. As he inspected the corpse I did so too. As he turned away, issuing instructions, I knelt and took a closer look at the shape and length of the wounds. And then I spoke: "Those wounds, Sir, were made by no woodsman's axe. I have seen countless wounds of every sort." I stood to face him. "Those wounds were carved by a battle-axe."

"Are you sure?" Sir Gabriel looked perplexed for a moment, then shouted, louder than before, "Then find it, you dolts, find it!"

I looked at White Whiskey John, standing beside Sir Gabriel, and thought I saw him flinch momentarily, as if a shadow had passed over him, and the thought occurred to me: you are one of the few here who carries such an axe – is that what you are thinking?

Sir Gabriel's men spread out in every direction, both the courtyard's buildings and into Fugglesham Hall itself.

Whiskey John was unusually still for such a commanding figure. He paced beside Sir Gabriel awhile before, as it seemed, gathering himself together, said, "I'll take a party and search the stables, Sir. There maybe blood there on one of the horses."

Sir Gabriel started as if John's voice had materialised out of thin air, then growled, "No, damn, you. I need you here with me. We must think this through. Who wanted him dead?"

"You're right, Sir, we must discover who had a grudge against Master Michael so great he would stoop to this."

I entered the house to begin my search of the chambers. Something strange drew me towards that chamber, that of White Whiskey John. Perhaps it was the simple fact of his possessing such an axe; perhaps, and I like to think this was my perception, it was that momentary flinching, so marked because so out of character.

I opened his door and made straight for the closet. Rifling through the clothing, my hands suddenly felt sticky and, withdrawing them, I saw them smeared black with half-congealed blood. I pulled out the bloodied jerkin and pants and laid them on the floor. Resuming my search, I felt deep into the cupboard and my hand touched something familiar, cold and hard. The blade I pulled out was White Whiskey John's without doubt. I had seen it wielded many times in the heat of battle and knew his skill with it, as with all weapons. It was heavy and coated with blood and as I dragged it out a gory gauntlet fell to the floor.

Pulling out its sibling, I laid the assemblage out upon the planks as if for a funeral.

I shouted out to Gabriel. He came running, closely followed by John. As if in disbelief, he ran the opposite way upon reaching the landing till summoned by my further calls.

Entering the room, the two of them stood staring at the bloody disembodied clothing laid upon the floor.

Gabriel turned and stared at White Whiskey John, who blanched for the first time in his life, realising his plight.

"Guards!"

"Whiskey John was arrested, arraigned, found guilty and condemned to death with astounding alacrity. Sir Gabriel's fury was unstoppable.

No appeals for justice, for postponement until officers of the law could be summoned, prevailed over his will to mete out the ghastly vengeance he called 'justice'.

Whiskey John, naked and face down, was tethered by his ankles to a horse and dragged around the cobbled court until senseless. Revived, he was eviscerated and had his heart torn out before having his head hacked off with a dull blade.

His head was mounted at the gate; his body and bowels fed to Gabriel's hounds.

Sir Gabriel watched throughout, hardly blinking, uttering not a word.

Seeing change in the wind, our Pastor Mew, his Mewlings and not-so Saith Fool vanished into the mist before even the crows had plucked White John's eyeballs out.

In his diary Sir Gabriel wrote of his satisfaction in warding off the curse of those wretched hags, at his frustrating the plot between the gullible Michael and that evil manipulator, White Whiskey John.

Little did he know how far wide of the mark his arrow fell, how misplaced his chosen target. But the old hags' prophecy was later fulfilled in the sisters' revenge, as I describe next.

"My true ambition thwarted through those years of its perversion, I now bent my mind to the purpose of rescuing the poor Amelia and restoring her in secret to her lost daughter and the son she had never seen. That surely would redeem me in the eyes of our Creator.

But even this good intent was thwarted by the actions of Amelia herself, for she cunningly wrought a tapestry depicting a scene whose meaning was known only to herself and Phyllis, her sister, a meaning that drew her sister into subtle deception of her husband to secure the key to the East

Wing and to their tragic meeting and decision to end the whole ghastly charade.

Yes, I had discovered them, yet not betrayed their murderous plan. With Phyllis's knowledge of her sister's plight, I realized the impossibility of my spiriting away that very prisoner whose disappearance Gabriel could never admit, while I myself had to admit the true justice in their desire to avenge their wrong and rid the world of such a monster.

I followed Phyllis up the stair that night, stood at her shoulder in the shadows by the door looking down upon the naked back of her husband bedding her beloved sister; watched her to the trunk and lift the boy's head by the hair and shout as she hurled it at him with her following lantern smashing at the bed's head, spilling liquid flame over the couple; watched her leap upon him, dagger in hand, and strike and strike; watched as he, trapped between them, struggled to rise, reaching for his sword to run her through; saw Amelia dart between them to receive the blow as the canopy blazed overhead and fell among them; watched his flaming body stagger towards the door – towards me.

I looked him hard in the eye as he reached the door, saw the realization in his face as I slammed it shut, turning the key; heard him pummelling the heavy oak; felt the heat and saw the smoke creeping under the door; listened till his hammering grew soft and heard his roaring turn to bleating and finally the crump of his collapse.

Counting slow to sixty, I made my way back down the stair and down into the servants' hall where, at last, I cried "Alarm! Fire, fire!"

The house was ablaze with frenetic shouting and running all about, fetching and carrying pails of water in human chains from the courtyard well through the great kitchen, through pantry and servants' hall, up the back stair and across the landing to the East Stair and to that fateful door, where axes thundered till it fell in splinters and a great blast singed the strong axe men of their hair and beards and eyebrows so that they fell back and cried out and doused themselves in those pails.

In all this mayhem, though all this pandemonium, from the moment Phyllis fell upon her lord, I never heard either sister cry out nor even moan in their death-agonies. For agony it must have been, martyred upon the funeral pyre of their wicked master. Such must have been their strength, their determination and their love for one another.

I confess, in this complicity, I find myself guilty and gladly so. You may ask what I did henceforth, since none knew of my part?

Even as the household and villagers brought the fire under control towards dawn I busied myself with a thorough search of all Gabriel's goods and chattels, seeking out evidence that might, in retrospect, incriminate me in any way, and found in his study two diaries.

The first was an official account of the great house's affairs and the doings of its occupants. The second was the intimate relation of Sir Gabriel's inner thoughts and true actions.

I also found the documents' case of White Whiskey John, in which I presumed all his secrets were hid. With these latter I absconded, for I deemed them to contain much harm, and hid them in a spot known only to me.

When, the next morning, the fire was finally brought under control and the servants sifted through the wreckage of the open-roofed blackened chambers of the upper story of the East Wing, they were surprised to find five bodies: those of their Lord and two women in one room and the desiccated remains of another man in a side chamber.

Mystifyingly to them, they also discovered a child's skull in the room with the bodies, and the disarranged bones of a child in the remains of a chest in the great hall.

"The lawyers reading the will of the dead lord discovered in it the existence of a bastard love child, Daniel, named as sole inheritor of the Linnece family, estate inherited by Sir Gabriel's wife, Phyllis, upon the earlier death of her parents. His elder, legitimate, son, Raphe, now known to be deceased, had been named heir to his own, de Tiercel, estates.

The whereabouts of this bastard child and his foster-parents, known only to me, now that Sir Gabriel and White Whiskey John were dead, were revealed, and the child was sent for. He was given the family name and installed as heir to both estates, under the tutelage of the good people who had been his fosterers.

After a decent interval, I resigned my post to that man who had so ably fostered young Daniel, and went away to the west and sought out that daughter whom I had rescued and myself secreted, years before, intending to unite brother and sister in their inheritance, thus undoing some of the harm to which I had been a party.

I told no one of my purpose, and just as well, for not a little blame might have fallen upon me had I so done. When I came to their safe-haven the birds had fled, flown the coop, no one knew where.

Perhaps young Robin had seen through my disguise at length and, wary of my purpose, taken his charge upon adventures unknown but away from certain peril, as he saw it? We will never know, here on earth.

When I stand before my Maker to account my sins and righteous acts and one against the other, maybe their freedom will tip the balance."

49

Shabby Tattler

"And thus end the Confessions of Black Martin," said Shabby Tattler.

"So Kate and Robin pass out of the story, never to be heard of again?" Kate spluttered.

"I'm afraid so, my dear," said Shabby Tattler.

"Oh my God," cried Kate, still wrapped in her own thoughts, "that means Black Martin saved them. Incredible, after all the hateful things he had done."

"So it is told," replied Shabby Tattler, stretching his legs straight out before him and wriggling his toes inside his soft leather boots that reached to his thighs.

She had never noticed his boots before. It occurred to Kate that these boots were strange, but not so strange as his knowledge.

"So what happened next? " Kate asked.

"Well, Daniel de Tiercel grew up good and just, bringing a new hope to the trauma-wracked community of the estate," said Shabby Tattler, smiling. "He had the East Wing refashioned in the style of the day without despoiling those parts of the shell of the old that remained intact.

From this son, the line of succession of the de Terciels, now Tercel, continued uninterrupted to this day.

But rumour spread in the villages around, rumours that persist to this day among the older folk, that the de Tiercel name is cursed and that there will be a final reckoning in which the last of the de Tiercels will be wiped from the face of the earth by a descendant of one of those massacred."

Shabby Tattler looked deep into her eyes and the sudden realization hit her that he must think that she, Kate, must be that descendant.

50

Kate

Kate returned home, confused and afraid but determined to discover what her role in this bizarre affair could possibly be.

Early that evening Kate took her keys and ran to the East Wing via the woods to confront the prisoner with the contents of her own diary. Entering the secret door, she climbed the stairs to the hall. She entered and had just begun crossing the hall, which she found empty, when she heard a strange whimpering sound coming from one of the rooms beyond.

She crept forward and peered through the arched door. She gasped. A powerful man was pressing Amelia to the bed. Amelia saw her, but her expression betrayed her. The man turned and let out a bellow of rage. Kate ran. Just as she reached the door to the stairs the man caught her by the throat and dragged her back into the hall, demanding to know her identity and how she had got there.

Choking, she was unable to speak and the man hurled her into the other room, locked the door, and stormed off.

Recovering her wits, Kate realized that she was trapped in her 'mother's' time, that this man must be the original Sir Gabriel de Tiercel and that he must return soon. Pondering all means of escape, her eyes lit upon the window. It was too high to reach. She pushed a table up to it, climbed on it and stretched her hand out. Its sill was still just beyond her fingertips.

Climbing down, she thought of throwing a stone or something heavy, with sheets attached, to break the glass then climb out and down. She found a paperweight and looked in a chest in the corner for sheets or blankets, but it was empty.

She realized she could not escape now without a miracle. Suddenly Shabby Tattler's words flashed into her head: "If ever you need me, whistle, like this…" She thought it too ridiculous. Then, in despair, she decided to give it a try. But with the windows closed, who could hear her?

She stood up on the table and flung the paperweight with all her strength at the window above. It shattered and shards of glass crashed down all around her.

Then, feeling ridiculous, she whistled shrilly in the way she had been taught and waited. Nothing. She whistled again and again. She listened.

Eventually she heard a heavy flapping sound and a large black shadow cast itself across the room. She nearly fell off the table in fright, jumped down away from the window and looked back. Silhouetted against the glooming there was a raven in the window above her, cocking its swarthy head from side to side, inspecting her first with one beady eye, then the other.

Kate's brain worked furiously. If a raven can answer my whistle, she thought, perhaps it can carry a message? But to whom? Anyone. It doesn't matter. I must find paper. Frantically she searched the room, in case the raven should fly off. There was none. What now, she thought. I know its absurd, she decided, but if a raven can come to my whistle, it must be Shabby Tattler's raven, or even the man himself. Therefore I should be able to talk to it and explain my predicament.

So she told the raven that Sir Gabriel had locked her in this room and that she must escape before he returned. The raven cocked its head, croaked and flew off. A while later she heard a scrabbling at the door, and cowered into the corner, fearing the lord had returned, hoping by miracle it was Shabby Tattler himself.

The key turned in the lock until it clicked and Kate saw the latch rising. The door opened and she could see a hooded figure silhouetted against the dim light of the hall, beckoning her. She jumped up and edged slowly at first towards the urgently gesticulating figure, then deciding it couldn't be Sir Gabriel, rushed quickly to the open door.

The hooded figure pointed to her exit door and urged her towards it, brushing aside her thanks. Kate rushed to the staircase door, pulling out the key she had hidden in her blouse, briefly looking back as she opened it to descend. She saw the figure lock the door of the room in which Kate had been imprisoned and flit into the shadows at the further end of the hall.

Just then she heard the main door from the house start to open. Quickly locking the staircase door, Kate ran down the stairs. As she reached the outer door and locked it too, she heard a roar of anger.

She fled across the grass, the bellowing diminishing all the time. Only from the safety of the woods dared she look back: at least no one was following.

Could it have been Amelia in that hooded cloak, or was it Shabby Tattler, responding to her call as he said he would, she asked herself as she hurried into the depths of the wood, and, if so, what would Sir Gabriel in his fury do to them?

Making her way by moonlight deep into the woods to return to her cottage, she became aware of a rush of wings above her head. She looked up but could see nothing but the shadows of trees swaying and rustling in the wind. Approaching the heart of the wood, she felt the same rush of wings, closer this time.

Shocked and bewildered, Kate ran to her cottage as fast as she could to make sure she was in her true present.

"What's your hurry young lady?" laughed her father, as she nearly knocked him over as she burst through the front door.

"Oh, nothing Dad," she panted, "I was just seeing how fast I could make from the great house to here through the woods. Tomorrow, after school, I'm going to run back via the road. I made a bet with Rob that I could beat him if he went one way and I the other, so I need to know which is fastest before Saturday's race."

"Really," her father looked dubious, "what a strange girl you are."

"I'm not a girl, father," Kate shrugged her shoulders as she elbowed past him into the kitchen.

"Would you like a cup of tea before your supper, young Lady?"

His exaggerated politeness made her chuckle, "yeah, ok."

After school the next day she left the cottage and sped back along the road to the great house's main entrance. No one answered her knocking. Knowing that the front door was never locked during the day, Kate opened it and crept in.

The hall was empty. "Is anyone there?" she called. There was no answer and so she ran on into the library to reread the historical account of the fire. This dovetailed exactly with Amelia's account of the events leading up to it.

All the elements here missing were given in graphic detail in Amelia's account, confirming the identity of all those found in the burnt-out hall. The rest of the story, horrible as it was, must also be true, she thought.

Suddenly deflated, Kate collapsed to the floor and sat there, with her legs straight out before her, like a bewildered little girl who had lost her first puppy.

"What's all this? What are you doing here, in tears, in my study?" It was the general, standing silhouetted in the French doors to the garden, clippers in hand.

"Oh, Sir Perry," she began.

Old Sir Perry comforted her and gradually drew from her the dreadful story contained in Amelia Linnece's diary. Kate told the whole story as she knew it now, but omitted to mention Shabby Tattler's part in the telling of it or of Shabby Tattler's suspicion that she was the descendent of Amelia.

"My God," he exclaimed, as she finished. "I half-expected something bad, but nothing as awful as this. Are you sure you've got it right?"

"Yes, of course. I can prove it. You can see the diary if you like," she responded.

"I think that would be best. Go and fetch it now, if you please."

Kate, a little taken aback by his sudden formality, looked at him nervously before replying, "Of course, I'll go now."

She ran back to the cottage and was halfway up the stairs when he father called out: "Did you win? I mean, which way is quicker?"

"Oh, I..." she paused. "Oh, yes, the woods are quicker. But I must hurry, the old general's expecting me back. He's helping me with my history project. I've got to run."

She had fetched the diary, placed it in her satchel, and was out of the door as she finished her sentence.

"Well, I never!" Her father shook his head. "What's the hurry?"

Taking the diary, the general looked at its cover, turned it over slowly in his hands, then opened it, flicking through the pages before settling on one and studying its handwriting carefully.

Without a word, but looking very solemn, he slowly put it down on the library desk and walked over to one of the glass-faced bookcases. Drawing a small key out of his waistcoat, he turned it in the lock, opened the wide glass door and reached up towards an old set of papers and manuscript books.

After half-pulling out several and returning them, he

appeared to decide on one and drew it out, walked slowly over to the table and placed it carefully alongside Kate's.

Kate's eyes opened wide. "It's the same! It's identical! How can that be?"

"I'm afraid it appears to be so. Look at the crest. It is precisely the same. And the leather – it's the same colour." General Tercel looked at Kate and back down at the two books. "To all intents and purposes, they're from the same set."

He opened each in turn, inspecting the fabric of the pages. "Yes, they're the same. I cannot see any difference in the paper at all. There's no reasonable explanation but that this one you brought was secreted in that niche you mentioned at or about the same period in which this other one originated. Its crest's form, as you see, is not identical to that of our family's today and since this document lies in my private collection, no forger could know that it took this form at that time."

"Wow! Then it must real, mustn't it?" Kate was twitching with excitement.

"I'm afraid so," answered Sir Perry. "We can eliminate forgery, so I am drawn to the conclusion that somehow we now have in your manuscript, if what you have recounted to me is accurate, something approximating a complete account of the events of that time that makes a more telling argument than any other version, because each of those has glaring omissions or discrepancies."

51

The General

After Kate had left, General Peregrine Tercel withdrew to his study to sit in his favourite old leather armchair and draw on his favourite old pipe and sip his favourite old single malt whisky while he read the secret diary of Amelia Linnece and contemplated the consequences of all he had learned.

To keep a clear head as the study steadily thickened with smoke, he stood a glass of plain water beside his neat whisky.

After several hours, out of the fog, a pattern grew discernibly until it achieved the status of revelation.

Young Kate, to whom he had taken such an instant liking to the point of breaking his self-imposed exile from society and of admitting her into his confidence, must be, without a doubt, that descendent of the original Kate Linnece, Amelia's daughter, through which folklore prophesied the downfall of his own family.

Why else was it given to her to discover a secret door, meet the doomed Amelia, be handed an impossibly authentic manuscript, written before her eyes in the hand of that Amelia of old and, finally, to find intact her hidden diary that survived the great fire?

These ideas wreathed and intensified about his brain, as in the breezeless room the smoke, until he felt, as if in his very lungs, a mental suffocation close to panic or despair.

The conclusion was inescapable. She would somehow be a

party to his death and that of his son, Gabriel. But how? She was surely incapable of any such dreadful act.

Heaving himself up, he staggered, coughing, to the window and threw the casement open, leaned out and breathed deeply the cool night air.

Clear as the stars appeared to him now, with their invisible lines connecting to one another depicted constellations to the ancient astrologers, he saw that line descending from Amelia Linnece to Kate through the mother, as his own line, through the father, reached back to Daniel de Tiercel and Gabriel, in whom those two distinct threads met.

He determined to commission genealogical research into her matrilineal family tree, to see if he could verify his hunch that she could indeed be a true descendent of his own ancestor.

With this determination came the inspiration that there might be a way out of this apparently inevitable doom. He had noted the growing affection between his wayward son Gabriel and this strange, lovely girl. The notion hit him that should they fall in love and get married, the two lines of descent would become conjoined, atoning for those misdeeds of the past. She would inherit the estate through marriage with his son, as was her right in this bizarre interpretation of history, and this would make a most appropriate resolution to the tale.

Then it occurred to him that, given modern technology, the surest way to confirm such a possible familial link between Kate and the members of his Elizabethan family, the General concluded, would be to establish a direct genetic connection.

To do this he would have to exhume the remains of that original Kate's grandmother and purported mother, Rosie Linnece, buried beside her husband Sir William Linnece at Runswick Abbey. He would also have to have tested the remains of the Amelia and young Kate Linnece who were supposedly massacred and buried alongside them, to eliminate them as directly related to that Rosie.

In addition, he would have to exhume the bones of Sir Gabriel de Tiercel, so easily identifiable after the fire that they were buried separately in a coffin in the family mausoleum. He would have to obtain a lock of Kate's hair to test to see if Kate carried any genes indicating descent from Sir Gabriel himself, as she would have done had the original Kate been his bastard daughter by Amelia Linnece.   And for good measure, test also the bones of the two women found in the East Wing fire to see if they were sisters and from them trace a matrilineal line to Kate if possible.

This he did and, explaining his intention to Kate, obtained from her a sample of hair to enable the appropriate genetic tests to be carried out on her mitochondrial DNA to establish if there was a direct matrilineal connection.

He also submitted his own DNA.

52

Gabriel

"As the pearled mists at dawn kindle the fire in your cheeks;
   as the light touch of dew upon your skin glistens in
reflection of the rising sun;
   as the rising sun, in whose light bathed, your beauty glows
and grows wondrous,
   so I touch your lips with scarlet, as with a kiss.

As the caressing whisper of the cool breeze of morning
quickens your slow lassitude with the pulse of love, an ardour
rising from the depths of sleep;
   as the low murmur of the brook in which you dabble draws
you down, through rivers of yearning, to the frothing surf of
the pebbled shore;
   so I, through raging breakers, drag you down into the
drowning of your Self in the dark Ocean that I am."

Gabriel lay beside her as she leaned against the grey smooth
bark of the beech tree, staring out over the Downs towards
the sea and the sun wrapped in the dissipating haze of early
morning.
   He had brought Kate here as the birds started their
chattering chorus in near darkness. She, snug in her winter
coat; he, dancing about her like a faun, laughing, cajoling,
egging her on as they climbed the steep slope through the

lower beech woods towards the ring of trees at this highest point of the Downs, planted over a century ago.

"That is so beautiful, Gabriel," she whispered, looking down at his face bathed in that golden light and stroking his cheek.

"Thank you, Kate, my darling," he replied, smiling back.

"It's so sincerely expressed," she added, "so unlike you."

"Somehow," he said, "when I am with you, I am inspired and feel so differently to my normal self..."

"So like..." Kate paused, playing her fingers through his tousled hair, "your father!"

"Ouch! What did you do that for?" Gabriel leaped up, clutching his scalp.

"Unfortunately, Gabriel dear, I have read your father's little love lyrics already. He lent them to me." Kate laughed. "How like you, though, trying to pass yourself off as something you are not!"

"You're wrong, how wrong you are," he retorted, "though the lyrics may not be mine, they are sincere, both in origin and expression. After all, to how many comes the gift of originality in expressing their desires? Not many. Are they then, expressed at second-hand, any the less sincere?"

"I suppose not," Kate answered, "Did I hurt you?"

"Yes, you did, as a matter of fact," Gabriel looked at his least insouciant, "more than you know."

Kate could not resist the false concern upon that beautiful face, with its pleading eyebrows and sadly pouting lips. "You're incorrigible!" She leaned down and kissed him hard and long until they both collapsed in laughter and rolled together on the cold dewy grass.

"Oh, God!" Gabriel yelled suddenly, "You've rolled me onto a pooh! Jesus! It stinks!"

"That's not a sheep's, either," Kate sniffed, "It's a dog's! Get away!"

Kate jumped up and ran off across the round-shouldered

down towards their homeward path, not stopping to look back as Gabriel ripped off his jacket and smeared it across the wet grass.

53

Robert

"Why should I?" Robert turned his back on Kate and stomped towards the yard. "Anyone can see you're after him, that dandy Gabriel, with all his money and grand living."

"I'm not, Rob, honest," she pleaded. "I'm not after him. If anything, it's the other way round; he keeps following me."

"But you let him, don't you? You don't exactly push him away." Robert brushed her hand from his elbow.

"He's just charming, that's all – fun – difficult to say no to."

"Well, you go it, that's what I say, and good luck to you." Robert ran to the estate yard and slammed the door to the office before Kate could stop him.

Kate, at a loss, wandered slowly home along the road, idling in the hopes of a change of heart from Robert.

Suddenly she heard footsteps crunching of the gravel, getting closer: running steps. She turned her head. Robert was racing towards her, cap in hand.

As he approached, she could see his ruddy cheeks were smeared with mud where he had wiped away tears. Her heart leaped. His blonde hair flying, blue eyes shining as a smile broke across his dimpled cheeks. As she turned he slammed into her, caught her as she fell, apologised and embraced her all in one move before kissing her lips with an incontrovertible passion.

Kate swooned, suffocating in the fierce grip of his embrace, and slid to the ground as he eased his muscular torso onto hers.

"What you doin' there Miss? Are you alright?"

A rough kindly voice burst into her consciousness. Kate opened her eyes. A farm worker was standing directly over her, legs apart and hands on elbows, head silhouetted, tousled hair flecked with sunlight.

"I saw you fall, like. So I came over to 'ave a look." He reached out a hand.

"What's happened? Where's Robert?" Kate looked bewildered.

"Didn't see nobody else, Miss. Here, take my hand, I'll pull you up."

Kate complied without thinking.

"There was just you Miss, walkin' along slow. I was admiring you, if you don't mind me sayin' so, when sudden, you just slips to the ground without a sound. So I came."

"Thanks, er…"

"Henry," the man smiled, "I work for the estate. Often seen you about, with Rob and that Gabriel…" The man's voice tailed off as if he realized he was hitting a nerve. "Still, we'd best get you home to your dad, eh? I'll walk with you in case you take another of them turns."

"I'll be fine, honest," Kate began.

"No, I'd never forgive myself if you fell over again. No, I'll see you home."

With that the pair walked back to Kate's cottage, with the farm worker chatting about anything at all.

54

Gabriel's revelation

Paper and bamboo lanterns of every hue hung that evening from the lower branches of the tree-lined avenue leading past the magnificent wrought-iron gate and on up to Fugglesham Court, lighting the drive and the gaily-decked horse-drawn carriages crammed with guests.

Old General Tercel had arranged for a magnificent party to be held for his heir's 21st birthday. It was to be a grand masquerade and ball. Throughout the grounds close to the great house paths were lit by lanterns arranged on poles leading to various foci of the entertainments of the evening. All guests were required to be dressed in the most elaborate disguise, and the old general had had many carnival costumes and masks flown in from Venice for those who found difficulty acquiring such.

Cars were abandoned in a park by the old fishing lake and a marquee set up with changing rooms for those guests who had failed to arrive in appropriate fancy-dress or whose costumes too closely resembled those of their host, Gabriel Tercel, or his guest of honour, Kate Pegler.

As the guests arrived they were ushered to the West Terrace where champagne was served as they watched an extravagant display of warrior horsemanship by a troupe of Don Cossacks, dressed in their traditional outfits. Dummies' heads were severed, horsemen somersaulted on or beside their mounts while performing manoeuvres of dazzling complexity all silhouetted against the glorious oranges reds and purples of the dying sun.

Just as the sun reached the horizon in a carmine ball, the horsemen synchronously lit torches, swirling about one another until finally they formed a solid phalanx facing the crowded terrace, raised their glittering swords and flaming torches and trotted towards the throng.

Picking up pace, they reached a gallop and thundered full pelt, swords and torches held high, and in unison leaped the ten foot wide dip onto the ha-ha wall, stopping at once only feet from the guests, some of whom, terrified, jumped backwards, spilling drinks and tripping over one another.

The horsemen dipped their swords in salute to the old general, resplendent in his old dress uniform, with its medals, braid and long ceremonial sword. He saluted back, and then clapped twice and the horsemen turned sideways and filed off docilely in two columns to north and south.

The crowd started clapping too, at first out of sheer relief, then with enthusiasm as they realized the sheer panache of the drama that had been played out before them.

At the centre of the terrace, the general raised his glass in a toast: "To my son and heir, Gabriel!"

The assembled guests raised their glasses in response, shouting: "Gabriel!"

As if an angel had been summoned, on the balcony above a figure appeared in a white cloak with an Harlequin mask and, mounting a hidden step, leaped into the air, his great cape billowing in the breeze like great wings, revealing his lithe form in a tight harlequin's diamond motley.

A gasp wheezed from the crowd as the flying figure landed lightly, caught by two men in black, and mounted the low dais on which stood the General. Lifting its mask, its glossy black mane shook free to reveal Gabriel's beautiful smile as he beamed in triumph at this successful beginning to his 21st birthday extravaganza.

Raising both his arms to quiet the hubbub of awed appreciation and speculation as to what might come next, Gabriel announced: "And now, my special guest, my Darling Columbine!"

The double glass doors opened behind him and Columbine stepped out, her diamond patterned blouse matching Harlequin's, and her skirt billowing white. Kate's auburn hair with its white streak accentuated the paleness of her face as she stepped up to acknowledge the applause of the much more extravagantly attired guests.

"To the Grand Masquerade," shouted the Harlequin, Gabriel, as he led his Columbine back into the hall. As they entered, an orchestra struck up a comic dance. The guests filed through the series of French windows lining the series of rooms along the West Wing and began dancing.

An atmosphere of license suffused the air as the music played and the dancers danced, each free behind his or her mask to engage with others in brazenly lustful or coquettish gestures leading to transient pairings seeking the cooler air outside to discover the nature of their small conquests.

At the appropriate time, the master of ceremonies announced the banquet, and led the assembled multitude through into the Great Hall on the South Wing.

This banquet was of many courses, starting with seafood antipasti prepared by chefs flown in from La Corte Sconta in Venice, the General's favourite restaurant there. He had game birds, large and small, arranged fancifully, decked in feathers. He had a wild boar from the Maremma roasting on a spit on the patio outside the great hall, and great cuts of beef and venison from Scotland.

The guests circulated as they picked dainties or sat to eat meat, if their dresses allowed, at the various tables scattered through this hall and spilling out onto the terrace outside.

After the banquet, during the grand masked ball in the evening, with a small orchestra playing alternately romantic and comic pieces, Gabriel, dressed as Harlequin, entertained and bewitched and seduced Kate, his Columbine.

He took her by the waist and led her to the centre of the floor and in his arms the night became like a dream to her, and in this dream it was as if she was floating above the dance floor looking down upon herself and Gabriel, gliding effortlessly amongst the fantastically masked costumes, kaleidoscopically spangled with colour and dancing lights, pulsating hypnotically in concert, entrancing in their beauty.

In the middle of a romantic tune Gabriel suddenly started a fierce balletic dance totally at odds with the music and in so doing cleared a large space in the centre of the great hall, then, at the moment of greatest tension and attention, fell upon one knee before Kate.

"Marry me?" he implored.

At first she giggled at the sheer absurdity of his gesture, then as she looked into his utterly serious eyes, she softened towards him and held out her hand, saying quietly, in a speech in keeping with the baroque atmosphere of the place: "Dear Gabriel, much as I find you irresistibly charming and hugely entertaining, I am too young to think of marrying. And much as I am hugely flattered by your proposal, which I surely don't deserve, I cannot say 'yes' just like that. For me, love is something that takes time to discover and I can't jump into a decision.

But I do thank you and hope you will give me the time I need to consider your sudden proposal."

As he stood she kissed him on the lips, took his hand and led him out onto the terrace amidst sporadically enthusiastic bouts of clapping among the confused guests, some of whom, not having heard her words, seemed to think she had accepted. A frenetic buzzing spread through the milling crowd like the murmur of bees following the rumour of nectar.

The evening culminated in a huge theatrical fireworks display performed by a Catalonian troupe, whose actors ran around the stage performing scenes derived from ancient mythology.

Kate was wholly mesmerised by the elaborate fireworks exploding amongst and on their bodies in a display that culminated in the marriage of the Bull-god with the Earth-goddess. His huge phallus erupted into a shower of silver rain that spilled over the heads of the astonished audience.

"This is absolutely amazing," she said, turning to Gabriel. But beside her, where he had been standing seemingly only a moment before, stood a rotund stranger. He was gone! How strange, she thought, perhaps he's upset at my refusal.

Kate went off in search of her Harlequin. Not finding him in his distinctive multi-coloured diamond motley among the crowds on the terrace, she went into the house. Then, not finding him in the main dance hall or any of the rooms in the South wing, she mounted the stairs.

As the last of the fireworks erupted and lit up the night sky around the house, she made her way to his room and quietly opened the door.

The sight that greeted her astonished her. The naked body of a beautiful young man lay face down in intimate embrace with another. She thought it was Gabriel and cried out his name. But then Gabriel's face emerged from under that of the young man.

A silent scream issued from her lips and she rushed out of the room. Gabriel threw his lover to one side, leaped out of the bed and, hastily pulling on his outfit, raced after her. He, half-naked, caught her at the head of the stairs.

"Get away, you bastard!" Kate lashed out at him, scratching and kicking and pushing him so that he, with his tights not fully pulled up, tripped and fell headlong down the

stairs, tumbling and rolling till he crashed against the wall of
the half-landing.

He sat, stunned, with his thighs, crutch and belly naked,
still pulling at his tights as if trying to cover his modesty.

Kate rushed down the stair toward him, and knelt beside
his pathetic figure, crying, "How could you be so deceitful?
Tonight of all nights – humiliate me like this so soon after
declaring your love down there, in front of all those people?"

Gabriel groaned incomprehensibly. Kate, seeing his pain,
could not help touching him, "Are you hurt?"

He groaned again, shook his head and said: "I am just so
stupid to think I could have it all, have you and…"

He broke off and looked away from her.

"For God's sake, cover your crutch," she said brusquely.
Then, more tenderly, "Am I so undesirable to you?"

"It's not you. It's not you – it's me. I love you, I do. But in
my own way. I don't know if ever I could make love to you. I
don't know if I could, but only because you're not like other
girls to me. It was easy with those I didn't care for, because it
didn't matter if I was being dishonest in my taking them for
pleasure." He looked at her, pathetically lost in his anguish.
"You see I've only really felt comfortable with – intimate
with – men. I am, I must now admit, homosexual, gay, queer,
a bloody bum-basher, if you like." He sneered and looked
away.

"Gabriel, stop now!" Kate shook his shoulders. "Don't talk
about yourself like that. It's disgusting."

"Isn't it?" He sneered again. "And I hate myself for it.
I should never have dragged you into this. But it's that
incessant pressure from the old dragon, the 'Look here, old
man, don't you think it's about time you got yourself a Gel?'
You know, to get a bloody son and heir to his little empire!
Chip off the old block and all…"

"Shut up! You're not doing any good, talking like this."

"I know, I'm sorry," he smiled faintly. "Look, you know I

327

respect you hugely, too much to deceive you for long.

I admit that at first I thought that I could just play along with my father's dream, using you as my play-partner. You had serendipitously arrived on the scene and I had merely taken advantage of that fact.

But I can't go through with it now, you see? I realized when Gerald came to me, all forlorn, I just couldn't do without him."

"I see. So it's over between us, then? Your charm, your seduction, slowly undoing my resistance, leading me on and now – this?" Kate slowly stood up, grasping the banister.

"It never was, never could be, with you, sexual" he replied, "I love you dearly, but I'm gay, and there's the end of it."

Eyes blurring, Kate turned without another word, ran down the staircase and out into the rear courtyard, away from the crowds at the front of the house, straight into the old General's arms.

"Hey, Hey? What's all this? Tears, from my lovely Kate? Tonight of all nights?" General Tercel took her shoulders and held her at arm's length, looking into her eyes.

Unable to meet his gaze, Kate burst into tears and collapsed into his arms, her chest heaving with uncontrollable sobs.

"There, there, my dear," the general turned and, supporting her with one arm, started walking them gently up the yard away from the house, "Now just you tell me all your woes and I'm sure you'll find they're not so bad as you think."

"But they are, they are!" Kate spluttered and before she could help herself, blurted out, "He's gay! Gabriel's gay! His proposal to me in front of all those people? Just a sham! A complete humiliation!"

"What! Gabriel? Gay? Ridiculous! Don't be absurd!" the general pushed her away.

"He is! I caught them at it – him and another man – in his bed."

"When? Here? Tonight?"

328

"Just now. I was looking for him and I found him, naked, with another man." Kate burst into tears again and sank to her knees.

The General Tercel's face went puce and began to blow up like a toad's. His arms stiffened, his fists clenched. His scowl deepened as his body went rigid. He was transfixed for a moment.

"Where's that boy?" he shouted. "Gabriel! Gabriel! Where are you, you sulking coward, you damned queer?"

"Please, General, Perry, stop! Don't confront him now. Not like this, with this anger. Let yourself calm down." Kate clutched at his sleeve, "Let it rest till morning after all your guests are gone?"

"Damn the bloody guests!" Before Kate could stop him he was away, leaping up the steps to the rear hall door. "I'll deal with you, boy! You disgrace!"

He ran into the house to confront his son and soon their row exploded into the great hall.

Kate could hear them arguing furiously. She heard, as did all the guests, General Peregrine Tercel, loudly and publicly disinherits his son and orders him out of his house.

Gabriel left without another word. He passed Kate, glancing swiftly at her in a way that made her feel awful, and strode out through the arch into the gloom beyond.

"Out, out! All of you, out!" The General swept through the ground floor rooms, driving all before him like parti-coloured sheep.

The party broke up in a chaotic scurrying for carriages as the hugely embarrassed guests almost fought with each other to escape the suddenly poisonous atmosphere.

Kate watched as those who could not get carriages flung off their tawdry and ran as fast they could down the drive. It was pandemonium.

The general, having dispersed his guests as means of venting his spleen, returned at length to back court where Kate still stood rooted to the spot.

Suddenly calmer, Peregrine Tercel turned to face Kate: "I think you had better sleep here tonight, my dear. I would fret for you wandering about out there all on your own."

"But, General, reconsider," Kate began.

"No, Kate, no. No more tonight. Enough – too much – has been said already." The general suddenly looked very tired and very very old.

"You're right. I'll sleep in the room you showed me before. Goodnight, Sir." She kissed him on the cheek and walked away into the house.

Soon after she heard the old man retire to his private apartments and wondered at the misery he must be feeling now. She was shocked by his sudden transformation, this weakness in his armour: this manifestation of sheer intolerance so out of character.

As she made her way to the guest room, she determined to try to reconcile him to his wayward son the next morning or in the days following.

55

Morning

At dawn the following morning a cry from the courtyard brought Kate, followed by the general and servants, running to the rear entrance.

In the blue grey mist that hung over the courtyard, framed in the great archway that led to the further courtyards, hung a body. The sun at that moment broke through the mist to highlight a white figure, its face a white mask of painted sadness, its body clothed with a baggy suit of white pyjamas with large buttons, hanging like a shroud. The pointed hat it wore still further accentuated the pathetic figure. Below it a tall kitchen stool lay on its side. From the ghostly body's feet hung a heavy iron anvil. On its white chest were two perfect sets of black handprints, crossed over as if in supplication.

They both knew immediately it was Gabriel. As they approached, the general read the small notice that hung over its chest:

> "Without mother,
> Without father's love:
> No One
> Dies here,
> Unforgiven."

General Tercel stepped close and pulled away the mask.

Gabriel's face was all but unrecognizable. His head hung askew, the skin bloated and purple. His eyes were protruding from his head, and his tongue lolled to one side, looking almost black in the early morning light.

"Cut him down and cover him." The general curtly ordered the gathering crowd of estate workers. He turned sharply on his heels and marched into the house, not looking back.

Kate watched as Gabriel's body was laid gently on the ground and covered. The women were weeping for this beautiful boy who had taken his own life in such a horrible way.

Kate asked for the police and doctor to be called and waited until they arrived before following the general inside. She went to Gabriel's room first, hoping for a clue, a letter, perhaps as to his extreme action. Then to the general's bedroom, but finding the general in neither place, she returned downstairs and made her way to his study.

As she entered she saw him reclining in his chair with his back to her, in his slumped posture he looked utterly defeated.

Gripped in his left hand, hanging over the arm of the chair, she could see a letter, scrumpled up in his tight fist. Guessing this must be Gabriel's suicide note, she approached cautiously, fearful of upsetting the old man further.

As she came to the side of the chair, she looked down at him. His head hung to the side and his eyes were closed and his tongue hung out in a grotesque parody of that of his dead son in the noose.

Kate realized he had had a stroke or heart attack and put her ear to his chest. He was still breathing and his heart beating. She rushed out to fetch the doctor. Returning, she noticed, as the doctor attended the old man, that the letter had slipped to the floor.

As she picked it up, she noticed a flame burning in the hearth, and looked to see another charred piece of paper, now disintegrating, begin to break into pieces and float up the chimney. Beside the hearth was an envelope.

This she picked up. It was addressed to the general in Gabriel's hand. She opened the letter in her hand. But this was addressed to her. It read...

"My Darling Kate,
I loved you in my way. I deceived you, it is true, and I deeply regret my deception. But in my love for Gerald and in his for me I found the unconditional acceptance I could never gain from my father, hard man that he is.
In your warmth and beauty I found that love of my mother's, rekindled, brought back to life – as I believe did my father – so my love for you was always ambiguous, but real for all that. Being such, whether I could ever have consummated it as a husband should I will never know.
Goodbye, dear Columbine,
Forgive your Pedrolino."

Tears in her eyes, Kate turned to the general. No wonder he had had a fit. She wondered what Gabriel had written to him. It must have been cruel and dreadful for the dear old man to have thrown it in the fire and taken such a turn.

The general was laid on a stretcher and was then carried out to the waiting ambulance. The ambulance that was called for his son, Gabriel, now bore them both away.

There was no room in the ambulance for Kate so the doctor volunteered to drive her to the hospital. He explained en-route that old Perry had had a stroke, as she suspected. Not fatal. But, as it turned out, paralyzing his left side and his tongue, so that he never spoke again coherently.

56

Robert

Rob arrived that morning for work to find the courtyard in turmoil. Piece by piece he discovered what had happened.

Desperate to rush in and comfort Kate, he was frozen by his uncertainty as to her affection, given the strange stories circulating among the staff: that she had accepted his proposal of marriage; that she had found him in bed with another man immediately after; that Gabriel had been expelled by his own father; that Gabriel's suicide had precipitated his own father's stroke.

He stood in the shadows watching as Kate came out of the house following the old General to the ambulance, looking for any sign of her perhaps looking out for him. She seemed too distraught to notice him.

He was about to step forward to offer his help when Kate was ushered into the doctor's car and it sped off after the ambulance.

He hung about for days outside her father's cottage, watching her dash to and from the hospital, uncertain how to approach her. She seemed so utterly absorbed in looking after the General: a devotion he found difficult to comprehend but which he dared not question by thrusting himself into her world at this time.

Over the next few days Kate attended the old man in

hospital and then nursed him in his recuperation back at the house.

Rob maintained his vigil when not engaged in his duties on the estate, which ran mechanically on as before, as if by doing so uncertainty as to the future of its workers could be staved off.

On day Kate emerged from the front door and sat down on the steps. She looked utterly drained and so sad that Rob left his hiding place and tentatively walked across the courtyard towards her.

Kate, noticing the sound of his feet on the gravel, looked up.

"Hello, Miss. I hope you're all right. What with everything that's gone on, here," began Robert, "I mean…"

"Oh, Rob!" She leaped to her feet and ran towards him. "Where have you been all this time? I've missed you so much!" She threw her arms around him, hugged him tight and buried her face in his jacket.

"I didn't want to interfere. You seemed so busy, like, and I didn't know whether you cared for me any more. Not after that row we had, and Gabriel's party an' all."

Kate looked up into his eyes, took his face in her hands and kissed him. "Oh, Rob! I was thinking you thought I had accepted Gabriel's proposal and hated me for it. I hadn't. I was so gobsmacked when he proposed like that in front of everybody I didn't know what to do.

I suddenly realised that General too thought I was Gabriel's girlfriend and it came as a huge shock to realize the level of that expectation that I would naturally accept his outrageous proposal.

I was flattered, yes. Hugely! But I never loved him. It took me some time to work out just how I could turn him down without upsetting him, for I thought he must really love me to have acted as he did.

When eventually I decided I must tell him firmly but

sympathetically that night, before these expectations got out of hand and took on a life of their own; that's when I went looking for him and found the pair of them…"

She paused, blushed, and gathered herself. "When I caught Gabriel and that boy having sex. I was so humiliated I ran out and that's when Sir Perry found out and went wild, throwing Gabriel out. It was all my fault, don't you see? If I hadn't…"

"It would have come out, anyway, sooner or later. Everyone on the estate knew, or suspected, he was gay. Only the poor old general refused to see it." Rob lifted her chin with his forefinger till she was gazing into his eyes. "I couldn't tell you before. It would have seemed the act of a jealous rival, don't you see?"

"Oh, Rob, I'm so glad you still like me. I've been lonely without you, with all the burden of the poor old man and his grief and guilt to bear."

Kate took his hand and led him out of the courtyard towards the woods and sat down on a bench overlooking the house on that side where all her adventures had begun.

"Promise me you'll always be here for me, if you really care for me, as I will, for you. Don't doubt me, even when I seem to be preoccupied in looking after the old man. You see I feel a debt of kindness towards him I must fulfil."

57

The General

Kate continued to care for the old man in his recuperation back at the house with the help of a trained live-in nurse. He had taken up residence in his study, with a bed placed in one corner, so that on good days he could potter about to reach his books and papers.

On one occasion she entered his study to find him with the doctor and a solicitor, huddled around the desk. The solicitor explained to her that the general, mindful of his condition and impending death, had drawn up a new will and testament in her sole favour. The doctor was there to attest to the old man's sanity at the time of making this new will.

Kate sat down beside the old man, and taking his hand in hers, kissed it, saying that it wasn't necessary. He shook his head gravely, denying her. She embraced him and kissed him. The general held her with his good arm for a long time, tears rolling down his cheeks, watched silently by the doctor and solicitor.

On another occasion, after he had suffered a second stroke, the general beckoned her to fetch him paper. On it he wrote…

"And so at last, dear Kate, it has come to this. I am struck dumb, just as your own dear ghostly mother, Amelia, was, all those centuries ago. I am a prisoner in my own body and am killed by my own son's actions as surely as if he stuck the blade between my ribs.

The tale has come full circle, my dear. This is the end of the de Tiercels, just as Amelia and her sister, Phyllis, intended so long ago. Have you been back into that hidden room, seen her since all this has happened? My guess is, no. She has gone now; her mission fulfilled in my death. She has no further reason to haunt this home.

You, my dear, take my blessing with you, and live. Marry that boy, Robert. He is a stout lad, and true. Look after this place for me after I'm gone, my dear. And remember me kindly as you might a long-lost uncle."

The general died after a third stroke two weeks later. Only his estate workers and a few old close friends attended his funeral, at Kate's insistence.

He was cremated and his ashes buried beside those of his wife in a corner of the walled garden he had tended for her all these years beneath the massive wisteria that he had planted when she died.

58

Pierrot

Kate moved into the great house and set herself up in the West wing. Her father, John, refused to join her for the moment, saying that it was her future now that she had become wealthy and independent and that he was comfortable where he was, a stone's throw away if needed.

Respecting this, Kate bought Old Tom's cottage secretly so that he could continue paying his rent while protecting him from rent increases or eviction.

She hoped to gradually persuade him to take up residence in his own quarters. But she was glad for the moment to be able to keep the general's portrait of the ghostly Amelia hidden from him while being able to look at it as often as she liked. She felt the shock of seeing his 'wife' in this house could cause him severe distress.

Kate's relationship with Rob had deepened during this time until he finally moved into her bedroom, bringing with him all his things, and it was, from that moment, just as if this was how it had always been.

On a walk in the gardens one day Kate spotted a familiar figure in the shade of the gazebo close to the lake. She walked over calmly and sat down beside Shabby Tattler.

"There is a story about the Pierrot," he said, turning toward her, "which relates how a small naked boy was found outside the gates of Heaven.

It was winter, and as St Peter picked up the child and blessed him, the snow on his body turned into a suit of pure white clothing. St Peter adopted the child and gave him his own name – Little Peter or Pierrot.

But there was one condition. Pierrot was not to be allowed to play with any of the human children he might come across as he wandered outside these gates of Paradise.

Of course, this was almost impossible for a small boy, and one day on his return from just such a meeting he realised that his white suit now had black marks on it where the hands of ordinary children had touched him.

These marks proclaimed his guilt, and little Pierrot was excluded from Paradise forevermore."

Shabby Tattler looked up at the blue sky and it was reflected in the colour of his own eye. Slowly standing, he bent over her and touched her forehead with his fingertips. He turned and walked away.

59

Amelia's sectret

A week later, a bill arrived at the house for the DNA testing. Kate had forgotten all about this in the storm that had engulfed the house and its terrible aftermath.

She phoned the company and spoke to its managing director, a personal friend of the general. She told him she had not yet seen the results of the tests and wished to receive a copy, since she had inherited the general's estate.

The man, an ex-army colleague of the general's who had founded a genetic testing company as business venture on leaving the forces, prevaricated, stating that the general had already seen the report and that if he had wanted her to see it he would surely have shown it to her.

She explained that the general had been very poorly and it might have slipped his mind. The man thought that highly unlikely, in view of the findings, which tantalized and frustrated Kate all the more. Under her persistent questioning, he eventually relented and agreed to meet up with Kate to give her a complete account of what had been discovered, since it was not a simple matter.

Meeting him at the house a week later, he showed and explained to her the results. Yes, indeed, she was descended directly through the female line from Lady Rosie Linnece, but also evidence showed she was descended from Sir Gabriel de Tiercel, giving credence to the theory that the original Kate

341

was his illegitimate daughter.

Kate's heartbeat quickened with a mixture of elation and dread at this news. She asked, "But why would Sir Perry not tell me this?"

"Maybe he never got a chance, because it was after his stroke that my results came through," replied the man. "But more than this, there is something else. Something that may well have persuaded him not to reveal the truth. Something that, even now, I am not sure I should reveal, now that he is dead and unable to censor my account."

"What do you mean, censor? What is there to hide?" Kate became quite agitated, "You can't stop now, after what you've just told me! Anyway, now that he's dead, all his property is mine, as you know, and that must include your report. You can't refuse and leave me in the lurch!"

The man looked thoughtfully at Kate, measuring her. Eventually he began: "Well, it's like this. Quite a long time ago now, about five years after he married Cordelia, the General fell in love with a much younger girl from the district, and had an affair with her that lasted about six months or so.

They met, he told me, during that terrible storm that blew half the trees of southern England down. A falling branch trapped her car. He rescued her and drove her home in the dark, through pelting rain and howling winds.

It was an extraordinary meeting, followed by a torrid romance that ended when the general's wife discovered it, confronted him and made him choose between them. The general chose his wife and children, Gabriel, whom you know, and his younger sister..."

"But Gabriel hasn't got a younger sister," Kate interrupted, "or at least he never mentioned her. Nor did the general."

"He had, at that time. But she died, not long after her mother's death, of a childhood leukaemia. I guess the double loss was too much for them, and so they have never been willing to talk of her.

Anyway, to get back to the story: Perry, who had gone back to his wife, Cordelia, now left the children, Gabriel and Annabelle, who knew nothing of what had happened, with their grandmother while he took Cordelia on a second honeymoon to the South of France. It was on that holiday that he crashed the car, killing his own wife.

He never got over the guilt of that accident and the relationship that led to it, and vowed never to touch a woman again. Never did, so far as I know."

"Oh," Kate felt a twinge of pain and sorrow for the general, "but why are you telling me this story? What has this got to do with your results? I can't see the relevance."

"Nor can I affirm it, but it may be the only viable explanation for what I am about to tell you."

"Go on, for God's sake. You are so roundabout in the way you talk, it's maddening."

"Listen. I don't know how to say this in a tactful way. You are the general's daughter. The DNA evidence is conclusive, undeniable."

"Don't be stupid! I can't be! My father is alive and well and I live with him. Have done all my life. He and my mum were always blissfully happy together until she died a year ago."

"I'm sorry to have to be the bearer of this shocking news. But that was the most controversial and yet the clearest result of my genetic research. You, Kate Pegler, are the daughter of General Percival Tercel. There is no denying it. What was your mother's name? Her maiden name?"

"Amelia…" Kate paused, reluctant to go down this road.

"Amelia Cashel, aged nineteen," the man completed her sentence for her quietly.

Kate burst into tears and sat down, crushed. Her whole life exploded. Her childhood unravelled before her eyes. Her mother, unfaithful? Having a bastard child, herself, Kate, and bringing her up as the child of her husband?

Does her father know that he is not her father, but a surrogate? He can't possibly. He would have betrayed it somehow, at some time. When they argued, for instance. And her mother, never revealing her, Kate's, true identity, even on her deathbed? It was inconceivable. She suddenly felt horribly betrayed by those most dear to her.

The general's old friend grasped her shoulder and squeezed gently. "It is entirely possible, my dear, that neither knew. You see, your mother and your present father were together before Perry's encounter with her, and they married shortly afterward. Perry told me at the time. So there may have been no reason to suspect that the Perry's short romance with your mother bore any consequences. Your parents may have just put it behind them and got on with their lives and yours, loving you as their own daughter. And Perry, of course, lost touch with her before you were born, because they moved away from here…"

"To London. That is where I was born, in 1988, the year after the great storm. Yes, I suppose it is possible they never knew," whispered Kate, praying that it was true. She knew she could never ask her father that question. It would destroy him to discover such a truth if he had lived in innocence all these years or, if he had known but never revealed it, their beautiful relationship.

"So the portrait of the lady in his bedroom…" Kate began.

"…is of your mother," continued the friend, "I came down personally to break the news of this report gently to him, knowing that too great a shock could spark another stroke. Old Perry showed it to me after he had recovered from the shock of discovering your true identity. It turned out that he was pleased, joyful even to know you were his daughter.

"He told me that it was shortly after meeting you that she appeared so lucidly to him in a dream that he knew he could paint her at last. He told me that he painted her as you see her, ambiguously cloaked, to avoid controversy. When it was complete, he said, he felt as if he laid the ghost of that woman, whose beauty had haunted him through all these years but whose image had eluded his brush, finally to rest.

"Knowing what he knew, the general would only have been doing the right thing in making you his sole heir, mending both the wrongs of long ago and of his own recent past in that action. So you Kate, his only surviving daughter, are truly the legitimate heir to his estates." The general's old friend patted her shoulder gently, adding, "I think it is time I ran along. You really need a little space to allow you to take this all in."

And so the old man left her, sitting in the general's armchair, its worn leather still faintly reeking of the tobacco he always smoked, looking blankly out through the tall Elizabethan windows of the library towards the hazy downs, blue-green in the distance, and the silhouettes of deer grazing in the nearer parkland of this great house, but seeing all the while the words of the poems from the general's story floating before her across the pale clouds: words of an enchanted love, expressed so tenderly, for the woman who was her mother, Amelia.

60

The Book

Kate rose from the chair and walked over to the bookcase where Sir Perry had placed his copy of his book, 'Daisy Chain,' and drew it out.

This book of poetry and prose seemed to be his way of assuaging his guilt for that affair that had led her here, so she felt she must read it again, in one sitting, by way of closure.

Then, going to his secret drinks cabinet, she pressed the button to open it and poured herself a glass of his favourite whisky.

She sat down again in his comfortable chair and, perching the tumbler on one arm, opened the book and started reading...

(Daisy Chain is printed as an addendum to the main story.)

61

Kate

Kate closed the book, her eyes and lay back in contemplation.

Why had the General inverted the tragedy to make himself the victim? She could only think that the truth was so painful to him that to portray it starkly would have made it impossible to make public this homage to the two women he loved as plainly he wanted to do.

No one would then have read into it the depth of sentiment expressed but merely grubbed about seeking a psycho-biographical exposé of its author.

She wondered at the glamour her mother's beauty must have cast over him to so tear him from his family, if only for a while, and yet which persisted through years of regret at the consequences of his actions to once again become manifest in the incredible portrait he had painted of her all those years later.

Putting the book down, Kate left the study and went to look once again at that portrait both of the haunted Amelia of yesteryear and of her own dear mother.

As she stood before the painting, she became convinced it would be dangerous to keep it hidden from her father, John, for too long. For, if discovered, as surely it must be sooner or later, how could she possibly explain to him its being secreted from him?

Her choice it seemed, was either to destroy it and the results of the investigation and leave her father peaceful in his ignorance or to reveal the portrait to him, perhaps pretending it was indeed an ancestral painting that happened to mirror her own mother, or face the truth and reveal all, hoping he could bear the pain and, looking on the beauty of his own beloved wife, forgive her youthful indiscretion and accept what had come of it.

Kate took down the portrait and carried it into the drawing room of the East Wing, the ladies' wing, and replaced the painting over the mantel there.

Standing back, she thought how perfectly it suited the room and how, ensconced there, it was as if the original Amelia, her own mother, and Kate herself had finally found reconciliation and peace here.

It looked so beautiful, hanging here, that Kate couldn't bring herself to lift it down. How could she destroy something as perfect as this?

She determined to go to her father and somehow explain to him the whole saga and bring him round to an understanding and acceptance of its consequences.

Robert had gone out that morning as usual. He was undertaking a management course at the local agricultural college, about 12 miles away with a view to eventually taking over the running of her vast estate.

She decided to walk through the woods to the cottage along that route that had led to her first insight into the tragedy of this place.

She walked out of the courtyard and past the East Wing to reach the shortcut through the woods to reach her father's cottage, thinking hard on how she should broach the subject.

Looking at the walls of that wing, she realised that its shape was again as it had once been, and she automatically made for the nook in the wall in which her secret door had stood.

The door was still there. A little confused, she reached into her bag where she still kept her key, pulled it out and unlocked the door.

Ascending the spiral stone stair, she wondered why the stair had become open to her again. Was her 'mother', Amelia, still there? If so, why? Perhaps she was going to say goodbye, now that it was all over?

Opening the door to the great hall, she saw Amelia, just as she had first seen her, hood outlined against the light cascading from the high windows.

Kate walked quickly across the hall towards her and, as she drew close, gently called out her name, "Amelia, mother darling, why are you still here?"

She touched her on the shoulder.

Slowly Amelia's head turned towards her as she rose from her seat to face her. In the light reflected from her own dress Kate saw Amelia's pale face under her hood.

Kate impulsively reached out to clasp her to her bosom: "Why, Amelia, are you so sad?"

In that moment she heard a voice behind her, a voice like her mother's.

As she turned to see who this was, she saw a flash of light and felt a burning sensation in her chest. Another flash. She felt warmth rising in her throat. She felt breathless and started choking.

A second cloaked figure stood before her as her knees buckled. She sank to her knees. Hot iron pierced her spine. A cracking as of bones. Kate turned her head... ...cried out! Blood gushed from her lips.

A voice, distant: "Amelia!"

She put a hand to the floor to steady herself. Her hand slipped in her own blood. She crashed, headfirst, to the floor.

"At last," she heard, faintly, through surging waves of panic roaring in her ears, "Sister, it is at an end," drowned out in a rushing whirr of wings, of wild fluttering birds.

DAISY CHAIN

Peregrine Tercel

01.

The pale oval of her face. The fall of her hair in two strands over half-closed lids, shading under dark lashes the water-green of her irises. In stolen glances, a flashing iridescence seemingly reflecting his joy in beholding her.

The subtle curves of her lips, quivering intermittently in half-smiles as if in some private pleasures recalled. The occasional dropping of her lower lip, in tantalising self-forgetfulness.

Her hair, pulled back from her face by two clips, gradually released by the movements of her head and the jerking of the speeding train. Individual locks flopping forward in a gentle sliding into loose abandonment, periodically compelling her to reach behind her head, unclasp the clips and shake loose a swirling flame of lustrous hair before gathering it carefully on either side to clamp it once more in hard steel jaws.

This cycle of abandonment and self-control is reflected in the way she talks and laughs and is silent in succession. With no turn holding sway for long, her face bears mobile witness to her character, so fluid in its metamorphoses of mood, rippling her surfaces as succeeding waves make manifest on the shoreline of appearance the deeper ebb and flow of emotion under the influence of a changing moon.

The slow deliberations of this tussle with her hair reveal the smooth underside of her bare arms, whose hollow swoop leads his eye as in a sensuous big dipper to the up thrust mounds of her breasts, softly responsive to her every gesture."

Her sides, exposed in this lifting motion, curve inward and downward to a narrow waist and the smooth broadening of her hips.

It is with a tumescent guilt that he finds himself stroking her every declivity with such passionate imagination that it is as if she were physically drawing his yearning down into the deepest, most private recesses of her body. With the peculiar anguish of the famished his eyes ravish her with a brute appetite.

As the train approaches its destination she rises, walks to the door, turns, casts a glance — transfixes him to his seat.

He sits naked before it. His crude imaginings – in which he would seek to fascinate her with the subtle sheen of silken words, mesmerise her with delicate gestures plucking at her binding threads, spinning a cocoon of desire about her trembling form – are sliced through by the keen blade of that penetrating gaze; reduced to mere gossamer floating on empty air.

Wordlessly she alights: untouchable. Her enigmatic smile now stroking as if with the tips of her nails the nape of his neck, charging his skin and the hairs on his skin with sudden electricity.

When at last he moves, the burden of his loss wells up and congeals his lungs with a damp asthmatic pressure. With laboured breath he shuffles aimlessly from this seat of his transfiguration.

Disappointment winds like a steel band about his chest, contracting ever tighter as he stumbles idiotically towards the barrier like a drunk, breathlessly fumbling for his ticket...

The image of her, smiling.

Smiling, turning and walking away.

He strains after her dwindling form in the bright shafts of light barring the concourse, consuming her as she passes under the great glass-arched roof towards the city's anonymity.

He is distracted.

Her image is elicited by any chance form or gesture reminiscent of those he so tenaciously recalls. It as if she has become a template by which reality is measured.

The world's shadowed beings spring brightly into focus wherever similarity shines its spotlight. He sees her everywhere, fleetingly, as if she were a stalking presence, always vanishing teasingly before he can grasp her reality.

So many times embarrassed by his own half-gestures of recognition occasioned by some seemingly familiar motion of a figure, hands or glance, he is reduced to a state of extreme anxiety, both for her, sought after, and for his own blundering folly in the seeking.

The only respite from the absurd rigours of this impossible pursuit of a chimaera among the millions of the great city comes to him in the haven of his own home, where he can lose himself in the comfortable reaffirmation of routines insulated from the world.

Here is an other universe, with its own laws and cycles of activity and quiet that continue of their own accord, their harmony only occasionally disrupted by the more extreme dissonances of mood its members bring in with them from the fractious world outside.

03

How subtly she comes; stands at a distance, regarding him. Her gaze sets its stark snare upon him. Her intent, like a sudden predator, empties the thickly peopled room of its creatures, fled into the shadows. He is entranced.

Turning in the threadbare light, her silhouetted breasts, her waist, smooth dark thighs, embrace the body of his vision - leave him wide. Duskily framed against the light, she returns with studied innocence a direct stare.

And in staring, opens again the sluices to that giddy torrent, syphoning his strength into the main channel of her eyes, her deep-pooled eyes, calmly watching him gulp like a stranded fish boggling for a phrase of cool liquidity, choke out a desiccated farewell and stagger away, leaving in his glass the tell-tale measure of such unseemly haste.

He walks now, slowly, against the slanting rain in the dim unfamiliar streets of the capital. Depressed and elated by turns, he reflects upon the extraordinary coincidence of this second encounter that has driven him so precipitously into the night, away from that peacock gathering, whose strutting participants were so suddenly eclipsed by her presence.

Without exchanging the simplest of phrases she, who will exert such a devastating influence on his life, has already staked a claim on him as surely as in law.

As he recovers his self-possession, his awareness of his surroundings returns and the streets become familiar. He has made his way towards the station whose trains will carry him home to his family and the everyday.

04

Shattering him like splintered glass, the sound of his own heart in his ears. A memory, unbearable, to which he cannot help but return.

Oh, god, those eyes - how they liquefy him as in fire... How does she elicit in him such disquiet as to so totally unnerve him in the presence of so many?

Through the searing pain of these thoughts grates the sound of a voice, vaguely at first, then more distinctly, demanding attention.

He blinks uncomprehendingly. His wife, Jessica, is trying to tell him something.

"Ben has got a hernia. He is going to have to have an operation. Are you listening?"

He sits up, leans back against the pillow and begins to sip his tea. He is gazing out of the window over the far hills at the rosy clouds emerging from their purple.

His wife looks at him. "You seem increasingly... how should I put it? ...Apart from the rest of us."

He turns to her, takes her hand in his, and steadies his cup: "I'm sorry."

"Do you know what he said, when I tried to describe the operation to him?" she asks, "he said: 'but Mum, lots of little boys have tails, you know.'"

He is alone. In the midst of his family, in the chaos and noise, he is alone and waiting. He is awaiting a token, a sign.

There is nothing now that keeps him enervated more than this surrender of his will to the consequence of his desire for this woman who has him so enthralled.

"A small thought, a feeling, settles upon my shoulder, as a butterfly, surprising my slow wit with its delicacy. Its powder-winged fragility, like a snowflake upon the nape of my neck, traces an icy vibrancy, teasing to the pit of my stomach.

I turn my head, so carefully, for fear of it melting away in my gaze. I reach blindly towards it with slow trepidation, fearing its flight from the monstrous groping of my limbs, that it may alight on my finger, that I may bring it gently into the compass of my gaze, into my comprehending.

For it is a strange, rare and delicate thing that has settled upon my shoulder just beyond my gaze.

And will I destroy it in the act of so regarding this sweet passion which has silently crept into my heart with an eloquence which leaves me dumb?"

He puts down his pen and picks up the telephone.

06.

This is the beginning of the affair. It will lead step by step through tenderness and pain to its inevitable yet wholly unexpected ending.

He is thrilling with anticipation. He ponders the nature of the forces that can draw two lives into a mutual recognition in which each accedes to an unwonted vulnerability in such a pact of unreserved responsiveness? He smiles. She is so much younger than he and yet so wholly at one with him. It is as if she discerns and reciprocates his every feeling before even he is aware of it.

He is suddenly reminded of the early days with his wife, and his elation dissolves in a miasma of doubt. His throat tightens as guilt grips him momentarily.

Her lovely figure approaches him through the mist which parts as she passes, revealing in the valley behind her the tarn they have climbed so far to see.

She takes his hand and they sit on a mossy rock. She nestles between his legs and rests her head on his shoulder. He enfolds her in his arms, stroking her belly and her breasts. Shafts of sunlight penetrate further into the valley below, illuminating the whole mountain scene in a quiet ecstasy.

At this moment they are one and at one with the landscape. It is a moment they will repeat often, but with a frequency diminishing in time as commitment strictures opportunity.

It is a strange fact about those early days, he recalls, that the weather in the mountains was always benign, no matter when they visited. They went mainly out of season, the more to enjoy their own company in that magical place.

At those times he achieved a tranquillity only attained in one other place: a great circle of beech trees upon a hill, which once, as he sat alone watching the rising sun burning through the cold mists enveloping them, revealed through their pale forms a landscape of downland rolling to a glittering sea, inducing in him a feeling of calm transcendence.

He is walking alone on these downs. He is walking to a rendezvous with a destiny he cannot control. He is walking to this source of his solitary ecstasy on that dawn long ago.

But it is night. It is night and the moon is rising.

The moon is rising and she is coming to him.

Here.

In this place made sacred.

This place made sacred by solitude and the rising sun.

He leans with his back upon the smooth bark.

Since those times the heart of this magnificent circle on its hilltop has been ripped out. There is now just a ring of bare-boned trees, those that withstood the force of the great gale.

Perhaps it is this loss of the centre that has led him here, circling his past, searching for renewal.

She kisses him gently, without a word, and draws him down.

07.

"Green - shadow green
dark upon the mould-rich loam
close-canopied, the deeping coomb
marches hard upon her flanking down.

Under her suffocating glance
her concupiscent thorns advance
their promiscuous entanglements
in swathes across the virgin down
bursting bloody to the quick, bitter farrow of the Hag.

I pause now,
in this dusky close,
abandoned, beside myself and breathless;
love's frenzy coursing through my veins
the leprous track of her vengeance.
Anis-enraged, her night-spawned host
stalks, phosphor-eyed, through the shadow-footed margins
of the cold bog pool, whose rippling reflects, hypnotically,
the laying of the moon's silver wreath upon me,
spell-bound victim of her passion,
drowning in the death-hallowing pitch
of her fierce exultation.
Strife-ridden through thickets of blasted thorn;
driven to ground, fire-racked and torn,
pierced through and through, love-incensed,
I embrace again whole-hearted Anathema
feel the deepest shades of her yearning

rise, rubescent, into the pale flesh of my days -
feel the wrench of half-remembered roots entwine about my
limbs,
lashed in communion - cloud, wind and rain -
drenching the earth, mud-puddles, rank weeds,
rough rivuletted bark, glistening dew-speckled webs,
shivering - the leaves sing the wind,
the wild fluttering birds..."

He has become a sleepwalker since that night. His feathered
steps carry the assurance of a lunatic. He is calm in his flight.
From reality he exacts no demands.
He is barely conscious of the passage of days.

08.

He is walking slowly along the riverbank, holding Ben's
hand. Ben is still stiff and tender from the hernia operation.

Laura is running ahead, through a field of giant
camomile daisies, her curls bouncing, her flowered smock
complementing the spray of flowers she now carries proudly
back.

Jessica, his wife, kneels to hug her as she accepts this token
of her unconditional love.

She weaves for her a garland of the daisies, intermingled
with coloured meadow-flowers like small jewels. Laura's eyes
sparkle in anticipation: "Crown me, Mama!"

She dances round and round her brother, laughing; finally
stopping before him to plant a wet kiss on his cheek. "Ugh."

Central America. The documentary displays the dreadful
spectacle of the victims of a Junta's wrath, staring out of the
screen at him, unblinking. Their bodies lie on the floor below
the concrete slab on which they sit. Blood sluices into a sink
beside.

The floor has skid-marks where shoes have slipped in blood.
Outside, men are shuffling the dust in boredom. Smoking and
laughing.

He turns away. Nausea grips him. How would they have
spoken?

"As a child stalks innocence
among the first blooms of spring
and returns, radiantly grasping

your reassuring skirts, Mother,
and their crushed heads,
severed dutifully to please..."

"So shall he, my little executioner,
take now my dark beauty,
  token to his Fatherland."

He is restless. Has nightmares of livid executions. Of
betrayal and revenge.

09.

He has arranged a journey for himself alone to a remote part of the coast. His wife accepts this need for time to "come to himself". She will agree to anything that helps him to return to his family.

This journey, he is aware, may be regarded as an act of betrayal, though this is not how he chooses to see it. For him it is a wonder and a blessed gift. It is an adventure into the landscapes of love: cliffs and coves, sands and castles, woodlands and waterfalls. A return to romance, to the license of youth.

How does he feel about this question of betrayal in so acting?

Disconnected.

It is not betrayal. It is other. It is apart from. He loves Jessica and his children. He loves his time with them. He has no desire to leave them.

This novel universe that his love has brought him is parallel. Is complementary. It has an aura of innocence and rightness.

He cannot explain this except to say that it is so. It has no justification. It has no need of justification.

10.

"As the pearled mists at dawn kindle the fire in your cheeks;
  as the light touch of dew upon your skin glistens in
reflection of the rising sun;
  as the rising sun, in whose light bathed, your beauty glows
and grows wondrous,
  so I touch your lips with scarlet, as with a kiss.

"As the caressing whisper of the cool breeze of morning
quickens your slow
  lassitude with the pulse of love, an ardour rising from the
depths of sleep;
  as the low murmur of the brook in which you dabble draws
you down, through
  rivers of yearning, to the frothing surf of the pebbled shore;
  so I, through raging breakers, drag you down into the
drowning of your Self
  in the dark Ocean that I am."

His eyes are upon her as she reads, the breeze playing in her
hair.
His eyes are upon her as they descend the steep stone-cut
steps zigzagging to the tiny beach below.
The sea is calm; more blue than green.
They are alone here and their low conversing mingles with
the rumour of the waves on the shore, and the deeds of this
day pass into a tale told across the tides, endlessly repeated.
Endlessly, archetypally re-enacted.

11.

"Thoughts, gathered with such care –
swept away as sudden,
with each new tide of emotion."

These days and nights beside the deserted shore are as vivid
to him as the image of her name inscribed in the shifting
sands, as fleeting.

For a while harmony and simplicity carry them beyond all
care into a state of wonder at all around them.

On the first day, with a bottle of wine, French bread
and cheeses in a knapsack, they wander where they will,
whimsically observing the smallest things.

They wander in a landscape of praeternatural brightness as
if through a Pre-Raphaelite painting in which every blade of
grass shines forth in idealised lucidity.

The cliffs, the shore, are as he would remember them, and
he half expects to see a straw-hatted sailor pointing out to sea
as he explains its mysteries to the two young lads at his feet.

They picnic on a cliff-top, feet dangling, watching the
distant sheep edging slowly in irregular fronts across
the undulating chalk downs, ignorant of the seemingly
determined passage through their ranks of stick figures
pursuing distant goals along the criss-crossing tracks which
make up the Coast Path.

Picking their way down the steep stone steps into the cove,
they undress, don their costumes, run slipping down the
shingle incline and dive into the clear cold water, still as a
lake, sheltered from the open sea by a outlier of rocks, mostly

submerged.

In this tranquil pool they play at first like children, ducking and diving to retrieve stones from the bed, disturbing small shoals of fish grazing the weeds.

Tiring of this, they take to exploring one another's bodies in a gravity-free ballet in which they discover themselves in the final act somehow free of all clothing.

Returning at last for their dinner in the hotel's dining room, their childlike amusement at the formality of those less familiar manifests in glances exchanged and secret jokes shared.

As the evening advances their mood softens and matures, their perception withdrawing from external amusements to an intense concern with one another.

The hotel has a piano in an out-of-the-way drawing room. She plays for him on this first evening a nocturne of extraordinary beauty and grace.

He leans over her, his hands upon her shoulders, and whispers playfully in her ear:

"Were I ivory, you would touch me, love;
fingertips lightly play over me,
filling the air with your music,
striking the deepest chords within me.
My resonance would enfold you,
wrapt in beauty."

She turns to him and rises, slipping within his embrace until their lips meet and the undulating waves of their inner music carry them away to strange islands of delight.

Later, they sit together on a terrace under the moonlight and even now words are forsaken in this time of quiet.

They experience a dim awareness of surroundings more clearly circumscribed in emotion than perception: of smell, of warmth's degree, of textures' subtle interplay, an immediate comprehension, closer to heart than mind.

12.

On succeeding nights, they repeat this performance, which
becomes a ritual of love, a haven around which the turbulent
intensity of their relationship revolves...

 "The slight touch of your lips,
like hemlock, suffuses my senses,
numbs my heart with a desperate joy."

   Even as they reach the heights of such ecstasy, shadows
creep through this landscape of bliss.
   His words reveal this ascending discord, whose timing and
sequence may only be guessed at...

 "Your sudden denial has blossomed
 like some deadly nightshade
among the scented tendrils
of jasmine with which you
have entwined the body of my love."

... whose tone hints at erratic moments of tension of
increasing frequency revealing the fragile reciprocity of
fears feeding upon themselves, whose causes he does not
comprehend...

 "Reeling, drunk with love, as if on ice,
unable to balance my emotions;
your slightest push topples me,
crashing hard upon cold indifference."

It is as if the sheer weight of his desire is overwhelming and stifling, ultimately bringing about its own destruction.

"You – rule your passion.
I, ruled by my passion,
must cast it into the void,
since it is unacceptable."

He cannot understand what has changed in her. It is as if she were challenging him to a commitment he cannot make.

This unspoken question is as a glass rising between them, so that he sees her as a reflection, mirroring, what? There is something strange yet familiar about her presence which he cannot reach; as if, by coming too close, the breath of his passion fogs the glass and makes her image evaporate when it should be most clear.

Thus they are slowly drawn back into themselves to face their futures, alone, discordant.

13.

"Gazing upon the beauty
of the full moon –
haloed with tears."

At first incomprehensive of the possibility of separation, he waits in hope of her return.

"Listening for your heartbeat
within this tiny shell –
only the lapping of a lonely shore."

At length, retracing those half-remembered paths, disconsolately he comes to accept the termination of this beautiful dream.

As he pays the bill to the rosy round-faced manageress, he

is almost surprised to see the signs of its having been so. In the dinners-for-two, the double room, the laundry charges and most poignantly in the casual remark of the manageress about "what a shame it was she had to leave so sudden, seein as 'ow lovely she was, an all".

He barely has the presence of mind to pay the bill in cash, as he thanks the manageress for her concern. He takes a taxi to the station in the nearest town.

14.

His return to his family elicits questions he must circumvent with lies and descriptions of the place without her.

The family accept in good faith his jolly description of the joys of the place, and an aura of eager optimism bathes Jessica and the children.

In the evening, as they approach bedtime, he makes a playful approach in keeping with the mood of the day.

She draws him to her and says: "We can't my dear. Not just now, not for a while yet. As soon as I found out, I knew I had to let you go. I just had to."

Tears well up in her eyes and roll heavily down her cheeks. She buries her face in his chest as he wraps her in his arms in slow fearful comprehension.

15.

> "My love has lost her desire.
> Her hot tears are blood.
> There is no stanching
> This torrent of her anguish.
>
> Close, now, to the world.
> Expel the bitter residue
> Of cloying expectation.
>
> In silence, endure the snows.
> In silence, succour the inward
> Potent bloom of another spring."

For several weeks despair hangs over the family. Silences of moody incomprehension roll like thunder across the landscape of self-recrimination.

It is little Ben who picks the deadlock with his key to the citadel of reconciliation. Jessica is leafing through his school exercise books when she comes across the following answer to the question: what makes you proud of your family? "I'm proud of my Mummy and Daddy because they feed me."

"Oh, darling," she cries, hugging her husband, "whatever can they think of us?"

16.

"Hello, it's me."

He is sitting in his office when the phone rings.

"It's me. I'm sorry."

It is she.

"Sorry? For what?"

"For not being all you wanted of me."

"Wanted? But you were... you are..."

"No. I saw your unhappiness."

"But... that ... wasn't you... to do with you... with anything you did, or said, or were. It was me. It was my stupidity, my predicament, my ridiculous dream... that I could have it all. You're not angry with me?"

"Angry? For what?"

"For what happened."

"What happened was beautiful... wonderful."

"Really? I want to see you again. When can I see you?"

"Wonderful and unique. Unrepeatable."

"Are you trying to tell me you won't see me again?"

"I can't."

"Why can't you? You can. You must."

"I cannot. Not until you have made a choice."

"A choice?" His face sets in a pallid alabaster mask of terror. "A choice?"

"A choice between us. You must now choose between us." Her voice assumes a firm conviction he has never heard from her: a certain practicality that reminds him of Jessica.

"I can't. I won't. How can I?"

"You have known us both. I know you know me. I gave

373

you all I am. And god knows you know your wife loves you."

"What makes you say that?"

"I have met her."

"You can't have. How? When? You told her then. How could you?"

"I told her nothing. She trusts you implicitly. That's how I know."

"Oh, hell."

"So. You must choose. You may not have both. Goodbye, my love, until then."

17.

"I think I understand." Jessica turns to look at him as he finishes telling her about his affair.

"You do?" He asks, in wide-eyed incomprehension.

"I think so. When I was young, I had an affair with an older man."

"Did you? When? You never told me."

"Why should I? It was before your time."

"Oh, did you love him?"

"Yes, I loved him... I wanted to marry him."

"Did he want to marry you? How did it end?"

"You're here, aren't you?"

"Yes. But did you really love him?"

"Yes."

"And you would have married him?"

"Yes."

"But he wouldn't?"

"He was married."

"But why didn't you just continue with the affair — if you loved him so much, I mean?"

"He had to choose. He wanted to continue the affair. But I wanted him to choose between us."

"But... You say you loved him, yet you'd have broken up his marriage?"

"Yes."

"Did he have a family... children?"

"Yes."

"And you still wanted him to choose between you. Why?"

"I couldn't lead a double life... have him lead a double life.

It would have destroyed what we had."

"But you did, anyway."

"I know."

"I don't understand. You left the man you loved because he wouldn't leave his wife, and destroyed your own love in so doing?"

"No. I've always loved him. I always will."

"What? More than me?"

"No, not more than you."

"But as much as?"

"As much as."

"So if he turned up tomorrow and said he did love you after all, would you leave me for him?"

"No. I've made my choice."

"But that doesn't seem fair. You wouldn't leave me for him, and yet you tried to force him to leave her?"

"No. I gave him the choice, and he chose. He couldn't have both of us."

"I don't know what to say. I never realised... that you had this great love in your life."

"Why should you? I never told you."

"Why didn't you? I told you about my previous girlfriends."

"It was none of your business."

"Then why tell me now?"

"Because you need to know now. How else could I explain that I know what she is going through?"

"She? What about me?"

"You too."

"Just that? You too?"

"And me."

"But, aren't you angry? Don't you hate her? Me?"

"I've been through that already. I have seen both sides. I was her; and she is me, if you see what I mean"

"I don't know that I do. I don't know what to think any

more. How can you not be angry if you really love me?"

"I told you. Because I know her better than you do. I've experienced what she is... what she wants. And I want it too. It's up to you. Its your choice."

"How can you be so understanding?"

"I could have hysterics, if you like. I could throw you out."

"Why don't you?"

"Because that lets you off."

"Lets me off? Losing my marriage, my children, my home? How is that letting me off?"

"Of the hook. Off having to choose. Off having to make the most difficult decision of your life."

"And if I chose her? You would just let me go?"

"What else could I do? You would be hers."

"But, what would you do if I chose her?"

"Live. Die. What difference does it make?"

"But the kids... if you killed yourself, what would become of them?"

"When you undo the knot binding it and let it go, a ball of string will run where it will. Life unravels itself from each moment, each choice. And now that moment is yours. Its entirely your responsibility."

"But that's blackmail! Saying that you would commit suicide if I left."

"I didn't say that. I did say that, once unravelled, that ball could never be retrieved as it was before. Whatever you choose, it can never be the same between us."

"You mean you wouldn't want me, even if I chose you?"

"No. I don't mean that. I would accept your choice. If you chose me, I would love you. If you chose her, I would love you still."

"How could you?"

"As I still love him."

"Who rejected you then? I can't cope with this. I need to think. To clear my head."

"Do you need to talk to her?"

"What? I can't. She won't."

"She will if I ask her."

"You've talked to her? About this?"

"We met. I knew. She knew I knew. That is why she knew you had to choose... that it couldn't go on as if there were no consequences."

"I don't know — if I need to talk to her. I'm so confused."

"Perhaps you'd better go away for a few days; to that place where you were so happy together?"

"You know about that?"

"Yes. Perhaps it's best you go there: to the heart of the matter. To the place where your relationship was... consummated. Discover how real it all is, or whether it is just a dream, a fantasy. But don't come back till you have chosen."

"But..."

"And if it is her, you won't come back anyway."

"This is absurd. This isn't happening."

"It is happening. You brought it about. Now, go. Face yourself."

As he stands there, limp and dumfounded, she walks over to him slowly, takes his hands in hers and looks at him one last time. She stretches up towards him on tiptoe and lightly kisses his cheek, whispering: "Go now."

She walks to their bedroom and closes the door behind her. He hears the lock click. A quiet sobbing.

He turns, leaves.

378

18.

"That gnarled trunk, fallen
– a void in the wayside –
no longer familiar."

He walks the final mile from the station down to the
isolated hotel.

"So you're alone this time, then?" The marginally raised
eyebrow of the genial lady of the house. "Here are your keys.
I've given you that room overlooking the sea again. Enjoy
your stay, my dear."

He has arrived. Retracing those steps of happiness and
hope, he finds himself alone, wandering the sea cliffs, the
dunes and woodlands, through the ruins of their brief love.

"I come to this sweet wood
and find myself
in a forest of uncertainty.

Each place, here,
thicketed
with barbs of remembrance."

....

"These trees have withstood
so much, while I?
One breath from you...

Like a great gale
you have uprooted me,
exposed my heart
and passed me by."

Gradually he passes from this sense of acute loss into a
feeling of profound abandonment, as if those he most desires
and needs have somehow deserted him, leaving him in a
wilderness, isolated from all that is dear to him.

"Among the shadowed stones
of this ivy hung ruin,
my thoughts return to you...

The way your presence
has clung to me,
slowly tearing apart
the fabric of my life."

He looks out of the window. There is no sky, no moon. His
joyless eyes look out upon no thing.

That night he dreams.
He dreams he is walking towards a distant forest.
He is crossing a decaying wasteland of abandoned fields.
It is as if time itself has slowed, so endless is his march, so
pitiful his progress.
He approaches at last the forest's dark rim. The trees
themselves seem now to be rushing to overwhelm him. The
bloody discus of the sun skews its incandescent arc to earth
through giddy vortices of cloud. Winds rip through the
haggard traceries of the forest's unroofed colonnades, keening
for the dying of the light.
A sudden rush of wings, a shrieking terror, beats through
the branches. Feathered with darkness, it brushes against his

skin, claws him, seizes him and drags him...
into wakefulness, away from the dreadful heart of the matter.

19.

He remembers this. He remembers he is afraid. Afraid of losing something he cannot grasp. He knows it only by an acute absence within him.

His melancholy withdrawal is telling upon those around him. The rosy-cheeked landlady's concern is evident.

She frets.

She wishes she could contact the nice young lady with whom he had come previously, with whom he had seemed so happy.

Behind pleasantries she plans subterfuge. She bustles into his room that afternoon while he is out walking. For clues she searches the room, his belongings. She reads…

…and determines to save him from himself.

She makes a telephone call.

"You see - I didn't mean to - but when I did. I'm worried, so worried, you know," the kind lady stammers over the phone in her confusion and panic and sheer excitement, "nothing like this has ever happened in all my years. Not that it has happened, like - I mean to say - but it might! Mightn't it? And I thought you ought to know, just in case?"

Her voice trails off momentarily as she flushes, panting.

"Yes, thank you. You did right. I'm coming. I'll come right away. Thank you."

"Oh good. Thank you, Ma'am. I didn't mean no 'arm by it. But I was worried so."

"No, you were right. Have you a room for me?"

"A room? Seprate, like? Of course. He'll need his rest,

won't he, when you've come? And your bein' here will set him straight. Yes - a seprate room - its for the best..."

"Thank you. I'll be there as soon as I can. I'll be there by morning, hopefully."

"That'll be a load off my mind, it will. I've been so worried, an' all."

She rattles on distractedly over the dead line for a few more moments before realising.

"I'd better go and see to it, then. Yes. That's what I'll do." She hastens upstairs, glad of the release into activity.

When he returns for dinner she fusses over him anxiously, until in irritation at her exaggerated solicitousness he retires to bed.

20.

At dawn he gets up, dresses hastily and plunges out into the half-light, impelled as if by necessity to escape an approaching doom.

Awakened by the creaking of the stairs and clacking of the door latch, the curious landlady peeps through her curtains… watches his stealthy figure slip into the darkness along the path to the headland.

Through a fine rain he walks, on the cliff's edge. Glasses misted, head bowed, gravel oriented, he myopically stumbles over the path's rocky undulations, careless of the precipice beside him.

Even as the rosy-cheeked landlady scurries upstairs ahead of Jessica to hide her confusion at the appearance of this new 'wife', he is climbing with faltering steps the rocky crags of the headland.

"And I found this. You'd better read it, Ma'am."

"In the rain,
towering haughtily on uninviting hill, a solitary house.
Wrapped about, it's avowed wilderness of silence.

A shimmering heavy-beaded screen veils it from them.
A jewelled surplice of tawdry covers its sombre penitential cowl.
A mouldering habit, festering opiate dream,
threads illumination through its innermost recesses.

384

Sprouting down callowed walls,
rapacious filaments find out
each last flickering rumour of life;
husking the meanest whisper of a once-vital
cricket-prattle with its acrid suffocating fumes.

No mourning Ruth with her salt tears,
but a trembling cowed aversion greets its stark Sodom stare.
Through this gate no one returns. Its rusting hinges cry out
no more.
Heart's blood engraves its rubric on stone:
Condemned"

   She puts down the note, and quietly asks: "Which way did
he go?"

   "That way, madam. Up towards the cliffs. Oh, ma'am,
I'm so sorry," the landlady calls after her, "You see, I was so
worried."

21.

He lays down his coat, and sits down upon it.

This is the end of his journey. This is the place to which he has come, at last.

Feet dangling over the precipice, he wipes his glasses with a tissue.

The rain has given way to a pink and amber sunrise. The seas to the East are a shimmering gold. He looks back across the land, across the downs rising steeply to the height on which he sits.

The grass is steaming. The vapours hover, float and swirl, giving evanescent form to the breezes that move them.

He watches with some contentment these swirling wraith-like dancers, pirouetting and dissolving into one another's arms.

Even as he stares in fascination, the vapours appear to condense into a form more familiar, an ethereal embodiment of his desire. And in his mind the realisation flashes that, like these wraith-like dancers, individual manifestations of Beauty, seemingly met face-to face, separate and distinct, are but motifs woven into the labyrinthine patterns of Her elemental dreams. That the recalcitrance of this Enchantress' love is this - though of itself all ecstasies' dispensation – possession, it will not endure.

She approaches him now through these mists, clothed in grace, a golden aura about
her body, substantiating with every step into her own unique and perfect form, ascending towards him.

He turns and rises to embrace her, arms outspread.

22.

The staccato rattle of pebbles and stones subsides into the wheezing roar of the surf far below, throwing up its white frothy arms in cold embrace...

She peers over the cliff's edge down into the thundering surf. There is no cry beyond the surging roar of the waves, the mewling of the gulls.

23.

As she closes her front door, Jessica notices in the pile of mail in the hall an envelope addressed in a familiar hand. She drops her bag, bends down and picks it up.

She walks slowly to the kitchen. Her hands tremble as she boils the kettle and makes some tea. She sits for some time with her tea at the kitchen table, just staring at the handwriting on the envelope in front of her.

Suddenly she tears it open and unfolds the letter:

"My darling Jessica…"

The words swim out of focus. She wipes her eyes before continuing:

"…I have spent the last days thinking of nothing else except our relationship and my sudden infatuation with this strange and enchanting young woman. I had sought to explain it to myself through the small story enclosed with this letter.

I had reached such depths of despair and bewilderment in the face of this impossible dilemma that it seemed I had only one course open to me before I came to a realisation so sudden, strange and impossibly dream-like in its illogicality that I could not countenance it and still count myself among the sane.

In spite of that, so many small clues lent it a credibility that, once envisaged, could not be otherwise.

I scarcely, even now, dare put it to paper. Its absurdity is such that, if not true, you also must surely deem me mad as I seem to myself,

Things you said during our last conversation sowed the seed of this notion. That, and your understanding, which at the time I found so incomprehensible.

And then again, the contradictory nature of my love for her; it seemed so appropriate, so innocent. Dare I use that word? But yes, our mutual affection felt so innocent.

It was as if we were intended for one another. The depth of her intuition for my feelings, almost before they entered my own consciousness, made it impossible for me not to love her.

I say her.

I love you.

How can I say this and at the same time presume to tell you of my intense passion for her?

It was certain phrases you used that unravelled this knot; that give me the courage to write this.

You said: "I've experienced what she is, what she wants. And I want it too." And again, "I've seen both sides. I was her, and she is me, if you see what I mean."

You meant that, darling, didn't you?

Literally.

You are she, and she, you. This sounds insane, but I know it is true. Somehow, as in a dream, you have come to me as the Other Woman - seductress, mistress - to show me the nature of my love for you. To bring me to myself.

I cannot fathom through what means this came to be, except perhaps through the sheer intensity of your love for me, as I choose to believe. But it has brought me back to you in a way I never thought possible.

Again, that story of your affair with an older man when you were younger. That was me, wasn't it? And she, you, with your intent to wrest him away from his wife. Failing, as she has.

It was you and I, wasn't it?

Then and now.

Endless and repeated. A cycle of love rediscovered?

I ask your forgiveness, and plead only that, as I once fell for you, then how could I do otherwise than repeat that falling in love with you again, my darling?

I will return soon, unless I hear that I am mistaken, and unwelcome.

All my love,
 Oliver."

Jessica paused for a long time. Turned to this, his last story:

"The Tale of Boy-who-is Fish

Boy-who-is Fish is swimming, as fish do.
He is swimming in Sea, who is clear, blue and very, very warm.
She and he are closest.
Sea caresses his skin with rippling strokes, tickling his skin as he swims through her as fishes do.
She has been there always, like this, carrying him warm and snug in her belly. Her belly so huge there is no end to it he can see.
He flies weightless in her caressing warmth and she lets him do as he pleases.
Sand there is below: white, white Sand. And Sky above, bluer than Sea. Through Sky scud little patches of Cloud, which sometimes fill Sky, rippling just like wavy ripples in Sand below, so that Boy-who-is-Fish sees above as below, Sand as Sky.
But Boy doesn't care as he spins and turns and flies hither and thither, free and weightless, for it is all the same to him: up and down.
Boy-who-is-Fish sometimes burrows in Sand, so that white Clouds follow him just like in Sky, but burrows not so deep as to lose Sea, his Mother.
Other times Boy tries to burrow into Sky, but Sea follows him into Sky, reaches out with many silvered fingers to fetch him back with laughter splashing all around.
So they go on, Boy-who-is-Fish, his great Mother Sea, Sand and Sky, from day to sunny day.

At night, Sea strokes him to sleep and purrs, "Shhh...,
shhh..."as he slumbers on her shoreline. She laps about him
and rises to embrace him.
Always, when her fingers stroke the nape of his neck, Boy
awakes and drowsily lets him be taken into her huge warm
belly.

Bye and bye, Boy-who-is-Fish crawls further out of Sea-who-
is-Mother, out onto Sand-which-is-White, and leaves her
fretful lapping behind.
He learns to stand, and finds himself in Sky-which-is-Blue
with his toes in Sand, finds himself somehow with a heavy
Heart, something like regret, leaving Sea behind, if only for
a while. But this new feeling too excites Boy, and wiggles his
toes into the hot hot Sand and stares up at the bright yellow
eye of Sky watching him.
He feels the last tickly caresses of Sea as she trickles down
him into Sand.
As days turn one into another, a whispering is heard among
the Green-that-is-Leaf on the shoreline between Sea and Sky,
a soft whispering in the winds:
"Oh, look at Boy-who-is-Fish,
How Sea drops away from him like Scales.
See how smooth and white is his skin, smooth and white like
Sand."
And they whisper this, these Leaves-in-Wind:
"How like Palm tree he stands, so tall and erect, how like
Palm his hair grows thick and bushy.
Strange, his hair, so white upon his head.
But see his eyes, strangest of all. Not Blue like Sea and
Sky, nor White like Sand; not Green like Palm, nor yet like
Coconut, fruit of Palm, Green.
Not bright colour, like these, but Brown. Brown like old Sea-
worn-Coconut, fallen and all dried up."
And this strangest-of-all brown, Brown Eyes betrays him to

392

his Mother Sea, who cries to herself softly, "Am I losing you, my son?
Where are your silken scales a-shimmering with lights?
Where your sleek tail swishing freely through my warm belly?"

One day at dawn, as Boy-who-is-Fish slumbers at the shoreline as he always does, neither in nor out of Sea, strange Creatures happen by: Man and Woman, arm in arm.
Seeing Boy-who-is-Fish at the shoreline, neither in nor out of Sea, Woman cries out:
"Oh, look at that beautiful Boy, half-in, half-out of water!
Oh, Man, rescue him before he drowns!"
And Man leaps bravely into Sea, right up to his ankles, leans down and snatches Boy from Sea, who murmurs angrily, and Man shouts:
"He's alive, thank God. He's alive!"
This sudden snatching and loud shouting wakens Boy-who-is-Fish, who cries out in alarm and struggles to be free of this iron grip and return to Sea, to the warm womb of his Mother.
But Man will have none of it, and holds firm onto Boy, while Woman coos:
"Our own little beautiful Boy, it's a Miracle!"

So Boy was taken away from Sea, from his warm mother, and taken far from there.
Man and Woman, they took him far away to a cold, cold land, far from Sea, and called him their own little Boy.
Boy-who-was-Fish became Son-of-Man and Child-of-Woman, who both possessed him because he was theirs.
They brought great Fuss with them to take care of Boy in the best manner of that country.
Great Fuss was called Nanny, who looked after him wherever he tried to go and brought him back and up.
He was brought in daily to show Man and Woman and Man-

and-Woman's friends and relations what a Good Boy he had become. Boy was much admired for his beauty and his never-speaking-out-of-turn.

But Boy's silence was a great hole in his heart - was a void of longing for the warm caress of Sea, his Mother.

He was burned by Eyes all around him, which touched him like hot pokers, prickling his skin with their hard scrutiny.

Because he was their Prize Possession, their Pride and joy, Boy was sent away to be with his own kind who were not, but were cruel and hard, whose prying was harsher than Eyes.

Boy cried at night for his mother, Sea, and his tears trickling warm down his cheek brought him briefly close, feeling her soft caress.

His own kind didn't like Boy's tears, which frightened them, so they rubbed them harshly away and handled him like rocks in a storm of bruises, dark clouds across his Sand-white skin.

When Man and Woman, who called themselves Father and Mother, came to inspect Boy they were proud of their Son, who was learning so well to hide his feelings.

But one day his yearning and longing for his warm mother, Sea, swept away all his learning and impelled him to return.

He was found and brought back and his Father said: "You belong here and here you will stay until you learn to forget this foolish Childishness."

And Boy's mother, when he tried to touch her and hug her and have her run her fingers through his hair all trickly down his neck, started and said: "Don't be silly Dear! You're a growing Boy now and that's not how we do things here."

And she looked away from him, as far away as possible to hide her own silly Weakness-of-Woman and made an end of it.

Boy behaved.

He behaved so long he grew to learn to forget and became for All-the-World like every other Young Man.

Except in that space which he kept secret: where his Heart beat, "Sea... sea..." which he could hear when it was dead-of-night and all was quiet around him.

Thus he carried Her within him, rhythmically surging through his arteries and veins, washing warmly through every part of him - invisibly all though him - Sea.

He learned to adapt to the cold ways of Man. He learned to "measure up," and to measure others, too. He acquired Talent, Success and Possessions, as all Men in that country want to do.

One day he found himself an Asset: he acquired a Wife, as most Men do, and Family to go in House, which is called Home when fully equipped with these Possessions.

He had Happiness, which was measured by Success and Wealth, consumed by Family, and so on.

To all outward appearances Boy-that-was-Fish had become Man-of-Substance.

He was entirely Normal, just as he should be, Praise be the Lord.

But deep down a worm gnawed. A little Sea-Worm, such as burrows in Sand-below-Waves, hungering for Sea and all her Gifts.

Worm burrowed into his Heart a tunnel, always in the direction of Sea, down which poured a torrent of yearning for that pure Grace in which he had once swum free.

Then one day came Otherwoman, who carried with her something of Sea.

In Her he tasted Saltiness-of-Surf, smelled Fish-of -Sea, felt in her rhythmic caresses, his once playful Carefreeness.

He knew he must follow Her to the far sea-girt land from whence she came.

He was sure she could lead him Home.

Her home was a Land-almost-sea, formed of the lapping of waves on sand, and its sea grasses rippled in the breezes like blue-green waves of the sea.

Otherwoman too, he thought, was born of Sea.

She swam in Surf's surge with an ease born of Nature, and joyful Ecstasy broke over him in waves.

As he watched her run and dive, disappear and re-appear in that grey choppy swell against the grey-clouded sky he laughed.

She emerged, laughing too, and skipped over the wavelets towards him and dragged him, so willing, towards the great Sea swell.

He felt "Now, at last, all will be well."

Ice.

Icy cramp seized him, dragged him from her.

Its grip tightened on his chest like a clamp and its claws dug deep into his heart.

It suffocated him, strangled him, bloating him purple like a corpse.

Monstrous!

His own Mother Sea!

Frigid, cruel, winterblast counterfeit!

Breaching the waves, he clung desperately to her surface, crying out for release.

In the distance, he saw Otherwoman, sitting on a rock, perfect in form, in substance perfectly remote, remote from his comprehension.

Mermaid, Ice-Maiden, impenetrably smiling, looking out far away, oblivious to his agony.

He slipped beneath the waves, icy fingers dragged him down, heart growing cold.

Suddenly she was lifting him to the surface of the grey icy sea, guiding him gently to shore.

He lay on the shore, bloated, burning with cold, gasping for breath.

Otherwoman looked down at him with Pity in her eyes for this Man-who-could-not-swim and she could not help him.

She slipped quietly into the waves so icy and her wild hair in

the frothing surf was the last of her.
Man-who-was-once-Fish left the cold unfriendly shore of that
Land-almost-sea and returned to his place.

But from that moment on Despair took up residence under
his roof and ate his bread, starving the Hope that sustained
Yearning.
He never recovered from the cold shock of that day.
His breathing became short and laboured as if the air in
which he swam was alien, choking him.
From that first cold swelling of his body, eruptions
volcanically spread in crusty flows across his skin, slowly
encasing him as he withdrew inside himself.
All around stared in awe at this Transformation in him.
Doctors came to inspect and name its parts. Cold Urticaria.
Chronic Asthma. Psoriasis.
These were some of the names.
But their naming of parts did not drive out those demons of
despair.
As the days dragged, wheezing, one after another, ever slower,
he withdrew entirely.
His last breaths gurgled, a gentle bubbling, whispering,
"Sea… sea…"
And, as they covered him over with a sheet, one doctor was
heard to remark to another:
"His skin – so scaly – almost like a Fish."

Notes.

- The myth retold in the Elizabethan section of the book is adapted from that of Philomela, Procne and Tereus as told in the Metamorphoses.

- Apart from the sisters, Phyllis and Amelia, the brothers, Gabriel and Michael, and the two priests, John Ball and Jack Straw, all names in the Elizabethan recounting are derived from colloquial names for British birds.

- The sermon of the radical preacher, 'John Ball', is that delivered by the historical 14th century Lollard priest on Blackheath in 1381.

- The great house, Fugglesham Hall (later Court) is loosely based upon facets of both Parham and Wiston houses in West Sussex. The lands depicted are those of the South Downs and the neighbouring Weald.

- Not long after writing the episode of Black Martin's overhearing the sermon in the woods and the subsequent massacre, I was taken on a private tour of Parham House by Lady Emma Barnard. I was shown, in the 'blue' bedroom, hidden behind the wood panelling, that popular quote from John Ball's sermon scrawled on the plaster as 'discovered' in the story by the modern Kate. Lady Emma had no knowledge of what I had written and I none of the existence of that graffito.